Warning!
Violence and the Supernatural

The fictional World of Rifts® is violent, deadly and filled with supernatural monsters. Other dimensional beings, often referred to as "demons," torment, stalk and prey on humans. Other alien life forms, monsters, gods and demigods, as well as magic, insanity, and war, are all elements in this book.

Some parents may find the violence and supernatural elements of the game inappropriate for young readers/players. We suggest parental discretion.

Please note that none of us at Palladium Books® condone or encourage the occult, the practice of magic, the use of drugs, or violence.

An epic world book for the Rifts® series.
Compatible with the entire Palladium Books® Megaverse®!

Dedicated to the unsung heroes at Palladium. The troops who are always there in the trenches, working hard.

Maryann Siembieda, vice president, typesetter, bookkeeper, office manager, world traveller, wife and my dearest friend. Maryann does the work of at least three people without most people realizing it. I'd be lost without her.

Henry Siembieda, warehouse manager, my terrific father, the fellow who introduced me to drawing (my first love), and the deadliest ping-pong opponent I've ever faced!

Alex Marciniszyn, editor, researcher, idea man, confidant, Defiler, and my best friend since 8th grade. A fellow daring adventurer who has accompanied me on many escapades — Megaton, A+Plus, Dream Con, the DGC, Palladium, Robotech and many others. Life wouldn't be half as fun or interesting without him.

Steve Sheiring, sales manager supreme, business analyst, budding writer (another great idea man), Defiler, dear friend and Acquire playing god!

James Allen Osten, editor, fan liaison, information director, an artist and writer in his own right, and my long time college pal.

Julius Rosenstein, contributing writer, editor, mail order supervisor, warehouse assistant, Defiler and the friend who introduced me to role-playing games. Without Julius' showing me the wonders of role-playing, there would be no Palladium Books. Thanks Jules.

Lawrence R. Jordan, Esq., protector of Palladium's intellectual properties, defender of artist/creator rights, advisor and friend. A lot of folks insist attorneys are devils, this one's on the side of the angels.

Thom Bartold, computer expert, research and development guy, special projects director, Defiler, globe-trotter, rocket scientist and dear friend. He'll always be a part of Palladium no matter where he is.

Ken Bartold, one of Palladium's most stalwart supporters, who is always ready to lend a hand (or a few bucks). Plus he's a pal and one of the greatest of the Defilers. Thanks Ken.

Adam Donald-Siembieda, my teen son who helps out in the warehouse, offers ideas and serves as a sounding board.

Monica Donald-Siembieda, my daughter, for just being there for support.

Kevin Kirsten recently left the Palladium team, but we may still see him around as a freelance editor and budding writer. Kev's an all-around nice guy.

Wayne Breaux Jr., my most dedicated and hardest working freelance artist, and still just a young lad in his twenties. He came through big-time on this one and his work continues to grow with every book. Wayne's been with Palladium for years now, and although officially a "freelancer," we all think of him as one of the gang!

Note: *The Defilers* were characters in my original Palladium Fantasy campaign; an epic adventure that built lasting friendships and memories none of us will ever forget.

Kevin Siembieda — 1996

Second Printing — July 1997

www.palladiumbooks.com

Copyright Palladium Books Inc. & Kevin Siembieda 1996

Rifts® World Book 11: Coalition War Campaign™ is published by Palladium Books Inc., 12455 Universal Drive, Taylor, MI 48180. Printed in the USA.

Palladium Books® Presents:
Coalition War Campaign™

Rifts® World Book 11

Written & Created By: **Kevin Siembieda**

Additional Text & Ideas: **Patrick Nowak**
 Julius Rosenstein
Senior Editor: **Alex Marciniszyn**

Editors: **James Osten**
 Julius Rosenstein
 Matthew Walhiem
Cover Painting: **John Zeleznik**
Interior Artists: **Wayne Breaux Jr.**
 Vince Martin
 Martin McKenna
 Kevin Long
 Jim Lawson
 Peter Laird
Art Direction, Maps & Keylining: **Kevin Siembieda**
Typography: **Maryann Siembieda**

Special Thanks to Wayne Breaux Jr. for his outstanding designs and artwork. Martin McKenna for pitching in at the last minute, and John Zeleznik for a great cover painting that got people's imaginations burning months before the actual book saw print. Julius and Pat for some cool ideas and their contributions to the book. And to Maryann, Steve, Alex, Jim and the usual Palladium troopers for all their hard work and efforts.

— *Kevin Siembieda*

Contents

Contents

Quick Find

5

Building the Campaign

The Coalition States and Emperor Prosek are the villains everybody *loves* to *hate*. I know I do.

I've been itching to write this book for over a year now. That means I've been formulating plans for *our* favorite villains for a long time.

The following pages will reveal more about Emperor Prosek, Joseph Prosek the Second, the CS high command and other key characters. You'll get some frightening insight into the mind of Emperor Karl Prosek and the inner workings of the Coalition States, Chi-Town in particular. You may not believe it, but Prosek and his High Command are more despicable and duplicitous than you may have ever imagined.

This book focuses on Emperor Prosek's vision of the future for the Coalition States. A future that seems assured by the launching of his *New Army* and plans for regional domination and continental expansion. It was his and Joseph's decision to give the new "Dead Boy" body armor and war machines a more frightening appearance. The new designs are intended to intimidate the enemy, as well as being tougher and more lethal. The light assault SAMAS and Super-SAMAS now fly alongside the old, famous "Sam." The Glitter Boy Killer, Hellraiser IAR, new Skelebots, tanks, aircraft and weapons have all been added to the Coalition's arsenal. New alliances are in place, old ones have been shattered, and the battlelines drawn.

To help bring this all to life is the artistry of Vince Martin, Jim Lawson, Peter Laird, and Martin McKenna, but it is Wayne Breaux Jr. who really gave this book his all. We worked closely together to create an entirely new front line of massive and menacing CS combat vehicles. He pounded out one terrific design after another and worked ceaselessly for over two months to produce (what I feel is) the best artwork of his career! When one artist backed out of the book at the last minute, it was Wayne who jumped in to take up the slack along with Jim Lawson and Martin McKenna. Long-time fans will remember Jim Lawson and Peter Laird from Palladium's **After the Bomb**® mutant animal line (not to mention the *Ninja Turtle* comic books). As for Martin McKenna, the smattering of incredible artwork in this book is just a glimpse of things to come from him. If you can't wait to see more of his work, take a look at the **Palladium Fantasy RPG 2nd Edition**. Besides, if you like fantasy you'll love the Palladium Fantasy RPG, now *compatible* with **Rifts**® (some modification is necessary).

As if all this raw excitement wasn't enough to give our fans heart palpitations, it appears *Palladium Books* is single-handedly holding down the price barrier for role-playing games. We couldn't believe our eyes during a visit the other day to our local game shop. 96 and 128 page books for $18 to $20 dollars! With prices topping out at $28 and $30 dollars! Holy cow! I guess we've been so busy getting out products and sending new product into production that we missed the price hike of the century. And to think, we worried when we raised our cover price by one thin dollar in January.

But enough of my ramblings. See what Emperor Prosek has in store for the Americas. Learn and tremble.

Kevin Siembieda — 1996

Prelude to War

The Secret Army

For the last year, rumors and conjectures about the Coalition States' involvement in a secret campaign of genocide, experimental weapons tests, and all sorts of treachery have run rampant in territories along the western borders of the Coalition States. The now famous *Juicer Uprising* seemed to be part of the Coalition's diabolic plot, but it turned out to be the machinations of a hidden alien invader. Still people wondered what the CS might have up its sleeves.

It began two years earlier with the appearance of mysterious raiders clad in black and white skeletal armor. No one knew from whence they came, where they went, or why they attacked. Like harbingers of death, these armored warriors would bear down on a village or a caravan and decimate it. They struck without provocation, rhyme or reason. They left no witnesses and took no booty. Their only purpose seemed to be destruction for its own sake. Or was it genocide?

The "Skeleton Raiders," as they became known, seemed to target nonhumans — the only two exceptions were an encampment of mercenaries hired by Tolkeen, and a town known to supply and harbor members of the Federation of Magic; both known enemies of the *Coalition States*! Speculation soon turned to a Coalition plot. Was it coincidence that these armored devils wore the infamous Death's Head that had become the Coalition States' trademark? The armor and markings were different, more alien and frightening than the famous black Dead Boy armor, but could it be a variation for a special division? Perhaps field tests of an experimental prototype armor using D-bees as guinea pigs? While it was true murderous aliens emerged from the Rifts with terrifying frequency, and bones, skulls, and death's heads are a common motif among Juicers, bandits and warriors of all kinds, many felt the similarities and coincidences were more than mere chance.

Many contended that the Skeleton Raiders had to be tied to the Coalition States. They attacked only D-bees and enemies of the Coalition. They never ventured into the heart of CS territory and not a single human citizen of the States was ever endangered, let alone injured or killed. At least 90% of the attacks occurred in territories west of the Coalition States of Chi-Town, Missouri, and Lone Star (Texas), with occasional incidents in Arkansas, Minnesota and the Ohio Valley. A tiny handful of survivors reported close encounters of the worst kind with Skeleton Raiders in flying power armor and giant airships reminiscent of the Coalition's Death Head Transport. Most of these survivors frequently disappeared without a trace. Two were captured by CS soldiers and charged as subversives.

Only the Coalition State of Free Quebec (the furthest away from the actual incidents) expressed concern about these raiders. Chi-Town authorities issued the following statement:

"After a thorough investigation, we have found no evidence to support the existence or activities of a threatening force from another dimension. Rift activity has been light to moderate. Those who suggest otherwise are alarmists and rabble-rousers."

Despite their claim of a "thorough investigation," there was no evidence that even the most cursory investigation was actually conducted, more evidence of CS deception and a possible conspiracy.

The CS propaganda machine continued to routinely suggest that these "reports, rumors and wild imaginings are the result of unsubstantiated paranoia, mass hysteria, coincidence, D-bee activity, the deliberate acts of terrorist groups, the work of sorcery, and hallucination." In a calculated move that only benefited the CS, Emperor Prosek authorized the mobilization of 80,000 troops, "... in an act of good faith, to allay the fears of those who call upon us for help." In addition to the troops, *new border outposts* were established "... to create a sense of increased security in the areas most troubled by these 'phantom' raiders."

The deployment of troops only served to more firmly entrench the CS along its borders and raised more speculation that the CS was somehow involved.

Gossip fueled by hate and terror spread like wildfire. One of the most popular rumors was that the mysterious raiders were actually a new branch of the CS Army conducting military maneuvers in non-allied territories. Another was that the Coalition was conducting field tests of experimental military equipment. And one of the most far-fetched (and terrifying) was that the Skeleton Raiders were really a CS army battalion from a parallel dimension that had formed an alliance with the CS of Rifts Earth in an action to conquer both planets.

The inhabitants of North America would soon learn that the first two rumors were closer to the truth than anybody would have liked to believe.

Shortly after the *Juicer Uprising*, Emperor Karl Prosek addressed his people to fuel the fires of their fears. He used the incident as a springboard for his announcement of a military campaign he called, "the Crusade for Humanity," and the unveiling of the *New Coalition Army*.

The following are excerpts from Emperor Prosek's speech inaugurating the "New Coalition War Campaign."

Emperor Prosek

"To embrace the inhuman is to lose our humanity.

"To accept the alien is to lose our identity.

"To use magic is to forsake technology.

"Magic and the acceptance of the monstrous, alien and inhuman is the poison that eats away at our people!

"They represent an enemy obsessed with eradicating humanity from this Earth. Our Earth! But we shall not succumb. We will not be like the weak fools in Tolkeen, Kingsdale, Lazlo and other domains where men consort with monsters and are seduced by magic. Unlike them, the people of the Coalition States are proud and strong. We have not forsaken our humanity. Our humanness is precious and pure. We will not allow the destruction of human civilization without a fight!

"We are human! We are the people of Earth! This is our world! Ours alone!

"I cannot and will not stand by idle and mute while our identity as a people and our very existence is strangled by the hands of demonic invaders! I refuse to let my race be obliterated! I will fight till my dying breath, or until man is again the master of his fate and his world! That is my solemn oath. That is my promise to humankind.

"I am your salvation! Trust in me! Follow me! See that my words ring with harsh truth and justice. Do not allow the inhuman invaders to tread on you or your neighbor. Together we can push off the heavy foot of oppression that seeks to hold us down and crush our spirit.

"Do not be afraid to stand with me in the pursuit of triumph and justice against our inhuman enemies, they who would murder our children, enslave us like cattle, and rape our beloved planet. Join me for the good of all mankind! I shall lead you to freedom and glory, though it be down the long and painful road of war. Remember, freedom and justice are never easily plucked. They must be earned through hard-fought battles and heroic sacrifice.

"War is what binds us and gives us direction and hope. Hope that we will one day be free of the tyranny of the creatures from the Rifts! Free to walk outside our walled cities without fear. Free to let man's genius and creative spirit soar without being beaten and mocked by easy magic and alien powers.

"It is our resolve that makes us strong and unites us as a people. A resolve to reclaim our world from the monsters who seek to enslave us and the madmen who call upon dark magicks.

"I have been called ruthless. I have been called mad. If I am ruthless, it is because I fight without mercy against the enemies of humankind. I will not loosen my fierce grip on my humanity or my identity. Nor will I sacrifice my race to the alien hordes! I am human. This is my world, and I lash out at the enemy without hesitation and with brutal force. I conduct a war of annihilation against the alien, the grotesque and the unnatural. They are the abominations who seek to usurp humankind's place in the world, and I will not allow it. I sing out to all D-bees, mutants, aliens, demons and monsters, this is my world and you cannot have it! My people and I will fight you to our last breath. Go back to your hell pits and abyss of magic. Remain on our planet and prepare to be destroyed! If not by my hand, then by the multitudes who stand with me and who will not succumb! If this is ruthlessness, then I am ruthless!

"My dream is a dream of peace and prosperity for all humankind. I fight for the generations that will follow me so that they can walk our planet without knowing the fear and chaos that we must endure today. If my dream of salvation, freedom, and peace are those of a madman, then I welcome my insanity and bid you all to share in my madness!"

Cheers and applause erupted throughout the speech, but the Emperor's last statement elicited a standing ovation that lasted 15 minutes. Televised close-ups of the Emperor showed him so moved that a tear ran down one cheek. News commentators praised him for his leadership, compassion, courage and conviction.

Phase One: A Campaign of Unity

The Emperor continued by outlining "a new military offensive." Phase one was a "Campaign of Unity." He proudly announced that the Coalition States of Missouri, Lone Star, and Iron Heart completely supported his plan. **Iron Heart** was recognized as a major manufacturer and political power. The Em-

peror described Iron Heart's renewed commitment to the Coalition States and the leadership at Chi-Town, and their offer to work closely and completely with him in both the new military offensive and the Campaign of Unity. The Emperor praised them for their commitment and how their open cooperation could only strengthen the ties between Chi-Town, Iron Heart and all the Allied States. The Emperor waxed on about their spirit and dedication to creating a powerful and united Coalition States.

Emperor Prosek also proudly announced the candidacy of the territory of Arkansas for Statehood. Reportedly, the events surrounding the *Juicer Uprising* has convinced the people of **Fort El Dorado** to accept the Coalition's standing offer to join the States. The CS is presently helping their long-time ally to recover from the destruction caused by the Uprising. To help in the rebuilding process and defenses, the Emperor has dispatched an entire field army of some 23,000 troops; at the request of the kingdom's leaders. The troops are assigned to help with the clean-up and rebuilding of Fort El Dorado as well as the defense of its oil fields and borders from brigands who might try to take advantage of their weakened condition. The first of several major CS military installations is currently under construction on the outskirts of the kingdom as the "cornerstone in the frontline defense against such menaces as the Pecos Barbarians to the southwest and the denizens of the Magic Zone to the northeast." Fort El Dorado is expected to be back on its feet within one year. When Arkansas is ratified as a State of the Coalition, Fort El Dorado will be its capital.

Part of the "unifying process" and qualification for Statehood will include the "pacification of rebels and inhuman invaders," already underway (Translation: CS forces are marching on the scattered feudal kingdoms of Arkansas, smashing their defenses and conquering human communities — cooperate or suffer and die. While D-bees who may have inhabited the region for generations are being forced out or risk annihilation). The CS has successfully turned the disaster of their involvement in the Juicer Uprising into a positive political and propaganda campaign that serves only their interests. Its success is unparalleled in recent years and harkens back to the great, anti-Federation of Magic campaign of 12 P.A. It has given the CS an excuse to significantly increase its military presence in outlying regions and enemy territories "... to protect our human neighbors from the tyranny of alien enslavers and hostile elements allured by the recent conflict."

The Coalition States are so well positioned that they could easily seize control of the Arkansas Territory with little resistance and make major pushes into several other enemy held territories, including Minnesota. **Note:** Although Arkansas has been accepted as a prefered candidate for statehood, its official status as a Coalition State is a few years away (1D4+1).

Newtown (Arkansas), the site of the Juicer insurrection and the secret base of the UTI aliens, has been renamed *Redemption*, and is now under the jurisdiction of the CS, with the complete approval of Fort El Dorado (see **Rifts World Book 10: Juicer Uprising** for all the rocking action and complete details). It is currently being turned into a CS military base with a full Coalition Juicer conversion center and army training complex.

The Emperor further stunned the nation by reporting that the Coalition States recognized **Ishpeming (Northern Gun)** and the **Manistique Imperium** as independent nations and *allies* of the CS! As evidence of their good will, the States have entered into a free trade agreement and nonaggression pact with the two new nations. Furthermore, Ishpeming and the Manistique Imperium are working jointly with the Coalition to destroy the alien threat represented by *Naruni Enterprises* — hereby branded as an alien menace and marked for "eradication from the continent."

The CS has also strengthened its ties with the *New German Republic*. This relationship remains something less than the full alliance desired by the Germans, but is considerably more than what has existed in the recent past.

Rebellious Quebec

The Emperor pauses for dramatic effect and puts on his sad face. All the news is not good. In a solemn tone, the Emperor explains that the State of Free Quebec has seceded from the Coalition States.

"It is with sadness that I now speak of **Free Quebec**. This eastern jewel in the Coalition States has become the wayward child that must be brought back into the fold. It is with a heavy heart that I must declare the leaders of this State *traitors*.

Agents from Chi-Town and Iron Heart have confirmed that Quebec continues to ignore the laws and policies of our nation. Time after time they have resisted conformity with the rest of the allied States. They have lost sight of our goals.

"In their arrogance they have never truly embraced the needs and rights of the people under Coalition law. Their maintenance of forbidden technology over the decades, such as the Glitter Boy and Juicer technology, are but just a few examples of their insolence and detachment from the rest of us. While I, myself have recently sanctioned the inclusion of an elite Juicer force into the Coalition Military, Quebec has done so in secret for years. These are but a few of their affronts. Recent developments have further illustrated their lack of unity and defiance.

"They have openly condemned *our* great Campaign for Unity and refuse to participate. When we insisted they support the people of the allied States, they dared to threaten retribution if Chi-Town or the other States should try to force their involvement. To defy the Coalition States is to spit in the face of humanity. Suffice it to say, that I have just this morning asked the government of Quebec to step down without fear of persecution, and to let a Chi-Town interim government step in to reestablish the proper order of things.

"They have refused and declared Quebec a free and sovereign nation.

"Before the eyes of the world, I repeat the plea I made to the leaders of Quebec just this morning. I beg the old regime to step down. I will give them 30 days to reconsider their position. During that time, I ask that the people make their voices heard and implore their leaders to stop this madness. It is only together that we can remain strong. I know the people of Quebec believe in our allied States and rebuke their leaders for this pathetic attempt to steal personal glory and power for themselves. Thus, it is with great trepidation that the Coalition States has unanimously agreed to *declare war on Quebec*! The independent nations of Ishpeming and the Manistique Imperium support our position. They have agreed to participate in a trade embargo against Quebec, and will ask the leaders of Quebec to reconsider their current course of action.

"We are committed to use whatever measure of force necessary to reunite our nation. I find the very thought of using force against our own kind abhorrent. It makes me sick. Yet ... for the good of our nation ... and all of humankind, I will do what I must.

We must be a united people to win our campaign against the inhuman enemy. The people of Quebec are patriots who have become prisoners and pawns of their leaders. Thus, we shall liberate them and bring their treasonous leaders to justice."

— *Emperor Karl Prosek*

A Campaign of Terror

From the Diaries of *Erin Tarn*

As I watched the live transmission of Emperor Prosek's *Campaign of Unity* speech, I remember feeling cold and numb. If there was any conversation, I don't recall any. The twenty of us sat there with our solitary thoughts and fears, absorbing every terrifying word. It seemed like an eternity after the Emperor's speech before anybody could muster the energy to speak. I can't tell you who spoke first. I was in a haze. I heard words buzzing around me like someone calling me from a dream, but I don't recall what was said. When I came out of my dreamlike daze, I only needed to look at their faces and hear the tone in their voices to bring me up to speed. We had just been put on notice, our world was about to be torn asunder. After nearly a decade of relative quiet and peace, the Coalition was on the move.

Prosek had effectively declared war against all that wasn't human. To punctuate the point, he unveiled his new military war machine.

There were always rumors and suspicions about Coalition plots and war plans, but none of us were prepared for what he presented. The Coalition State of Chi-Town was far stronger than any of us had imagined. From the reaction of the citizens, at least as seen on the video, he had their full, blind support.

What nauseated me was Emperor Prosek's playing to his people's fears and patriotism. He was an expert at disguising his own hatred and ambition as a holy quest for peace, justice and freedom. I doubt the man knows the meaning of those words. But like it or not, his words are powerful and effective. Tonight they plunged a nation into war as his people applauded and thanked him for it.

His son, Joseph, probably wrote most of the speech. It had many of his hallmarks. It's a thought that sends chills up and down my spine. The devil has a son who is even more insidious, manipulative and evil than his father. We can expect a legacy of evil from a family solidly entrenched in the halls of power and which could remain in place for generations. It is hard to imagine. I pray that I'm wrong.

I wonder what the reaction of Free Quebec must have been. Did they have any inkling of what was unfolding? They are, well, until recently were, a member of the Coalition States. Did they know about the creation of the new Coalition war machine? Did they contribute to its creation? Or were they left in the dark with the rest of us? Whatever their suspicions may have been, it must have come as a shock to be declared the first target in the CS campaign of "unity."

Unity. The use of the word seemed blasphemous coming out of Prosek's mouth. A war of unity. The two words don't seem like they should fit together, yet in an odd way they do. The devil was right about one thing, war seems to bind and unite the people of the Coalition States. It gives them purpose and direction. I suspect it also empowers and strengthens them, giving both a sense of destiny and control that does unify the people. Those who fall under their boots are beaten into submission and absorbed into the fold; which is also a sort of unity from a certain, twisted perspective.

Free Quebec's mistake was not toeing the party-line. They struggled to maintain their independence and dared to question the great Emperor. I guess they didn't realize that Prosek is a brute and a bully. For him, the bottom line is to submit to his will or suffer the consequences. The consequences, of course, being forced into submission or death. Cruel. Brutal. But effective.

I forget who said this about Adolf Hitler, but it applies equally to the Prosek family and people like them; "Tyranny is a terrible habit that becomes a disease of barbarity." Karl Prosek is never afraid to use force. In fact, I think he's gotten quite used to it; even enjoys it. Force, fear and manipulation are the real weapons used by the Prosek family to build their Empire. Enemies who can't be broken are destroyed. Enemies who fear destruction often surrender and submit with little resistance, and once they submit, they are held in check with the same three weapons: force, fear and manipulation. I must admit it is a formula that has worked well for him, but a rule through force, fear, intimidation and ignorance cannot last. Or so I pray.

I still can't get over it. My mind keeps rushing back to his words today and his people's cheers at the promise of war. It exhibits a horrifying new level of nationalistic intolerance and a fanaticism I wouldn't have believed if I hadn't seen it myself. Has this madman and his son grown to such power that they can lead their people into hell with cheers and revelry? Is Prosek that powerful? That evil?

At the time, I felt overwhelmed by a great sadness and disbelief. I felt like I should cry, but I was too numb. It's two days later and I still can't believe it and I still can't cry. Our information network reports CS troops are already moving into position against Free Quebec and new forces have joined the standing army entrenched around Tolkeen. It would seem the Emperor has wasted no time implementing his Campaign of Unity. His brazenness has reached new heights.

The people of Tolkeen are as prepared as they can be for the inevitable. I just know this battle will be worse than anyone suspects, Emperor Prosek included. In many respects, the leadership at Tolkeen is as narrow-minded, manipulative, brutal and fanatical as their enemy. They wield magic that is more devastating than anything the Coalition has ever faced before. Ironically, it is as much the product of Emperor Prosek's mania as his own army. There was a saying in the old American Empire, "Necessity is the mother of invention." So it is, when faced with war and almost certain genocide, the sorcerers of Tolkeen have developed machines of war fueled by magic that rival anything the Coalition may have, and may even surpass the Federation of Magic in their range of mystic knowledge and raw power.

The Council at Lazlo has tried to stay out of the conflict. We have our philosophical differences with Tolkeen and cannot accept many of the things they uphold. However, the Coalition States may have pushed us all to a point where unpleasant compromises must be made to fight a common enemy. There are even rumors that the Cyber-Knights, led by Lord Coake, himself, ride to join the forces at Tolkeen. If this is true, it may polarize the entire region and bring many of the independent kingdoms, magic and not, to side with Tolkeen and stand against the Coalition States. This will be a terrible conflict.

As for the ex-State of Free Quebec, I must admit I was surprised to learn that they had opposed the Emperor's plans for military expansion. Even more surprised, and impressed, that they had the conviction to remove themselves as a member State under the threat of war. I applaud them and admire them, but fear for their existence. I couldn't help but notice that Emperor Prosek referred to the nation as "Free" only in the opening sentence of his speech. All other references to the nation were strictly as, "Quebec." The Emperor and Joseph choose their words too carefully and deliberately for this to be coincidence. If Free Quebec should fall, it will never be free again, you can count on it! The members of the current regime will be slaughtered, any resistance crushed and the government seized by Chi-Town. While this may be Prosek's plan, Free Quebec will not be a prize easily won.

From what I have learned, the other States, particularly Lone Star and Iron Heart, have been working in concert developing the new CS Army. The only notable exception was Free Quebec, who appears to have known nothing about it; although I imagine they had their suspicions. I find myself asking the same questions the people of Free Quebec must be asking themselves. Why keep them out of the loop in such an important political and military development unless one thought they were an unreliable ally, and/or one planned to use the army against them all along. It is no secret that the Chi-Town leaders, especially Karl and Joseph Prosek, have always seen Free Quebec as a thorn in their side. The government of that nation has never played by the Emperor's rules and have quietly defied him on numerous issues and positions.

Emperor Prosek claims that the people of Free Quebec do not support their government. I believe this is a lie to make himself appear to be the great liberator. The people of Free Quebec have always been fiercely independent and strong-willed. From the inception of that nation, they have always called themselves "Free." Even as a member of the CS, they called themselves the "Coalition State of Free Quebec." Looking back, it now seems inevitable that the alliance between Free Quebec and the other Coalition States was destined to fail. The bonds between them were never strong. The people of Free Quebec *have* always been arrogant and self-sufficient. They are not sheep that follow the leader. These are admirable traits to be sure, but Free Quebec is far from being sinless. They too, are militant human supremacists and can claim their share of atrocities and evil acts. If they rejected the Emperor's call to arms, one can rest assured that it was in their own self-interest. I have to wonder if their spies did not uncover a Chi-Town plot to undermine their power and position within the Empire.

My hope is that attacking Free Quebec proves to be Emperor Prosek's big mistake. Just as Hitler and Napoleon had underestimated the Russians (and Russia itself), attacking Free Quebec could be disastrous. It divides Coalition forces between at least

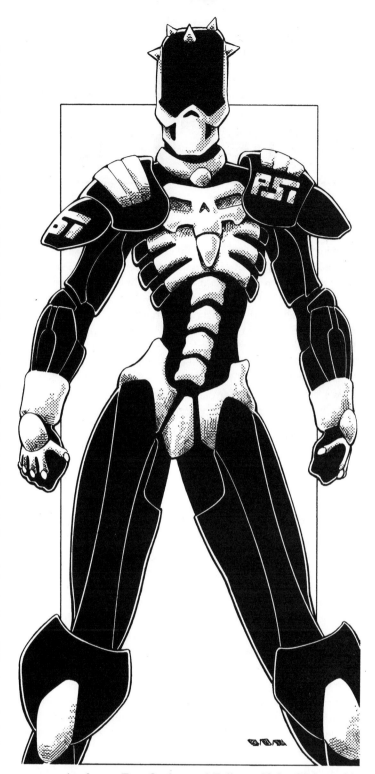

two major fronts; Free Quebec and Tolkeen. If the CS is unable to take Free Quebec quickly (and I suspect Free Quebec will not fall easily), it will drain their resources and will show the world that the new, allegedly "invincible" Coalition army is vulnerable. Furthermore, the division of the army and the strain on resources should leave holes in their defenses that others, such as the Federation of Magic, Pecos Empire, and Xiticix, could exploit to their advantage. I think Emperor Prosek and his Generals also underestimate the spirit and strength of both the people and military of Free Quebec. I have visited Quebec many times, and despite his claims to the contrary, I was always left with the impression that the people support their government completely and embrace their freedom as a nation and a people. I fear this will be a long and bloody campaign. God help us all.

— *Erin Tarn* — *Autumn 105 PA*

Declared Enemies of the Coalition States

Erin Tarn

Enemy Number One is the unlikely figure of the historian and outspoken champion of civil rights and freedom, Erin Tarn. She has been a thorn in the side of the Coalition States for forty years, but it has been in the last twenty that the famous rogue scholar has achieved legendary and heroic status. She is the most famous personality in North America and is more famous (and beloved) than Emperor Prosek. A recent (secret) survey conducted by the CS propaganda machine headed by Joseph Prosek II, showed that within the Coalition States 96.5% of all CS citizens knew about Erin Tarn and her writings, although only 3% admitted to having personally seen one of her books. In reality, an estimated 69% of the educated elite are believed to have read one or more of Miss Tarn's books, and an estimated 23% of the uneducated masses cloistered away in the fortified Coalition cities are believed to have read or heard excerpts from her books. Double or triple that number in the Burbs and outlying territories where Erin's accounts of history and her journeys are read aloud to the illiterate masses and taught by rogue scholars and scientists throughout the continent.

By contrast, 100% of all Coalition citizens know of and recognize Emperor Karl Prosek, 88% knew about Joseph, 87% of General Cabot, and 81% the legendary Joseph Prosek the First, founder of the Coalition States. In the Burbs, 98.6% knew of Erin Tarn, 92% in wilderness communities around the States and 67% in the farthest reaches of North America. She is even known by the Splugorth of Atlantis and 61% of their minions. Erin Tarn's name and literary works are also known to many people in Europe and by many educated men, women and D-bees throughout the world. Erin Tarn's name and courage are even known to *individuals* scattered throughout the Megaverse, including True Atlanteans and people on Wormwood and Phase World!

Her candid accounts telling the "true" history of the World (which conflicts dramatically with parts of the Coalition's *version* of history) and diaries telling of her adventures and observations about the world and the people in it (a combination travel log, geographic journal, political commentary and adventure story) are available on paper and computer disks, as well as on video and audio cassettes and disks. Her works are renowned in most free-thinking and liberal kingdoms of North America, like Lazlo, Tolkeen, and Ishpeming, as well as D-bee communities and even among the citizens (rich and poor) of the Coalition States. These books, particularly those that focus on the pre-Rifts American and Canadian Empires and Erin Tarn's political observations and commentaries on Emperor Prosek, young Joseph Prosek II, the Coalition's reprehensible policies of fascism, racism, genocide, rewriting of history, and its attempt to keep its

people ignorant/illiterate, have branded Erin as public Enemy Number One for the last five years (and earned her a place on the top 20 list for the last 32 years).

Periodically, Coalition spies, agents and bounty hunters have tried to capture Erin to bring her to justice, but she has managed to evade or escape all such attempts. She's been captured and rescued or escaped 11 times. On three occasions, her captors found her so charming that they released her on their own. Even among many of the citizens of the Coalition States, she is revered as the matriarch of history and truth, and regarded with compassion and favor.

The famous historian and adventurer embodies everything one would expect from a legendary figure. She is intelligent, inquisitive, observant, quick thinking, resourceful, modest, gentle, compassionate, selfless, and always concerned about others. She is a dynamic and strong-willed woman driven by an insatiable curiosity and indomitable lust for life. Although Erin would argue otherwise, she is one of the greatest heroes of the age.

In an earlier time, Erin was a slender beauty with long, flowing hair. Many of her readers have a romantic image of her based on her books, writings, and stories about her (many entirely fictional; created by well intentioned fans and circulated through the rumor mill). The fact that she has never allowed her photograph to be printed in any of her books, only adds to her mystique. Some photos and artists' portraits of a young Erin Tarn have seen print in unauthorized editions. As a result, most people think of her as a much younger, athletic looking woman. They are surprised, then, when they first meet the present day Erin who appears to be in her fifties, but is really around 67 years old (by the year 106 P.A.). Her short, silver hair, gentle round face, warm eyes and sparkling smile gives her the appearance of being somebody's kindly mother or grandmother. **Note:** Only in the New German Republic is a romanticized, Hollywood-style portrayal of a young Erin Tarn in her late twenties found everywhere: on books, posters, billboards, videos, and computer generated films (both fictional adventure movies and educational films). The German people are crazy about this American antihero!

Erin finds great amusement in people's reactions to her appearance. Inevitably, somebody will remark something like, "Please don't take this wrong, Miss Tarn, but ... you don't look anything like what I imagined." Or, "... you just don't look like a philosopher or adventurer." At which point she'll flash that disarming smile and ask, "Oh? And what does a philosopher or adventurer look like, dear?" A question most cannot seem to answer.

These preconceived notions about her and her appearance enables Erin to travel the countryside unrecognized and evade Coalition agents. She's had many brushes with CS soldiers and

citizens without incident (they never suspected her true identity). On two occasions, well-meaning Dead Boys protected her from a monstrous threat and sent her on her way.

Erin has always thought of herself as common in appearance and has never considered herself a philosopher or political activist, although she is renowned as one. An adventurer? Yes, in the sense that she loves to explore the world around her and all the marvels it contains, especially its people.

Although Erin can be soft spoken and motherly, she is a resourceful, brave, charismatic, and natural leader. Not only is she willing to stand up for what she believes in, but time and time again she has stepped forward to speak the truth when no others could find the courage to do so. Her honest, no nonsense, often uncompromising words have made this gentle woman the enemy of such world powers as the Coalitions States, Emperor Prosek, and Mrr'lyn of England, among others. She has been a source of inspiration to millions — she is the "every" woman who transcends racial, social, political, and economic boundaries. She has touched people in all walks of life, human and inhuman, wealthy and poor, king and peasant.

Over the years, Erin has earned the admiration, love and friendship of some very powerful people. Among them, Lord Coake (founder of the Cyber-Knights), Plato (leader of Lazlo), and most of the members on the Lazlo Counsel of Learning. Her companion, friend and protector for the last several years has been a noble Cyber-Knight named Sir Winslow Thorpe. He has sworn never to leave Erin's side except in death, or until she retires and settles down in one place. She finds Sir Thorpe's devotion both touching and troublesome. She fears that she is taking him away from greater adventure (not likely) and a more fulfilling life. She has tried to convince him that she can take care of herself, but Thorpe will not hear of it. The fact that he has protected her from many potential dangers and has saved her life on three occasions tends to refute her claims to the contrary. On the other hand, she has come to his aid nearly as often and saved his life once. Sir Thorpe values her life more than his own or any other and will not abandon her for any reason.

True Name: Erin Tarn

Family Note: The oldest of seven daughters.

Alignment: Scrupulous

Attributes: I.Q.: 19, M.E.: 24, M.A.: 23, P.S.: 12, P.P.: 10, P.E.: 22, P.B.: 14, Spd.: 13 (it used to be 15, but she's slowing down a tad).

Hit Points: 70; **S.D.C.:** 25

M.D.C.: Since her return from England and Africa, she wears a Millennium Tree leaf poncho with 60 M.D.C. or some other light type of adventurer armor (typically with 40-60 M.D.C.).

P.P.E.: 17

O.C.C.: Rogue Scholar with an emphasis on history and anthropology.

Level of Experience: Fourteenth

Natural Abilities: A natural leader, high intelligence, a curious mind, strong will and pleasant personality.

Psionic Powers: None.

Magic Knowledge: Erin Tarn cannot cast spells, however, she has a reasonable understanding about the fundamentals of how magic, spells, ley lines, and magic pyramids work. She can also read and use magic scrolls (provided they are written in a language she can read)!

Combat abilities: Hand to hand basic (9th level proficiency).

Combat/Attacks Per Melee Round: Four

Bonuses: +1 to strike, +2 to parry, +2 to dodge, +2 to roll/pull punch, +2 to S.D.C. damage, critical strike on unmodified 19 or 20, and judo style body throw/flip (1D6 damage and victim loses initiative and one melee attack). +5 save vs psionics and horror factor, +7 to save vs magic, +12 to save vs magic sickness, +6 to save vs poison and drugs, +6 to save vs disease, +23% to save vs coma/death, and has an 80% ability to evoke trust or intimidation.

Skills of Note (includes I.Q bonus of +5%): Cook, preserve food, basic math, computer operation, radio: basic, anthropology, archaeology, demon & monster lore, magic lore, land navigation, wilderness survival, first aid, swimming, S.C.U.B.A., climbing, running, horsemanship, pilot sailboats, pilot automobile, pilot hovercraft, and pilot hovercycle, all at 98%! Erin can read and write American, Spanish, Euro, and Dragonese at 98% and speaks Gobblely at 85%. She also has W.P. knife and W.P. energy pistol at 14th level proficiency. Other skills include streetwise 72%, forgery 90%, palming 55%, prowl 60%, read sensory equipment 90%, T.V./video 42%, and intelligence 89%.

Appearance: A healthy human woman who looks to be in her fifties.

Special vehicles: A bionic horse, compliments of the King of England.

Equipment of Note: Articles of clothing and numerous items for carrying things, including a backpack, large satchel, small purse, utility belt with eight compartments/pouches, three medium sized sacks, hooded cloak with many pockets inside, and an extra set of travelling clothes, a pair of sandals, pair of boots, pair of walking shoes, sunglasses, leather gloves, six pairs of surgical gloves (for collecting and examining specimens and alien stuff), two air filters, and one environmental helmet with gas mask.

Hardware includes: a portable language translator, pocket mirror, small camera with 30 disks of film (36 exposures each), sewing kit, magnifying glass, pocket flashlight, box of matches, a lighter, a pair of handcuffs, 100 feet (30.5 m) of string, ten feet (3 m) of nylon cord, two spikes, first-aid kit with a half dozen RMK and IRMSS medical nano-bots, tube of protein healing salve, PDD pocket digital disc audio player and recorder (with 30 one inch discs), portable pocket computer (with 24 one inch discs), a pair of hand-held communicators, infrared distancing binoculars, multi-optics band, pad of paper and a dozen markers.

Weapons: Silver cross, large survival knife (1D6 damage), tiny pocket knife (1 point of damage as a weapon), Wilk's laser wand, Wilk's laser scalpel, Wilk's 320 laser pistol (1D6 M.D.; 20 shots), squirt gun (for fighting vampires) and six flares.

Body Armor: Millennium Tree leaf (60 M.D.C.) or Urban Warrior environmental body armor (50 M.D.C.), or similar light armor.

Special Weapons & Magic Items:

1. Millennium Tree leaf armor: 60 M.D.C.; two were given to Erin by King Arr'thuu, only one is left intact.

2. Millennium Tree wand of life with five buds. The wand was a gift from a Millennium Tree during her visit to England.

The powers of the Wand include:

- Superior healing, restoring 5D6 five times a day.
- Casts a total of five spells per 24 hour period. Spells available are negate poison, cure minor disorders, cure illness, purification of food and water, and water to wine. All are 7th level in strength and can be cast in any combination.
- The wand also gives her bonuses (+2) to save vs poisons, drugs, disease and coma (already added to Tarn's bonuses).

3. Magic Amulet: This necklace was given to Erin by Plato 34 years ago and has served her well. It provides her with protection against sickness (+6 to save vs magic sicknesses, including magic and supernatural types) and protection against the undead, including vampires, zombies, and mummies.

Cybernetics: Clock calendar, gyro-compass, and a universal headjack and ear implant. She also has two bio-system fingers on her left hand and a bio-system spleen (lost during her years of adventure).

Money: She rarely has more than 3D6x1000 credits and an additional 3D4x1000 in gems or precious metals. She spends much of her money helping the needy and on books and ancient artifacts for her collection. Her collection of pre-Rifts artifacts, predominantly books, recordings of all kinds, and artwork, is worth at least 150 million credits and is kept in her home at Lazlo.

Alliances & Allies: Erin Tarn is one of the most famous figures of Rifts Earth. Her name is known in almost every corner of the world and even in some other dimensions. She is most renowned and revered by people of learning, but even the illiterate have heard stories about her, her travels, adventures, chronicles of history and commentaries on the people and place of the times. She has won many friends and allies. Some of the more notable include Plato and the people of Lazlo and New Lazlo, Lord Coake and his legion of cyber-knights, the powers at Tolkeen, King Arr'thuu, the Nog Henge Druids, Lo Fung, Victor Lazlo and many others. She is especially appreciated by D-bees, mutants and practitioners of magic whom she has defended many times and because of her teachings regarding education, freedom, justice, and equality for all life forms, human and nonhuman alike.

This has also won her the animosity of the Coalition States, the Federation of Magic, Blood Druids, Mrr'Lyn and other despotic rulers, dictators, monsters and criminals. Even the New German Republic has some concerns about Erin Tarn, partly because her books are so popular among their citizens and because the CS has branded her a dangerous subversive and criminal.

Sir Winslow Thorpe

Erin Tarn's Cyber-Knight Protector

Sir Thorpe volunteered to accompany Erin Tarn on her trek to the Vampire Kingdoms. Little did he know that he'd be swept from one epic adventure to another. They were whisked from Mexico through a dimensional Rift to the living Planet of Wormwood, reappeared on Earth in England, journeyed to Africa to fight the Four Horsemen of the Apocalypse, became members of a gathering of great heroes, and fought side by side with an Egyptian God and the legendary Victor Lazlo (from the 20th Century), before finally being Rifted back to North America.

The valiant knight is pragmatic and practical, yet at the same time, surprisingly idealistic. He is usually a quiet and serious man who appreciates the simple beauty and wonders of life. He is of American Indian descent and Erin has often wondered whether he might be related to the famed pre-Rifts, Olympic athlete, James Thorpe.

The knight sees his association with Erin Tarn as a great honor. He feels that his entire life has led to this moment and that his courage and skills will make a difference in their struggle against evil and injustice. He has vowed to himself to put his best foot forward and to bring honor and glory to the reputation of Lord Coake and his fellow knights. He is a good strategist and tactician as well as an expert in fighting supernatural monsters. Much of his initial training came from Lord Coake and Plato, but experience has taught him some new tricks. His calm confidence has helped to bring a feeling of direction and positiveness to Erin under the most difficult situations.

The knight is extremely fond of Erin Tarn and has dedicated his life to being her protector, confidant, and friend. A friendship that has changed his life and helped him to build his inner strength, open his eyes to the world, and taught him the real meaning of honor, nobility and compassion. She is as much his mentor as Lord Coake or the dragon, Plato.

True Name: Winslow J. Thorpe
Alignment: Scrupulous
Attributes: I.Q.: 14, M.E.: 19, M.A.: 21, P.S.: 22, P.P.: 21, P.E.: 20, P.B.: 12, Spd.: 19
Hit Points: 74, **S.D.C.:** 82
M.D.C.: Environmental armor with 110 M.D.C. plus cyber-armor (50 M.D.C., A.R. 16).
P.P.E.: 19, **I.S.P.:** 78

O.C.C.: Cyber-Knight (psychic)
Level of Experience: Tenth (up a level since Africa).
Natural Abilities: A natural leader, high intelligence, a curious mind, strong-willed and a pleasant personality.
Psionic Powers: 78 I.S.P.; considered a master psionic. His powers include psi-sword (4D6 M.D.), mind block, sense evil, and see the invisible.
Magic Knowledge: None, other than common lore and rumors.
Combat abilities: Martial arts (10th level proficiency)
Combat/Attacks Per Melee Round: Five
Bonuses: +1 on initiative, +5 to strike, +6 to parry, +6 to dodge, +3 to roll with impact, +3 to pull punch, +7 to S.D.C. damage, critical strike on unmodified 19 or 20, karate style kick (2D4 S.D.C.), jump kick and leap kick (both critical strikes), paired weapons, +2 save vs psionic attack and horror factor, +3 to save vs magic, +3 to save vs poison, drugs, and disease, +10% to save vs coma/death, and has a 65% ability to evoke trust or intimidation.
Skills of Note: Literate in American 98%, speaks Dragonese, Gobblely and Spanish 98%, demon & monster lore 90%, anthropology 80%, paramedic 98%, basic math 90%, radio: basic 90%, land navigation 85%, streetwise 56%, pick locks 80%, intelligence 70%, swimming 98%, S.C.U.B.A. 98%, climbing 90/80%, body building, gymnastics (+5% on abilities), prowl 75%, horsemanship 91%, pilot jet pack 78%, pilot hovercraft 95%, pilot hovercycle 95%, pilot power armor 85%, W.P. targeting, W.P. chain, W.P. sword, W.P. energy pistol and W.P. energy rifle.
Appearance: A muscular human male about 32 years old. Indian from the American West — bronze skin, long black hair, brown eyes, and stands six foot, two inches (1.85 m) tall.
Special vehicles: A bionic horse, compliments of King Arr'thuu.
Equipment of Note: Articles of clothing, backpack, four medium size sacks, utility belt with eight compartments/pockets, extra pair of moccasins (great for prowling), pair of boots, tinted visor, pair of leather gloves, and tent.

Hardware includes: A small camera with 12 discs of film (36 exposures each), medical kit with a half dozen RMK and IRMSS medical nano-bots, four laser scalpels, tube of protein healing salve, sewing kit, magnifying glass, pocket flashlight, large flashlight, box of matches, a lighter, 30 feet (9 m) of nylon cord, grappling hook, four spikes, a pair of hand-held communicators, infrared distancing binoculars and a hand axe for chopping wood.
Weapons of Note: Large silver cross worn around the neck, large silver-plated survival knife (1D6+1 damage), pair of throwing knives (1D6 damage), wood nunchuku (1D8 damage), Triax TX-26 particle beam pistol (5D6 M.D.; 15 shots, 400 ft/122 m range), TX-43 light assault laser rifle (three damage settings: 6D6 S.D.C., 2D6 M.D., 4D6 M.D.; 2000 ft/610 m range), squirt gun (for fighting vampires) and four TW rain flares.
Magic Weapon: A rune flail named Isabart Wind. It is a greater rune weapon that was presented to him by Lord Coake and was created by ancient dwarves from Lord Coake's homeworld.

The powers of the rune Flail:

- I.Q. 11 and has a telepathic link with Sir Thorpe.

- Indestructible; blue grey in color and glows a light blue.

- Scrupulous alignment: If any creature of evil or anarchist alignment touches it, they suffer 4D6 points of damage.
- Mega-damage: 6D6 M.D., double damage to vampires, undead, mummies, zombies, animated dead and the Apocalypse demons.
- Spell Magic: The flail can cast four air spells per 24 hour period. The spells are float in air, fingers of the wind, wind rush and breathe without air.

Body Armor: Knight's armor from Wormwood, 110 M.D.C. He may also wear any kind of environmental body armor or use most types of power armor.

Cybernetics: Clock calendar, gyro-compass, and a bionic lung with gas filter and oxygen storage cell.

Money: He rarely has more than 4D6x1000 credits on him at any given time.

Alliances & Allies: Cyber-Knights are native to North America but are known and respected throughout the Americas and much of Africa and Europe. Other knights, warriors and characters of a good alignment are likely to accept any Cyber-Knight as a comrade in arms. However, the reputation of these knights is so legendary that great things will be expected of them. Along these lines, a good number of evil and anarchist characters may want to see just how tough, skilled and noble a Cyber-Knight really is and challenge the character to trials of combat and wits.

Among the more notable heroic figures who consider Thorpe an ally are Erin Tarn, Plato of Lazlo, Lord Coake (his mentor), King Arr'thuu, Sir Prrcyvel, Sir Dred, Lo Fung, Victor Lazlo and Katrina Sun (Isis) as well as most fellow Cyber-Knights. Sir Thorpe believes in equality and freedom for all intelligent beings and treats D-bees with the same kindness and respect as he would a human. This has won him many nonhuman friends and the animosity of the CS.

Naruni Enterprises

Naruni Enterprises has been branded an alien menace. They are accused of supplying and supporting the Federation of Magic, Tolkeen, Kingsdale, and Lazlo as well as D-bees, monsters, terrorists, bandits, rebels and numerous other "Enemies of Humankind." Among the list of crimes leveled against Naruni Enterprise is that they deliberately fuel dissension and instigate war, particularly among nonhumans in neighboring territories (which is true, because it's good for business). The CS edict against Naruni Enterprises goes on to note numerous (true and false) allegations against the transdimensional gun dealers by Ishpeming (the home of Northern Gun Industries) and the Manistique Imperium.

In a move that has left people stunned, both **Ishpeming (Northern Gun)** and the **Manistique Imperium** have been recognized by the Coalition States as independent kingdoms. What is even more shocking is the pair signing an open trade agreement and a nonaggression pact with the Coalition States! The

implications of this event are incredible and will undoubtedly have serious ramifications in the Midwest for generations to come. Many have equated it to a pact with the devil in order to eliminate their Naruni competitor.

As is common procedure, the CS military launched attacks against Naruni agents, reps, caravans and trading posts before any formal declaration of war — a deft and devastating move applauded by the nations of Ishpeming and Manistique. The new Coalition Army has destroyed all *known* Naruni operations. All agents, aliens and D-bees associated with them were gunned down where they stood. The coordinated attack on nine Naruni locations simultaneously, caught the aliens off-guard. Surprised and hopelessly outnumbered, the Naruni operatives didn't have a chance. Few escaped. It is the (welcomed) responsibility of Ishpeming and the Manistique Imperium forces to clean up, salvage equipment and hunt down escapees, other agents and their Earthly, human and D-bee accomplices.

After the devastating first strike, Emperor Prosek declared Naruni Enterprises an enemy of the States that had been dealt with swiftly and decisively. He vowed to destroy this alien threat and ferret out their supporters wherever they may hide. He pointed to the tragedy of Newtown and the plot of the UTI aliens (see **Juicer Uprising**), declaring that even the alien Naruni equipment could lead to corruption and infiltration of alien forces. Thus, it was decreed that possession of any Naruni weapons, equipment and technology was illegal. Anybody caught selling, trading or bearing Naruni equipment inside CS territory will be suspected of treason and collusion with the enemies of humankind. These individuals will be captured, interrogated, and dealt with as is appropriate. "Dupes" tricked into buying/using Naruni equipment will see it confiscated, but they will be held harmless and released without charges. Those who willingly use, sell or trade in Naruni hardware are enemies of the States and will be "destroyed without mercy."

The Emperor then announced that any kingdom, organization or people beyond the Coalition States will be regarded as associating with a dangerous alien invader and is cause for invasion and occupation by Coalition forces. Deadly force will be used on those who resist. Critics of the CS are outraged and have publicly rebuked this policy as nothing more than a thinly veiled excuse to invade and conquer neighboring D-bee and nonallied human kingdoms by claiming that these people represent a threat to the States and humankind.

Northern Gun and the Manistique Imperium have used the Coalition's declaration that Naruni Enterprises is a dangerous alien invader to declare their own war on the "alien menace." Both have dispatched special agents (hit-men and mercenaries) to hunt down and eliminate any trace of their hated competitor. Both have gone on record commending the CS for its insight and quick action to defend the continent from these foul beings. Both have also pledged their active support in eliminating the presence of the Naruni and to prevent Naruni Enterprises from ever re-establishing even the tiniest outpost in North America. They do so with the blessings of the CS (playing right into Prosek's hands, because such a commitment frees the CS of the Naruni and allows them to address other concerns, like Free Quebec and Tolkeen).

This turn of events has made Naruni Enterprises equipment rare and expensive. The day after the CS declaration of war, prices rose 50% above list price and continue to climb.

The Naruni outlook. Being businessmen, the owners and operators of Naruni Enterprises do not consider themselves to be at war with the Coalition States or anybody else. They see the Ishpeming and Manistique pact with the Coalition States as a smart business maneuver that may have very well leveraged them out of the weapons market in North America. The Naruni will swallow their losses and keep an eye open for any changes in the market that they may be able to exploit. However, for the moment, North America is a loss leader for them, and they have abandoned the market.

Always looking for a way to make a buck, Naruni Enterprises is likely to try to cut secret deals with Tolkeen and other communities who may be looking at the business end of a Coalition blaster. However, they won't hang around; they'll make a deal, arrange a drop point, exchange the goods for payment, and return to the safety of another dimension. Factions within Tolkeen, Kingsdale, small wilderness kingdoms and among some mercenary or criminal organizations *may* agree to purchase Naruni goods. *Lazlo, New Lazlo,* and *Free Quebec* will refuse any offers from the Naruni. The Federation of Magic, Psyscape, their allies and associates will also reject such offers, mainly because they prefer to rely on their powers and magic weapons. Most other people will be afraid of sanctions from the CS and trouble from Northern Gun and/or Manistique, so they will avoid the Naruni and their wares like the plague. Of course, the events in North America don't mean Naruni Enterprises won't appear somewhere else in the world.

Note: Also see the sections about Ishpeming and the Manistique Imperium, Erin Tarn's observations and the Emperor's speech in a *Prelude to War.*

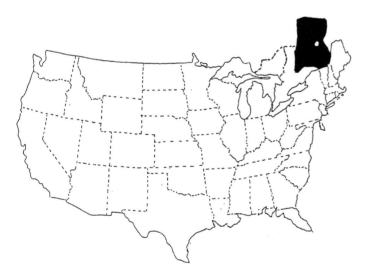

Free Quebec, traitors!

Emperor Prosek, with the support of the other States, has declared the entire government of Free Quebec of treason. They have been ordered to step down within 30 days or be forcibly removed. In response, the government of Free Quebec has declared themselves to be an independent and free nation. Despite the Emperor's claim that the people of Quebec are not behind their government, their declaration of sovereignty is the result of an emergency vote by the people. An overwhelming 87.5% majority voted in favor of seceding from the allied States, knowing full well that it was likely to provoke a war.

The speculations of Erin Tarn regarding Free Quebec's being cut out of social and political interaction between Chi-Town (the seat of CS government) and the other States is accurate, and did not go unnoticed by Free Quebec. It has spies planted throughout the States and many of the unallied kingdoms, including Whykin, Kingsdale, New Lazlo, Tolkeen, Fort El Dorado, and the Manistique Imperium. However, its greatest source of information regarding secret CS operations is through *Iron Heart* where Quebec has spies and sympathizers not only within the general population, but entrenched in the Iron Heart regional army and government! Consequently, although they didn't have complete details, they knew that Iron Heart was cooperating with Chi-Town in helping to up-grade the Coalition Armed Forces. It learned about the development of the Super SAMAS, light assault SAMAS and various other weapons of war nearly two years ago.

The *Quebec Special Investigations Task Force and Division of Strategy and Tactics (SITF-DST)* were also quite convinced that the so-called "Skeleton Raiders" were Chi-Town field troops testing the new weapons and armor. When Chi-Town denied any knowledge of these mysterious raiders and lied about conducting a special investigation that showed the Raiders didn't exist, the Quebec government became convinced that they were a very likely target of Chi-Town aggression. If there was any doubt, it was erased when the following memo to an authority at Iron Heart was intercepted by a Quebec spy.

Extreme caution and the utmost security should be exercised regarding *Project Unity*. The Free State of Quebec has dispatched several inquiries regarding the Skeleton Raiders operating in the Mid-West and what we are doing to investigate the matter. We also have reason to believe that security on YOUR end is lacking and that information vital to National Security is being leaked by various members of YOUR department. Rectify this problem immediately or suffer the consequences.

General Alexander Renton

Within 72 hours, security was increased ten-fold, 132 employees were dismissed under suspicion of being security risks and three were imprisoned for being spies (one actually was). The tightened security, followed by three months of instruction and reorganization by a special envoy of propaganda and security specialists hand-picked by Joseph Prosek II, Head of Chi-Town Propaganda & Communications, has tightened up Iron Heart security immensely. However, Free Quebec had enough information to act upon and still maintains a number of agents and sympathizers within certain areas of the Iron Heart government and military.

Quick to recognize the danger signs, Free Quebec sold the secret plans of Glitter Boy construction to Triax. This deal provided them with over a billion credits in cash and an equal amount of goods in the way of arms, equipment and a special order of Glitter Boys (see **World Book Five: Triax & The NGR**). In addition, the government secretly stepped up production of its own Glitter Boys, Juicers and "special" countermeasures, in case of war. As a result, Free Quebec is much better prepared for war than the leaders at Chi-Town imagine. It will be an incredibly difficult opponent to defeat. In addition to their readiness, resources, Glitter Boy force, and military expertise, they know and understand Coalition operations, strategies and tactics better than any other opponent who has ever faced the Coalition. After all, they were one of the allied States for over 40 years. If anyone can go toe to toe with the Coalition Army, it is Free Quebec.

Furthermore, most CS troops consider this to be a civil war, and civil wars are always difficult and awkward affairs. Meanwhile, the Armed Forces and people of Free Quebec are highly motivated and consider this a battle for freedom.

Two full field armies (some 46,000 CS troops) are already moving on the territory controlled by the ex-State. Another four armies are preparing to move in on Quebec within the month. Note that the firepower of one high-tech mechanized army of the Coalition States is easily the equivalent of 10 times as many 20th Century troops. Their initial task is to establish a military base, survey and assess the enemy and prepare for combat. The fortified super-city of Free Quebec is the ultimate target. When Quebec falls, the rest of the country will quickly crumble to the will of the Emperor. However, Free Quebec is entrenched and ready for a long and difficult war, they will not succumb easily. The matter is complicated by the fact that the Emperor does not want to obliterate the city. He needs and wants its secrets and its manufacturing capabilities. A Quebec that is demolished offers little of value. Furthermore, he and his military *are* conflicted about fighting and killing fellow humans. **Note:** Also see Erin Tarn's views about Free Quebec and the Emperor's Speech in *A Prelude to War*, located in the front of this book.

The Federation of Magic

Magic has been the "great equalizer," and one of the reasons the CS leaders hate and fear it so. An enemy who can cast mega-damage fire balls, call down lightning from a clear sky, summon a fog or storm to cover their movements or to slow the enemy, magically change their physical appearance, create magical body armor, fly, teleport and perform a host of other incredible feats through the force of mind and mystic energy is a formidable opponent. One which the CS military and political leaders do not take lightly.

When the Federation of Magic invaded Chi-Town in 12 P.A., CS society was forever transformed from a peaceful, introspective community into the aggressive, imperialistic Coalition States of today. Prior to that fateful event, the CS Military had both a Psi-Division and a small, experimental magic division. The members of the magic division studied the energies and functions of magic with an eye toward its application by the Coalition States in both military and civilian life. Two platoons

of magic users (mostly Ley Line Walkers; only 10% included Techno-Wizards, Mystics and Shifters) were an official branch of the Army.

Even then, there were grave misgivings about the use of magic in the military, or as a resource of any kind. The primary objections were concerns that the power held by practitioners of magic could not be effectively controlled, regulated and restricted. Nor could magic powers be eliminated after the soldier finished his tour of duty. This made retired soldiers entering civilian life a powerful and potentially dangerous problem. How would the soldier use his powers in civilian life? Did the existence of ex-military practitioners of magic create a powerful elite class of citizen? Did magic powers make these men and women more than human or less than human?

There was additional concern that if the CS leaders endorsed magic for the military, it would encourage ordinary people and members of private industry to also pursue magic. The potential corruption, damage and danger unleashed by magic upon human society was considered monumental and regarded as a threat to human society.

For evidence of this, they pointed to the citizens of Old Chicago, composed largely of practitioners of magic. Under the strong leadership of a Ley Line Walker named *Nostrous Dunscon*, the community had grown into a thriving kingdom and its association with numerous smaller magic communities in the south had earned it the name, **The Federation of Magic**. The place was a constant source of trouble. Dimensional anomalies and Rifts were a frequent occurrence caused by sorcerers and often unleashed monsters and mystic forces that the summoning mage could not control. They were also known to associate with creatures of magic and demonic beings; some as the controller and other times as the controlled. The mages engaged in slavery and blood sacrifices (granted, usually of inhuman beings, but still). The practice of necromancy also seemed to be sweeping the community. Yet most disturbing was the prevalent sentiment among the magic users and their associates that they were better than non-magic users. This bred arrogance and cruelty.

The sorcerers often spoke of the superiority of magic over technology and how magic had brought about a new era that made the old technologies obsolete. Many mocked the fledgling Coalition States and joked about how they would someday become the servants of the Federation. This talk of supremacy, war and conquest understandably raised suspicions and concerns. The CS government saw the magic nation growing in both power and decadence. They seemed to be losing their sense of history and humanity. While some argued that it wasn't magic but the leadership that promoted the sentiments of superiority and allowed the decadence of its people; this line of thought was ignored.

The decision was made to dismantle the CS magic program and to ban the practice of magic from the Coalition States. Laws making magic illegal and plans for making the policies part of the State constitution were created but languished. The CS leaders feared that its citizens would be reluctant to give up a potential resource like magic and that laws banning it would cause dissension among the young nations' people, and/or create an illegal underground of sorcerers.

Ironically, the **Federation of Magic** gave the Coalition leaders the opportunity they had been looking for. The atrocities and terrifying maelstrom of magic and supernatural forces rained down upon Chi-Town by the Federation in the siege of 12 P.A. gave the CS leaders the ammunition they needed to brand magic as something unnatural and more dangerous than a nuclear bomb! Even more ironic is the fact that the tyranny of Nostrous Dunscon would give birth to an even greater nation of tyrants, the Coalition States, with its policies of human supremacy and genocide.

The CS propaganda machine launched its first epic propaganda campaign to win the hearts and minds of its people and turn them against magic. They claimed magic was an unnatural and alien energy that came with the Rifts. Coalition leaders and scientists produced evidence (often theories presented as fact) that it was magic that caused the destruction of the Golden Age of Man (partially true), as well as being the source of the Rifts and the reason the Earth was under siege by monsters and insane wizards. They insisted that magic itself was evil, pointing to the numerous inhuman and demonic creatures who called upon its powers. The horrors of the siege and the tragic loss of life at the whim of the Federation of Magic was presented in excruciating detail. The public was bombarded by film, video, television and radio broadcasts, posters and public addresses about the war. Statistics about the attack focused on the horrific and paid particular attention to the murder of helpless women and children. 11,643 people died, nearly 80,000 others injured, and tens of thousands of homes and property were destroyed. All at the hands of humans and D-bees corrupted by the dark forces of magic.

The Coalition government produced magic experts, psychologists, and historians (claiming magic never existed in pre-Cataclysmic Earth) to support their claims. War heroes were interviewed to recount the horrors of fighting the insane Federation sorcerers and the creatures they commanded. They also presented repentant wizards who had forsaken the ways of magic, and captive members of the Federation of Magic to publicly confess their crimes and describe the power of magic (typically coerced through torture, drugs and psionic manipulation before they were executed).

The people, traumatized by the unprovoked attack and loss of loved ones, drank in every word and believed it all. Before the CS authorities could *suggest* legislation and defenses against magic, the citizens were demanding it. The illegalization of magic was not only implemented within a few weeks after the attack, but wholeheartedly embraced. Furthermore, the people were willing to pour vast amounts of money, resources and manpower into building a bigger and better army. This also gave birth to the idea of the great *fortified super-cities* to provide sanctuary for the millions of people contained within its mega-damage walls.

The so-called "war" with the Federation of Magic lasted less than a year. The initial attack that was so devastating, killing and injuring so many, lasted less than 48 hours. The Federation of Magic fell to the Coalition with relative ease because it was never more than a very loose association of sorcerers and their respective kingdoms. Most were tiny, with fewer than a thousand citizens, 10% or less of whom were actually practitioners of magic. The community led by Nostrous Dunscon on the edge of the Old Chicago ruins was the largest and most powerful with its 64,000 citizens and 12,000 sorcerers and creatures of magic.

It was the insane Nostrous Dunscon who stirred his people and many of the other magic communities into a frenzy. It was Nostrous who, for a few short months, united the scattered members of the Federation to rise and attack Chi-Town. His folly was not realizing that the people he led were not united in any true sense of the word. It was the promise of easy reward and a mob mentality that sparked the war. Like any mob, when the frenzy passed, the participants stood surprised at their own actions and scattered. Not even the charismatic and powerful Nostrous Dunscon could maintain the bloodlust. With each defeat, his supporters abandoned him. When Old Chicago fell four months after the initial attack, the rest of his supporters scattered like rats fleeing a sinking ship. Ironically, had they stayed united and fought together, they may not only have held their position but could possibly have destroyed Chi-Town. It would be the Federation's lack of unity, commitment and cooperation that doomed them.

After peace had been reestablished and the murderous sorcerers had been routed from Old Chicago, General Joseph Prosek the First (Karl's father; Joseph the II's namesake and grandad) drove the survivors of the Federation of Magic deep into the wilderness of the Magic Zone. There, he waged a two year campaign of genocide in an attempt to destroy "every last vestige of the hell-spawned mystics." He nearly succeeded. An estimated 30,000 sorcerers and their "accomplices" were put to death — most scholars outside the Coalition States estimate roughly half were innocent people, for anybody even *suspected* of being a practitioner of magic was slaughtered.

Since the war begun in 12 P.A., the Federation of Magic has been considered one of the Coalition's greatest and most reviled enemies. For the next two generations, the Federation of Magic was believed to have been "obliterated" as General Prosek had vowed. But around 60 P.A., rumors began to circulate that not only did the Federation survive as scattered communities hidden throughout the Magic Zone, but that a new member of the *Dunscon* family had taken the reigns of power and vowed to avenge the death of his family members and the destruction of "his people." Shortly thereafter, around 65 P.A., acts of terrorism claimed by the Federation of Magic were leveled at Chi-Town and other CS communities. Thus far, all the skirmishes have been small and brief. The few largest and most lethal encounters taking place among the ruins of Old Chicago and at the Devil's Gate (the Saint Louis Rift). Coalition patrols into the Magic Zone along the borders of southern Illinois and the Ohio Valley have found little evidence of any formal kingdom or Federation. In fact, according to official CS reports, the existence of Alistair Dunscon and the Kingdom of Dunscon cannot be confirmed and are believed to be unsubstantiated myths. However, investigators have found that there exists what they call a "cult network" of loosely associated magic practitioners, from individuals and clans to small villages. This "cult network" calls itself the *Federation of Magic*, but its members are scattered throughout the old American territories once known as southern Illinois, Indiana, Ohio and Kentucky. It is possible that *Alistair Dunscon* is its leader or a fictional character created to draw attention away from the identity of the real leader. The CS military rates the Federation of Magic as a minor threat.

Game Master Notes: The Federation of Magic and Alistair Dunscon are both very real and very dangerous. Most members of the Federation hate and despise the Coalition States; Chi-Town and the Prosek family in particular. The CS has had

trouble pinpointing the Federation because it is composed of hundreds of tiny villages, towns, clans and individual sorcerers scattered throughout the Magic Zone. From an outsider's point of view, most of these communities, typically numbering from 30 to 600, are "low-tech hicks" with few obvious resources and no *apparent* magic. For decades after the two year *Campaign of Blood*, as the Federation members call General Joseph Prosek the First's legendary purge, many members have been excruciatingly careful to conceal the presence of magic. Only the most brazen (and their numbers are increasing by the day) make no pretense to hide the practice of magic and welcome confrontation with CS troops, often bushwhacking them — 21% of all patrols into the Magic Zone vanish without a trace. However, even the most flamboyant or militant practitioners of magic, dragons, supernatural horrors and creatures of magic are difficult to find in the vast woodlands of the Magic Zone. Others use elementals and magic to conceal their presence from the world until they are ready to make it known.

Undoubtedly, *some* members of the Federation of Magic will join forces with Tolkeen. Others will bide their time and consider taking their own action against the Coalition States when they feel the time is right (Chi-Town and the Prosek family will be their primary targets). Such attacks are likely to take the form of guerilla operations, hit and run tactical strikes, banditry, unleashing ley line storms and creatures from the Rifts and isolated areas of combat.

A major siege is unlikely for two reasons. One, because no one leader, human or superhuman, has risen from the ranks who is capable of uniting the splintered underground society. Second, the Federation of Magic resents Tolkeen and regards it as a rival.

With the possible exception of *Lazlo*, no other kingdom of magic users has a better chance at establishing a nation dedicated to the practice of magic. Something the Federation considers to be its (lost) legacy. Thus, they are jealous and resentful of Tolkeen and will refuse to help. Some members have even suggested that if they stay out of the conflict, the Coalition will destroy Tolkeen, eliminating their rival in dominion over magic, and in the process, weaken themselves so badly that the Federation of Magic can rise up and strike the Coalition down! Less fanatical and more realistic members agree with part of this scenario, suggesting that the CS will be so weak after destroying Tolkeen that it will be unable to stop the Federation of Magic from resuming its rightful place as the preeminent magic society on the continent. **Note:** The World Book dedicated to the **Federation of Magic** will present much more information about this splintered and chaotic secret society and the Magic Zone. Tentatively scheduled for a 1997 release.

Tolkeen

The government and people of Tolkeen were not surprised or phased in the least by Emperor Prosek's announcement or his unveiling of the new army. They have come to expect the worst from their enemy. If anything, they have taken a haughty "we told you so" attitude toward other groups and kingdoms who had chastised their behavior as too extreme and their concerns about the Coalition as overstated. Although they are smug and confident in public, the leaders of Tolkeen were shocked by the alliance between Ishpeming and the Manistique Imperium and are gravely concerned about what it will mean during the impending war.

The Coalition States — the supreme power of North America —has formally declared war against their comparatively tiny nation. As ready and as powerful as they may be, it is doubtful that they can survive a full-fledged war against the Coalition States. Their only hope is that numerous other nations will join them and make the CS reconsider their actions (doubtful). Lazlo and New Lazlo are both considering such an alliance, and one flurry of *rumors* reports that Sir Coake is on his way with 2000 Cyber-Knights.

Presently, Tolkeen is not under siege, but Coalition troops continue to arrive and establish positions along its borders. Several of the small, allied and unallied kingdoms around it have already been attacked and conquered by the CS. Meanwhile, the Coalition troops work to "contain" Tolkeen by severing its supply lines, preventing mercenaries and sympathizers from joining them and disrupting communications. War could erupt within the year or the week.

Other Enemies

Archie-Three. The Coalition has no idea that the robot intelligence and its human partner, Hagan, even exist. However, Archie and Hagan are closely watching what's transpiring with the States, paying particular attention to the Quebec conflict which brings the CS very close to their operations in what was once known as Aberdeen, Maryland. They will probably stay out of things, although Archie has wondered whether he could best serve humankind by joining forces with Chi-Town. Hagan has tried to sway Archie from this train of thought, fearing that the CS will perceive the sentient computer as a threat and destroy them both.

Atlantis. The Splugorth and minions of Atlantis are interested in the events transpiring in the Midwest only as an entertainment and gambling event. Among the bookmakers and bet takers, the Coalition States are the favorite, with Free Quebec second as the favored underdog. Tolkeen offers some of the best odds, but is generally considered a sure-fire loser. Whatever happens, it is likely to have little impact on Atlantis, unless the Coalition States so weaken themselves that the Splugorth see an opportunity to invade and take over themselves (an extremely remote possibility). Splynncryth was delighted by the turn of events that saw the destruction of Splugorth rival, Naruni Enterprises. The Coalition's destruction of the Naruni on the North American continent prompted a six day festival at the city of Splynn.

Cyber-Knights: The Coalition has had little concern about the Cyber-Knights of the American northwest. Members of the two organizations have had a few nasty run-ins, but for the most part, the Coalition States consider the organization to be insignificant. Past altercations have been with one or two members of the group, never the knights as a whole. Furthermore, the knights have been more of a help in combating bandits and monsters in the western wastelands than a hindrance. As a group, the knights have never before sided with any CS enemy. If the rumors are true about Lord Coake and a legion of Cyber-Knights riding to join the battle at Tolkeen against the Coalition, they will have just earned themselves the enmity of the Empire.

D-bees & Practitioners of Magic: All nonhumans and sorcerers are considered to be enemies of the States and presumed to be armed and dangerous. Lethal force is suggested in the "dispersement" of these "enemies" from Coalition territories and war zones. This means it is open season for these two groups of people. Whether or not they are shot on sight depends on the commander of the Coalition force that encounters them. More often than not, such characters can expect a hostile encounter.

Kingsdale: This small kingdom's days are numbered. The Juicer Uprising has weakened it and put Coalition troops on its back-porch. The question remains only "when" will the Coalition invade. The answer is soon. Many people, especially D-bees and practitioners of magic, have already begun to leave the city and the state of Missouri entirely. The Juicer population and a number of wandering Juicer bands are ready to make their last stand at Kingsdale in one, final, grand battle against the hated Coalition.

Lazlo: The Coalition States considers this comparatively small, independent nation to be a danger to their quest for power. It is the home of Erin Tarn and a place where humans and D-bees live together in harmony. It is also a place where the practice of magic is commonplace and (in the opinion of CS authorities) the quest for knowledge and personal freedom is taken to dangerous extremes. Lazlo has been a refuge for peace-loving beings from all walks of life and has been outspoken against the Coalition States. However, because it has never threatened the States and is perceived to be populated by peace-lovers, scholars, and philosophers, and the CS has greatly underestimated its power, and considers it a secondary target. In truth, Lazlo is only slightly less formidable than Tolkeen. Unknown to most people of the world, it has one of the largest populations of dragons, True Atlanteans, Temporal Raiders and creatures of magic outside of Atlantis.

New Lazlo: This small kingdom is a lot like a teenager, young, full of vitality, enthusiasm, and high ideals and sees itself as strong and indestructible. Consequently, they are outspoken and brash. Up until now, they have been barely noticed by the Coalition, but if they continue to make waves and/or publicly support Tolkeen, even if only in words, they will be crushed.

Mercenaries: A number of mercenary groups, adventurers and opportunists (bandits and scoundrels among them) are presently considering their options, sympathies and best opportunities in the face of the impending conflict. One side or the other is likely to have some need that a merc can satisfy, whether it be smuggling supplies past the enemy, spying, sabotage or assassination to straightforward military operations. Inevitably, a number of mercenaries and opportunists will join forces with all the parties involved. Meanwhile, a juicy secondary market among the smaller, unallied kingdoms and wealthy merchants will also offer mercenaries and adventurers work. The worst freebooters will engage in banditry and crimes against all sides, attacking whomever seems vulnerable at the time.

Others: Characters of all O.C.C.s and R.C.C.s, both good and evil, are likely to be polarized by the Coalition's Campaign of Unity. This means characters from distant parts of the North American continent, and even the occasional character from Central and South America, Europe and Atlantis may travel to America to join one side or the other, or to try to get their share of the spoils of war.

The Pecos Empire: The Pecos barbarians of Texas are an irksome enemy of the CS, but are among the least of their worries. Unless these bandits provoke a confrontation by laying siege to the Lone Star Complex or Fort El Dorado, their destruction will probably be postponed for years. The Pecos Empire is composed of a motley crew of D-bees and monsters who terrorize lower Texas and parts of Mexico and the west as bands of marauding raiders and bandits. While they are certain to attack CS outposts and convoys, they are too unorganized and undisciplined to represent a serious danger to Coalition operations.

Xiticix in the north: For the moment, the Xiticix menace is of no concern to the Coalition States. However, as they continue to encroach on territories in Minnesota, Wisconsin and Illinois, they will become a threat to Chi-Town and other CS holdings. Likewise, the insectoids are a potential threat to Iron Heart. They will be dealt with after the Campaign of Unity has reunited Quebec, seen Arkansas join the Union, and Tolkeen is destroyed.

Coalition Allies

Ishpeming (Northern Gun) & the Manistique Imperium

These two nations have functioned independently for over 115 years. Ishpeming is most famous as the home of weapons, robots, and vehicle manufacturer *Northern Gun*; the disputed kingpin of arms manufacturing in North America.

The Manistique Imperium is the smaller and less technologically advanced of the two, but has also been in existence as a small manufacturing nation for over 100 years.

In both cases, the two nations rose to power based on pre-Rifts technology that survived the Great Cataclysm. Using factories, equipment, manufacturing designs and schematics, the two were able to reconstruct factories and production facilities for the making of weapons, armor and vehicles. With time, they became adept at pirating technology from other sources and creating "knock-offs," copies of items originally designed and built by other manufacturers. Their geographic location in upper Michigan, surrounded by the Great Lakes, helped to isolate them and keep them safe from bandits, monsters, D-bee invaders and the burgeoning Coalition States. Consequently, they avoided the strife that plagued the Midwest and other parts of the country, and slowly, but surely prospered and grew.

By the time people began to notice them, they were firmly entrenched and too powerful to be easily conquered. Furthermore, many small kingdoms, communities and organizations had become reliant on the two for weapons, vehicles, components, electronics and equipment used in all walks of life. Northern Gun and, to a lesser degree, Manistique Imperium products had become the life's blood of virtually every independent kingdom and community within 2000 miles (3200 km) of Northern Michigan. A survey conducted by the Chi-Town propaganda and investigations committee (under the supervision of Joseph Prosek II) found that 96% of all mercenary groups, 92% of all bandits and 89% of all independent kingdoms, large and small, purchased a substantial amount of weapons, equipment and materials from Northern Gun. 76% of mercs, 54% of bandits and 61% of all independent kingdoms made purchases from the Manistique Imperium. By comparison, roughly 12% purchased superior but expensive and hard to find Triax items (usually in small quantities), 19% from Golden Age Weaponsmiths, 24% from the Coalition State of Iron Heart and 41% from Wilk's Industries. Wilk's numbers are comparatively low only because this manufacturer specializes exclusively in precision and high quality laser weapons, tools and the occasional other item, while Northern Gun (Ishpeming) and the Manistique Imperium produce a full range of products from guns and armor to vehicles and electronics.

For decades, the Coalition States had ignored the activities and high volume sales of these two manufacturers for three reasons.

1. The weapons, armor, bots and general level of technology was inferior to the CS, and continues to be 20-30 years behind the States.

2. The two nations did not represent an obvious threat. They have never challenged the CS or engaged in any military campaigns. They conducted their business quietly, plus isolated in the Michigan wilderness, they were out of sight and out of mind.

3. The CS grossly underestimated the extent of the two manufacturers' positions in the marketplace — not that the Emperor, the CS military or any of the Chi-Town leadership would publicly admit it. Only Joseph Prosek II suspected the range of influence that these two quiet arms and technology merchants had built over a hundred years of manufacturing and promotion. Yet even he was taken aback by the final numbers of his investigation; a full 30-40% higher than what he had estimated. It is likely that even Northern Gun and the Manistique Imperium are not fully aware of the extent of their influence, wealth and power.

It was this recent study that led, in part, to the Coalition's recognition of the two as independent nations and its overture for

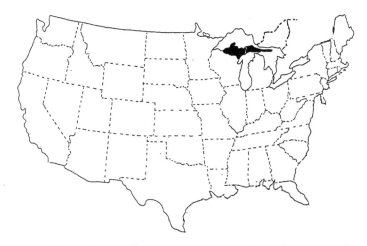

peaceful coexistence. It was simply smart and politically expedient to establish an open and friendly line of communication with these two sleeping giants. Furthermore, if the Coalition could build a friendly and mutually profitable relationship with the two, it could better monitor their activities and exercise some influence regarding to whom they sold their products. This influence comes in the guise of friendship, cooperation and mutual respect, not the Coalition's usual pressure tactics and threats. A good example is the embargo against Free Quebec and their aid in combating Naruni Enterprises. In both cases, Ishpeming and the Manistique Imperium's cooperation with the Coalition States has created an immediate, short term (1D4 years) economic boom for the two independent nations. In the case of the embargo against Free Quebec, Ishpeming and Manistique had nothing to lose since trade with that State had been minimal to begin with. The Chi-Town authorities sweetened the pie by presenting the two with a very open and liberal trade agreement that not only allowed them to continue to sell arms and supplies without limit to virtually everywhere else on the continent (despite impending war), but opened to them the expansive markets of the border towns and wilderness communities in the outskirts of the Coalition's Empire. This was a win, win situation for the Coalition because they had been unsuccessful in servicing this area of the market. With Northern Gun and the Manistique Imperium involved, the outer edges of the CS States and territories would receive superior service, making those people content and appreciative of their generous government, eliminating one more government headache and giving Ishpeming and Manistique a juicy bone that would hopefully build a lasting friendship and some sense of obligation.

Getting their cooperation to move against Naruni Enterprises was another example of mutual benefit and immediate results for both parties. For Ishpeming (Northern Gun) and the Manistique Imperium, the Coalition States helped them eliminate a serious competitor whose activities in less than three years had caused sales to drop 20-30%. The dramatic and literal "elimination" of the competition had an immediate and positive affect on sales.

For the Coalition States, it eliminated a potential alien danger, but more importantly, rid them of an arms dealer who sold weapons and equipment often equal to their own or even those of Triax. If Naruni Enterprises had remained unchecked, they could have supplied Coalition enemies with weapons and equipment equal to and sometimes superior to their own. This could not be allowed to happen; not with the launching of the new army and the (military) Campaign of Unity. Getting two other major na-

tions to agree with their extreme measures at eliminating the Naruni also helped to diffuse outcries from their other enemies, because they were not alone. Again the Emperor and his advisors have expertly maneuvered themselves into the best possible situation: eliminate a threat and at the same time, strengthen ties with two important allies. Such are the skills and machinations of Emperor Prosek and his minions.

Where this loose alliance will ultimately lead is anybody's guess. At least for the moment, Ishpeming and the Manistique Imperium remain strong and independent. Any changes or closer ties to the Coalition States is pure speculation and probably decades away (if ever). Neither has aspirations of becoming a member State. They regard the CS with suspicion and concern, but also see the Coalition as the dominant power in the land, and as such, a huge, untapped market and a dangerous enemy. Consequently, they chose to open diplomatic and trade channels to ensure their continued prosperity and very existence.

Other Allies of Note

Arkansas & Fort El Dorado: As stated previously, Fort El Dorado and the territory of Arkansas have been accepted as a candidate for membership as one of the Coalition States. Fort El Dorado is the center of CS activity and will become the capital of the new State. They will support the CS in any way they can, but it is their responsibility to help secure and defend the southern and southwestern territories from the Pecos Empire and other forces who might try to invade from the south.

Even after the nightmare of the Juicer Uprising, Fort El Dorado is a strong, fortified community, not to mention a source for oil and natural gas. It also has strategic value because it helps to restrict the Pecos Empire, can help defend the State of Missouri, and offers another line of defense against the Federation of Magic to the northeast.

Fort El Dorado and many of the friendly neighboring communities have had a good relationship with the Coalition States for years. The recent attack by the Juicer rebellion has driven home the value of a stronger, official tie to the powerful Coalition States. Ironically, the Juicer Uprising has made the authorities at Fort El Dorado more insecure and paranoid than it should. Although they suffered great damage and were nearly overrun, they managed to hold their own and survive against overwhelming odds from a surprise attack. While the incident has unnerved them, it impressed the Coalition, making Fort El Dorado a welcomed and rewarding addition to the allied States. Within a decade, Arkansas should rise to its potential and become the second most populated and powerful of the Coalition States!

CS Iron Heart: This mid-tech level industrial nation has always played second fiddle to Chi-Town and Free Quebec, the two genuine powers in the Coalition States. Consequently, the Iron Heart government welcomed the opportunity to become more closely associated with Chi-Town and accept the Emperor's plans for the future, provided Iron Heart played a major role in it. To this end, Emperor Prosek and the leaders of Iron Heart made a secret pact to retool and upgrade a full third of its factories with the most current and advanced equipment and manufacturing systems.

The farsighted Emperor made this arrangement six years ago. Even then, it was clear that Free Quebec was targeted for what

Chi-Town representatives referred to as a "restructuring" of Quebec's government to better reflect the goals of all the Coalition States (i.e. Emperor Prosek). The possibility for war against Quebec was very real and very obvious, still Iron Heart agreed. The decision was actually quite easy. The rulers of Iron Heart agreed with most of the Emperor's positions and they resented their haughty Quebec neighbors. They felt Iron Heart had languished in the shadow of Free Quebec long enough. It was time for them to shine and become the second greatest power within the allied States, even if it meant stepping on the battered body of Quebec to do it. Thus, for the last five years, Iron Heart has rebuilt, grown and become yet another weapon in the Emperor's arsenal against his enemies.

Chi-Town has lived up to everything it promised and more, thus winning the complete loyalty and support of the powers that be. While some citizens are suspicious of their close relationship with Chi-Town and uncomfortable with attacking Free Quebec, the vast majority (73%) are in agreement; roughly 10% are anti-Quebec fanatics.

The first step in the Campaign of Unity was the State of Iron Heart acquiring the renegade manufacturer known as *Iron Heart Armaments,* located in the independent kingdom of **New Kenora** (see **Rifts® Mercenaries** for details). Iron Heart Armaments was established by a handful of rogue engineers who discovered and absconded with several pre-Rifts designs for mega-damage tanks and armored vehicles. One day two months ago, the people of New Kenora woke up to find themselves surrounded by the Coalition Army. They had noticed a division or two of CS troopers on maneuvers along the border of Xiticix territory north of Minnesota, but had thought nothing of it. Additional forces came from the State of Iron Heart and caught the community by surprise. Resistance meant total obliteration, so the community surrendered.

New Kenora and Iron Heart Armaments are now the latest addition to the holdings of the Coalition State of Iron Heart. The city-state is quickly being transformed into a northern military manufacturing center and border fort, ideally located for dealing with both Tolkeen and Xiticix forces. The factories are being retooled to produce the new Coalition tanks and armored vehicles. The civilian population has been invited to stay and work for the CS at their old salaries. Many (30%), fearing to be branded traitors and shot down like dogs, agreed to stay on. About 20% liked the Coalition to begin with and saw this as a change for the better. Another 20% saw it as being as good as any other opportunity (a job is a job). Only 20% fled the area and 9% (mostly D-bees) were executed.

As a magnanimous gesture, the New Kenora factory owners and operators were allowed to keep their civilian positions and stay on to manage the factories. They get a good salary and any issues involving past disloyalty have been forgiven (at least while they work hard and exhibit loyalty to the CS). Only one owner refused and was summarily charged with treason and executed. The others accepted the offer and continue to work diligently for the CS military. They are too terrified to engage in acts of sabotage and several like the idea of working for the Coalition (better job security).

Note: This means Iron Heart Armaments (IR) tanks, vehicles and equipment described in **Rifts® Mercenaries** are no longer being manufactured. However, thousands of those items were

CS Free Quebec

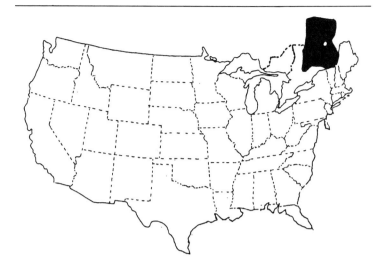

CS Iron Heart

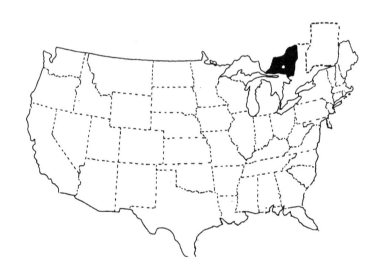

CS Missouri

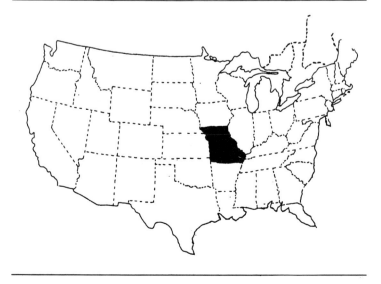

26

CS Lone Star

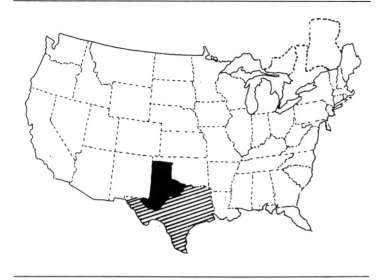

CS Chi-Town

The Domain of Man

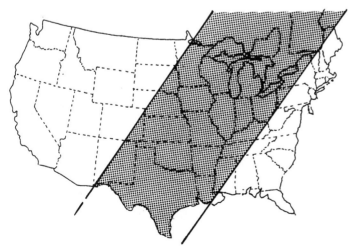

All Around is Hostile Wilderness

produced and sold before the CS occupation and will stay in service for years to come. The CS occupation force was distressed to learn that the original pre-Rifts plans for the tanks and other items are missing, which means they could resurface someplace new.

CS Lone Star: Lone Star continues to be an anomaly. All of old Texas is claimed by the Coalition States, but only the northern quarter is actually under CS control, and even that portion is lightly populated except for the military personnel located at the Lone Star Complex and military outposts.

The main resource of Lone Star is *Lone Star City*, a pre-Rifts military complex that sprawls across 30 square miles of land above and below the ground (three to eight levels below the surface). The complex is packed with some of the most advanced genetics laboratories, medical, bionic and robotics facilities in the world! It is the design center for all genetic experimentation and 50% of all military weapons designs in the States. It is the largest, most advanced scientific (military) research facility in the Coalition States, dwarfing even those at Chi-Town. This also means that 90% of the personnel are highly educated, literate scientists and engineers.

The Lone Star Genetic Engineering Division (GED) represents 40% of the entire complex. The very first Psi-Hounds/Dog Boys came from GED and 85% of all Coalition Dog Boys are genetically designed, mutated and grown at this facility. In addition to the creation of Dog Boys, the complex experiments with the genetic manipulation of other animals as well as cloning, the growing of artificial skin, cybernetic bio-systems, bionic reconstruction, molecular bonding, and, recently, Juicer augmentation. The GED labs are under the direct control of a genius named **Doctor Desmond Bradford**. He operates with complete autonomy as long as he keeps producing results. Unlike the other military and science divisions, Doctor Bradford reports directly to Emperor Prosek and must endure only one annual inspection. This means the work here is so ultra-secret that only the Emperor has any inkling of what is being conducted, and even he only knows what Doctor Bradford decides to tell him. Joseph Prosek II doesn't like or trust Doctor Bradford, whom he believes to be dangerously insane. The Emperor acknowledges that Doctor Bradford is *eccentric* and temperamental, but he won't consider installing any of the "safeguards" that his son has suggested for fear that they might interfere with the Doctor's creativity and productivity. For the moment, Joseph has allowed the matter to sit unresolved, but he keeps a nervous eye on the GED and prays that it is not a powder keg waiting to explode. Meanwhile, Doctor Bradford *seems* to have everything under control and continues to perform his duties admirably. Two full divisions of (over 10,000) Dog Boys have just come out of Lone Star to join the ranks of the military and SSI.

CS Missouri: This is the weakest and most vulnerable of the Coalition States. Much of it is farmland and cattle ranches, making it the bread basket of the Coalition States. In that regard, it is very important, but Missouri is far from a military or political power. Many critics of the CS have accused Missouri of being a puppet of Chi-Town and Emperor Prosek. While such accusations are denied, they are true. The State of Missouri always supports the positions of the Emperor and Chi-Town. Lone Star, virtually a giant military complex, is completely under the control of the Chi-Town regime and always supports the Emperor's position, effectively giving Chi-Town the clout of three States. The acquisition of Arkansas should give Chi-Town additional leverage, although the people of that fledgling State are not mindless sheep and will have some definite thoughts and plans of their own. Until the departure of Free Quebec, they and Iron Heart have always been the two most independent of the (then) five Coalition States.

Golden Age Weaponsmiths: This arms manufacturer is neither an ally or enemy of the Coalition States. They have built a successful business repairing, refitting and selling old, pre-Rifts weapons and equipment, primarily S.D.C. items. Their clients include the Pecos Empire, the Black Market, Tolkeen and numerous independent kingdoms, mercenary groups, bandits, and adventurers. It has only been with Emperor Prosek's recent speech about alliances, war and the Campaign of Unity, that the operators of Golden Age Weaponsmiths stopped to wonder how *they* might be affected. They surprised themselves when they realized that in their 25 years of business they have never had a run-in with the Coalition States. Nor have they ever been approached by the CS as a possible ally. They suspect they are too inconsequential to be of much concern, but wonder if that might change, especially with the new arrangement between the Coalition and Ishpeming and the Manistique Imperium. For the first time, the company looks at an uncertain future and wonders what it holds for them. For now, they continue operations as usual.

Mercenaries: A number of mercenary groups, adventurers and opportunists are already working for the Coalition Armed Forces in one capacity or another. Specialized combat personnel find work as spies, smugglers, saboteurs, assassins, scouts, and Special Forces. Most combat personnel find themselves as frontline infantry troops used as fodder to "soften" the enemy before Coalition troops are sent in. Cyborgs, Juicers, Crazies, experienced scouts (7th level and higher) and power armor and robot vehicle pilots are among the most valuable to the CS. An estimated 30,000 mercenaries have been employed for the Minnesota front alone, and that number is expected to triple or quadruple before the Tolkeen war is over.

Others: Characters of all O.C.C.s and R.C.C.s, both good and evil, are likely to be polarized by the Coalition's Campaign of Unity. This means characters from distant parts of the North American continent, and even the occasional character from Central and South America, Europe and Atlantis may travel to America to join one side or the other to get their share of the spoils of war.

Triax: Triax and the New German Republic (NGR) will watch from abroad and offer the CS their words of support, but there is little else they can do. Five hundred German, military advisors and observers are active among the Coalition Army and can be found at virtually any major outpost or combat zone. The NGR will also continue to provide moral support and a narrow stream of supplies. Military support is out of the question as they have their own intensifying war with the Gargoyle Empire.

Coalition Law

Laws & Penalties

Other than some notable and extreme exceptions, the laws of the Coalition States are fundamentally the same as those of 21st Century Earth, only the penalties tend to be twice as severe. The death penalty is used liberally for crimes that involve extreme brutality, murder, the practice of magic, consorting with the supernatural, and acts of subversion against the State. Most of the notable exceptions, some of which were not crimes in the 21st Century, are listed below.

Penalty Notes

Fines are typically given out for minor infractions. The amount can be as little as 30 credits to thousands depending on the crime. A character may also be forced to pay for any damages he may be judged responsible for.

CS Prisons are hell-holes with only the most basic facilities and freedoms for those contained within its walls. Morale is low and living conditions poor. Guards are authorized to use deadly force to quell troublemakers, rioters and those who attempt escape. Prisons are typically located in dangerous areas within the CS territories — the logic being to remove them from society and if they should perish by extraordinary means, little is lost. Every year, 26% of the prisoners fall prey to foul play, illness, enemy attacks, or monsters. "Lifers" and subversives are usually sent to prison to rot.

CS Prison Work Camps are similar to the minimum security prisons of 20th and 21st Century Earth. The prisoners are usually humans and D-bees who have no significant (known) powers and who represent a minimal threat to authorities. A typical day starts with a shower and breakfast, a 10 hour day of work and a return to a minimum security prison that often resembles a military outpost and barracks enclosed by a light M.D.C. wall or fence. These camps are always established away from Coalition cities and population centers, but may be found near military installations and outposts. They are frequently located along dangerous borders, enemy territory, wilderness regions and at the sites of military operations.

Work details typically include hard labor such as building/construction of roads, walls, homes, buildings and military facilities, clearing land, farming, mining, digging ditches, factory work, warehouse work, sanitation, and similar. Work Camps are often used to support military operations and reclamation of the wilderness. Every year, 37% of the camp workers fall prey to foul play, illness, or attacks by monsters, bandits or the enemy.

Expulsion from the City or Territory: Some consider permanent expulsion from a CS city as a fate worse than death. Expulsion means the character is forever banned from entry to *all* CS cities. If caught inside a city's borders, the perpetrator is captured, tried and executed, or slain on the spot. Most are considered dangerous sociopaths, career criminals and/or suspected traitors to their race and nation.

Those expelled from the Coalition States entirely are branded at enemies as the States and will be executed the instant they are discovered within CS territory (including the 'Burbs).

Expulsion is typically for life.

Serious Crimes and Penalties of Note

Note: In all instances listed, a death sentence is automatic if the perpetrator is a non-human or practitioner of magic.

Subversive Activities involving education and the dissemination of dangerous ideas: This includes rogue scholars and scientists teaching the peasant masses and illiterate citizens of the CS (even those of the middle and lower levels) how to read, write, mathematics and pre-Rifts history (or any history that differs from the official CS version). The penalty ranges from 15 years to life imprisonment, and even death.

Erin Tarn is the most notorious rogue scholar and critic of the CS government. She has been branded by the CS as an insane and dangerous subversive and has been Public Enemy Number One for the last five years. If she is captured, she will be publicly executed!

Possession of subversive and dangerous materials: Being caught with one of Erin Tarn's many books is considered an act of treason and likely to lead to interrogation and 15-20 years imprisonment.

Likewise, owning pre-Rifts books, maps, films, videotapes, and recordings of any kind is against the law. All such items are to be turned over to the authorities. First time offenders will be interrogated and frightened out of their wits but usually released with a harsh warning and a felony record. They may also be placed under secret ISS surveillance for several months to several years. Repeat minor offenders are considered subversives and shot in the street (resisting arrest) or condemned to lengthy imprisonment or execution. Known subversives and dealers/sellers of subversive goods are branded enemies of the State and sentenced to death!

Subversive activity involving the aiding and abetting or protection/concealment of practitioners of magic, known subversives, and enemies of the State. Penalty is life imprisonment without parole or death.

Consorting with Supernatural Beings: Including dragons and other creatures of magic or supernatural nature. Penalty is death.

Practice of Magic: Perpetrators are typically branded as a social misanthrope, dangerous criminal, mass murderer, or enemy of the State. Penalty is death.

Cyber-snatching: The stealing of cybernetic and bionic components for resale to illegal body-chop-shops, and usually killing or maiming the victim. Penalty is death.

Terrorism: Any act of deliberate violence that kills, injures or endangers the lives of innocent CS citizens for whatever reason. Penalty is death.

Kidnapping: The capture and holding of another human against their will, often involving extortion, torture and murder. Penalty is death.

Murder in the First Degree: The act of deliberate premeditated murder is subject to the death penalty (life without parole is a rarity in these cases, but is occasionally granted).

Murder in the Second Degree: A murder that is not premeditated; typically a crime of passion. The penalty can be as light as 15 years without parole or as heavy as life without parole. A life sentence in the CS means incarceration in prison or a prison work camp till the day the prisoner dies.

Laws Governing Cybernetic Systems

Note: The Coalition States strictly enforce laws regarding the use of implants and bionics to keep these augmented supermen in line and to protect the common people.

Repeat offenders, known criminals and citizens suspected of treason or anti-social behavior are legally *prohibited* from ever getting any cybernetics/bionics for the rest of their lives. Breaking such a prohibition is punishable by life imprisonment (40-60 years) and even the death penalty. Nonhumans living and working at or near Coalition cities are prohibited from getting bionics.

Possession and sale of illegal cybernetics or bionics (loose parts, not implants): The character will be suspected of cyber-snatching and subjected to an intense investigation and interrogation. If found guilty of cyber-snatching, the penalty is death, even if his/her involvement was fencing or acting as an accessory after the fact in such a case.

Illegal sale or smuggling of "clean" cyber-mechanisms (new and unused) is typically 1-3 years of prison or forced labor; often as an assistant in a CS science laboratory or manufacturing facility.

First time human offenders and small-time, back-alley repeat offenders are often "shaken-up," given a stiff fine and released. Of course all illegal goods are seized and retained by the authorities.

Illegal implementation and installation of unauthorized cybernetics and bionics: The perpetrator is typically a cyber-doc or body healer who is sentenced to 2-8 years of prison or forced labor. Typically to assist in a government hospital, medical facility in the 'Burbs or a military outpost or CS science laboratory — all low security clearance facilities.

Those operating large-scale body-chop-shops or involved in cyber-snatching or supplying criminals, subversives or nonhumans are sentenced to death!

In most instances, the penalty for having illegal cybernetic or bionic systems which have *not* been used in the commission of a crime is their removal, reimbursing the state for the cost of removal, plus 20% (can range from a few hundred credits to thousands), a permanent criminal record for the use of illegal cybernetics, and probation.

A character may try to appeal this ruling and petition the courts for legal authorization. The courts review each petition on a case by case basis, but only 10% of Lofties and Highbrows are given legal authorization to keep such ill-gotten enhancements. Less than 3% of the City Rats and Low Levellers make successful appeals.

"Custom" alteration of legal cybernetic systems may be considered illegal and subject to removal. In 67% of these cases, the person is charged with a misdemeanor and does not get a criminal record unless a repeat offender (six or more "customizing" charges). The courts tend to be lenient in this area because City Rats tend to be precocious, daring and foolish but aren't involved in criminal activity, they're just techno-junkies.

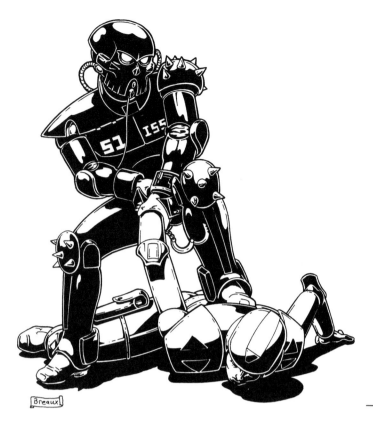

Breaux

implants and 1-4 years in jail. **Note:** Unauthorized bionics or illegal cybernetics will be removed and the prison time doubled!

Unpremeditated assault with intent to commit great bodily harm: 1000-10,000 credits fine, plus restitution for any damage inflicted as a result of the assault. Repeat offenders or particularly violent or unprovoked attacks may land the perpetrator in jail for a year and/or the courts may order to have the offending cybernetic feature and any other weapon systems removed immediately.

- **Premeditated Murder** with bionic or cybernetic systems: Life imprisonment or execution.

- **Restrictions for cybernetic augmentation:** No one under the age of 18 can receive cybernetic implants except for medical purposes. All authorized cyber-implants must be registered with and approved by the authorities.

- **Bionic reconstruction** or conversion is unavailable and illegal to the average citizen. Bionics are restricted to members of the military, ISS and the elite. All require special authorization — comprehensive records are kept throughout the Coalition States. Mercenaries and special agents working for the CS government or military are also allowed to retain and use cybernetic and bionic systems.

City Access Laws

All visitors must pass through a heavily armed and defended point of entry — the Coalition's idea of Customs and Immigration. At each of these checkpoints are ISS Inspectors and PRP Psi-Division officers. Psi-Stalkers and Psi-Hounds sniff and sense for the presence of magic, psionics, and the supernatural. Dog Boys and Psi-Stalkers can also detect human-looking D-bees (80% success ratio) and dragons and other shape-changing creatures (73%+ success ratio). These port of entry guards also utilize a battery of special sensors and optic systems to "scan" visitors for unnatural signatures and concealed weapons. Those who fall under suspicion are escorted to a holding area by two ISS Inspectors and a pair of Psi-Hounds for a more thorough examination. Such examinations may include a battery of tests, physical examination and further psionic scanning by high level Psi-Stalkers, Mind Melters or the most sensitive Psi-Hound. If there is the slightest doubt or suspicion, the visitor is usually declined entry and escorted beyond city limits.

Bribes are uncommon because the authorities involved are loyal and diligent protectors of humanity, and because each authorization team must sign-off on the entry permits. Visitors who undergo extensive scanning and allowed to enter must be signed-off by the team's top ranking officer and examining doctor. If a sorcerer, psychic, dragon, demon or nonhuman slips through, a full investigation is made and there is hell to pay.

In virtually all cases, visitor access to the city is limited to special shopping, services and communication facilities located on levels 2, 3 and 4. Access is usually limited to a short period of time, usually 4, 8 and 12 hour passes.

Day passes (24 hours), two day passes (48 hours) and week passes (five days; rare) are available upon advanced, special request and agreeing to wear a simple tracking device — a nano-chip the size of a fruit fly usually attached to the underarm or

Concealed weapons without a permit are illegal and subject to removal. Those in violation will have the weapon removed immediately, be fined the cost of the removal operation +20%, and placed on probation. Those with a criminal record will do time; 2-12 years.

Breaking a court ordered cybernetics/bionics prohibition: A serious offense that will result in the removal of all cybernetic systems, the usual fee, plus 50% of the removal cost, and a 2-12 year prison term. Repeat offenders may face a life term or the death penalty.

Using illegal cybernetic weapons, disguises, or bionic systems in the commission of a crime adds 10-20 years to prison time, in addition to the removal of the illegal systems. Repeat offenders may be executed!

Reckless use of cybernetics/bionics and endangerment (includes vandalism and accidental discharge of weapons): 500-3000 credits fine. Repeat offenders may be placed on probation or the courts may order to have the offending cybernetic feature(s) removed.

Assault with an authorized cybernetic or bionic system (includes brawls and duels): 5000-10,000 credits fine, plus restitution for any damage inflicted as a result of the assault. Repeat offenders or particularly violent or unprovoked attacks may land the perpetrator in jail and/or courts may order to have the offending cybernetic feature(s) removed immediately.

Manslaughter and murder using authorized cybernetic or bionic systems may result in the above and a slap on the hand if an officer in the military, ISS or highly placed government official. Otherwise, the character is likely to face a prison sentence of 10 years to life, expulsion or execution.

Assault with intent to commit great bodily harm/murder with an authorized cybernetic or bionic system — or manslaughter: Premeditated assault will result in the immediate court ordered removal of all bionics, potentially lethal cybernetic

behind the ear. Similarly, special passes are required for visitors to spend several days to several weeks with family members residing in a Coalition City.

All visitors get their forehead temporarily imprinted with a durable ink bar code that can be scanned by most business establishments, the military, and ISS. The bar code is roughly the size of a standard post-it note (2×1 1/2 inches). A quick laser/light scan reveals the name given by the visitor, an I.D. number, date and exact time of admittance, the exact moment of expiration, the type of pass, and the gate of entry. In addition, the bar code on the forehead enables the authorities and shop owners alike, to identify "visitors" at a glance.

City Access by Race

- **Dragons** and other creatures of magic are destroyed upon their discovery. They are *NEVER* knowingly allowed into Coalition cities for any reason!

- **Demons** and other supernatural beings are considered monsters and destroyed upon their discovery. They are *NEVER* knowingly allowed into cities for any reason!

- **D-bees** are not allowed, except under special and *rare* authorization permits. The owner of (D-bee slaves are allowed to powerful businessmen, traders and politicians, particularly as a labor force in manufacturing) or person(s) taking responsibility for the authorized D-bee must control the "creature" at all times and pledges 100% liability for "its" actions. This means that if the D-bee commits a crime, the creature is destroyed and the person taking responsibility for "it" will suffer the usual penalty for the crime; a fine, to the death penalty.

- **Renegade and Rogue Dog Boys.** All mutant animals are considered to be trained animals and the property of the CS government, like a pet dog or any animal. Free Dog Boys are considered to be runaways or dangerous rogues who deserted their CS masters and service to humankind. Frequently, the ISS, PRP and military will try to capture the wayward animal to see if it can be reindoctrinated to serve humankind (for which it was created). Those who cannot be reindoctrinated or who resist capture (90%) are destroyed like the mad dogs they are perceived to be. Psi-Hounds (other Dog Boys loyal to the Coalition) and CS Psi-Stalkers are often used to find and capture these rogues and renegades. For obvious reasons, most mutant dogs who have deserted the CS or escaped the Lone Star experimental complex avoid the cities, 'Burbs and CS outposts like the plague. Some won't even enter CS controlled territories.

- **Human Visitors (ordinary folks).** All visitors must leave all weapons, body armor, power armor and pre-Rifts or alien artifacts in a locker with the authorities. The character is frisked for concealed weapons and contraband, and all luggage, packages and personal items are inspected. Anything deemed inappropriate for any reason (real or imagined) must be left behind. The visitors pledge on video that they will avoid trouble and uphold the law and are forced to watch a 15 minute video presentation of fundamental customs and acceptable social behavior before they are allowed into the city. **Note:** Characters with a criminal record may be declined entry, especially if the crimes are serious or the character's past crimes fit the profile for current criminal activity or trouble in the city.

- **Human Mutants.** Human mutations are seen as dangerous aberrations that make the unfortunate soul less than human. Most soldiers and ISS agents feel a certain amount of sympathy for these people and may show them uncommon compassion. This is because the mutant's loss of humanity is not of their own doing — they are the victims of forces beyond their control. However, human mutants are *NEVER* knowingly allowed into the cities except under special and *rare* authorization permits.

  A number of human mutants are unofficially allowed to live in the 'Burbs or to gather in small villages within CS territory. The most fortunate are those whose mutations are not obvious and who don't possess any superhuman abilities. Some of these people are given work permits to perform the most backbreaking, dangerous and tedious labor (at incredibly low wages) in factories, mines and operations outside the city. Those who work at facilities inside the city are escorted in and out by the military. The work facility must have special containment measures to prevent any mutants from entering the city proper, and must have the sanction of the authorities. Escaped mutants who manage to enter the city are captured, lose their job, and permanently expelled from the city. Those who offer resistance or fight back are destroyed where they stand.

- **Super-powered and inhuman looking human mutants** are considered to be inhuman monsters or D-bees and are *NEVER* knowingly allowed into the cities for any reason. They may even be "purged" from CS territory (a CS euphemism for "exterminated").

- **Augmented Humans.** Juicers, Crazies, 'Borgs, Headhunters, Cyber-Knights, and other augmented humans must register with the Entry authorities, disclose all concealed weapons and abilities, leave all weapons, body armor and power armor in a locker with the authorities, and pledge on video that they will avoid trouble and uphold the law. They must then watch a 15 minute video presentation of fundamental laws, customs and social behavior before they are allowed into the city.

- **Psi-Stalkers** are the only human mutants accepted by the CS, but even these people are considered to be less than human. Even the Stalker who faithfully serves in the military, ISS or PRP is, at best, a second-class citizen. Official Psi-Stalker citizens of the Coalition States typically find employment in the Military and Internal Security Specialists Divisions or as independent security agents (private detectives, bodyguards, bouncers, etc.). Only occasionally are they found in other areas of work. Most are relegated to living in the low levels, 1-6, but live happy, productive lives and support the Coalition States wholeheartedly.

  Wild Psi-Stalkers are considered dangerous, unallied mercenaries or even as D-bees. They are *NEVER* knowingly allowed into the cities except under special and *rare* authorization permits.

- **Psionic Humans** must register with the Entry authorities, disclose their level of power (minor, major, master), classification (sensitive, healer, physical, super, or multi), and indicate all notable psi-abilities, typically a checklist marked off by the Entry authorities. The character must then submit to either a temporary IC bar coding or a permanent IC bar code and implant — part of the Psychic Registration Program (PRP). To entice psychics to participate in PRP permanent identification coding (an implant is placed under the skin and a scannable bar code tattooed on the back of the neck), the authorities give the psychic a 100 credit voucher that can be redeemed at all shops and banks, an additional 12-24 hours added to their visitor's pass free of charge and preferential consideration for future visits. The coding process is not harmful to the psychic in any way.

  In addition, like all visitors, the psi-characters must also leave all weapons, body armor and power armor in a locker with the authorities and pledge on video that they will avoid trouble and up-hold the law. They must then watch a 15 minute video presentation of fundamental laws, customs and acceptable social behavior before they are allowed into the city. **Note:** Nonhumans are not allowed in the city unless given special military or ISS authorization and are met by a military or ISS officer and escort (2-6 soldiers) and escorted wherever they go.

- **Practitioners of Magic** are considered dangerous criminals and even inhuman monsters. They are *NEVER* knowingly allowed into the cities for any reason. They may even be "purged" from CS territory (a CS euphemism for "exterminated").

- **City Level Restrictions in the Fortified Cities:** *Low Levellers (inhabitants of levels 1-22)* are not allowed public access to the higher levels where the more affluent and educated citizens live and work (a.k.a. Lofties, Highbrows, and Technocrats); levels 23 and up. A special work, travel or visitor's pass is required to gain access to the higher levels. Low Levellers (a.k.a. Grungers, Sludgers, and Downsiders) caught in restricted Highbrow areas are automatically suspected of wrongdoing and taken into custody for questioning. The fine for trespassing in Highbrow levels is 100-300 credits in addition to being a prime suspect for crimes committed on that/those levels.

Highbrows/Lofties can travel without restriction to any level lower than their own, although the ISS may look upon them with suspicion if found "slumming" or "sludging" on levels lower than 10 (suspected of smuggling, purchasing or dealing drugs, purchasing illegal cybernetics or contraband, rabble-rousing, etc.). Even the affluent citizens of the high levels do not have free access to the uppermost levels (typically levels 30-40) where the heads of government, the military, sciences and business live. These upper levels also typically contain research and development facilities, restricted science labs, the most advanced medical and cybernetic facilities, the ISS Headquarters and branch division headquarters (NTSET & PRP; typically found on level 30 or 31) and penthouses. Emperor Prosek, his family and top aides inhabit the entire top level of Chi-Town.

Death Statistics from Street Crime Encounters

Remember, as noted earlier, the police are given much greater leeway in the execution of their duties (and their suspects). Although the police are not endowed with the power to serve as judge, jury and executioner, they are free to use *their* best judgement as to the necessity of extreme and lethal force. Repeat offenders of virtually any serious crime, from malicious destruction of property and theft to murder and the practice of magic, are regularly shot and killed by CS law officers without the slightest negative impact or public criticism. **Note:** This does not include minor infractions of the law like littering or jaywalking. Likewise, the beating, harassment or killing of a citizen without good cause is not tolerated by the people or fellow ISS Inspectors.

90% of all supernatural beings who operate within a CS city (including dragons and other creatures of magic) are hunted down and destroyed on the spot. Only 2% escape and leave the area or remain at large. Of the 8% that are captured (none are released), they are either given a swift formal trial and executed (90%), or imprisoned and interrogated relentlessly for years (sometimes decades), or delivered to the military or elite science teams for a life (and death) of study and experimentation.

75% of all D-bees are slain in street encounters within the borders of CS cities. They are regarded as inhuman invaders and destroyed. Less than 8% escape and leave the area or remain at large. Of the 17% that are captured and reach trial, 80% are sentenced to death, 8% to scientific research, 10% imprisoned for 20 years to life and 2% are released (often after suffering physical and/or mental anguish).

55% of all practitioners of magic and rogue psychics are slain in street encounters. 12% escape and leave the area or remain at large. Of the 33% who are captured and reach trial, 60%

are sentenced to death, 30% imprisoned for 20 years to life (without parole) and 10% are released (most of those released are psychics).

42% of all augmented humans (Juicers, Crazies and Cyborgs) are slain in street encounters. 14% escape and leave the area or remain at large. Of the 44% who are captured and tried, 30% are sentenced to death, 40% imprisoned for 6-30 years to life, depending on the nature and severity of the crime, and 30% are released without charges or after paying a fine and recompense for damages attributed to them.

33% of most common, human criminals are slain in street encounters (the mortality rate is 10% higher when dealing with rogue scholars and rogue scientists). 7% escape and leave the area or remain at large. Of the 60% that are captured and tried, 18% are sentenced to death, 50% receive a prison sentence that varies with the nature and severity of the crime and 32% are released without charges or after paying a fine and recompense for damages attributed to them.

Less than 2% of all humans who are members of the elite, wealthy, educated and ruling members of CS society, including high ranking ISS and military officers, public officials, scientists, and members of high society (city levels 35-42 in Chi-Town and most major walled cities) are involved in serious crime.

Note: The "law" is nonexistent in the 'Burbs, because they are social and political no-man's lands where anything goes. See the section on the 'Burbs for details.

CS & Chi-Town Slang

Bot: Slang for robots with an artificial intelligence; unmanned.

'Borg: Slang for "cyborg."

Burbs: The shanty town no-man zones occupied by human squatters, refugees, rejects and criminals. Five to twenty percent of the population of a 'Burb will be nonhuman or renegades like rogue scholars and practitioners of magic.

Choppers: Scavengers and Vagabonds who scrounge through debris and garbage collecting valuables and salvaging parts; often chopping large items into smaller, more manageable pieces.

Citizen: An member and inhabitant of the Coalition States.

D-bee: Slang for "Dimensional Being" — humanoid or bipedal life forms from another world who are often refugees brought to Earth through a Rift, magic, or other dimension spanning force. Many have no way back home and try to make a life on Rifts Earth. **Note:** Alien creatures who are extremely inhuman or monstrous looking are considered monsters or demons.

Dead Boys: Coalition soldiers clad in the famous black armor with the traditional Death's head or new skeleton appearance.

Demon: Virtually any evil or monstrous looking supernatural being.

Dog Boys, a.k.a. Psi-Hounds: Intelligent, humanoid, mutant dogs created via genetic engineering and "designed" as well as indoctrinated to be loyal protectors of humankind and destroyers of magic and the supernatural.

Downsiders: Another name for Low Levelers or LL's, citizens who live on the lower levels (1-22). Also see *Grungers, Sludgers, LL's* and *Low Levelers*.

Ghosts: Characters living in the Coalition cities but who have no formal, electronic identity. As far as the CS census bureau is concerned, these people don't exist! Ghosts are typically City Rats, Rogue Scholars, Rogue Scientists, mercenaries, smugglers or assassins. They have no known identity or traceable records of any kind, other than 1-20 fake identities. The CS estimates for every 300,000 citizens, one is a ghost. Many citizens consider them to be urban legends and don't believe they exist.

Grungers: The citizens of the lowest levels of the fortified super-cities (1-10) and/or slums.

Highbrows: The residents of the upper levels of the fortified super-cities where the rich, educated and elite live. Also see *Sky Kings* and *Technocrats*.

High-Mayor: The political leader and city manager of cities with a population of one million or more or the mayor of highbrow and technocrat levels (typically levels 23-35) at the fortified super-cities.

ISS or Internal Security Specialists: The city police and protectors.

Lofties: A common slang term for citizens who live high up in the fortress super-cities (levels 23 and higher) or penthouses of normal cities.

Low Levelers or LL's: The least derogatory name for citizens who live on the lower levels (1-22).

Mayor: The political leader and city manager of ordinary CS cities or LL's (levels 1-22) at the fortified super-cities.

Nut-Set or NTSET: The ISS department that specializes in hunting and exterminating practitioners of magic, the supernatural, demons and monsters; "you must be nuts to take a job like that."

Pit, the: The sub-level of service, sewer and drainage tunnels below Level One of the fortress super-cities.

Psi-Net: The city, psychic defense force. A division of the ISS that specializes in detecting, containing and eliminating rogue psychics and psionic menaces, including the supernatural. They also enforce PRP (Psychic Registration Program) laws.

Rejects: Human residents of the Burbs whose application for CS citizenship or residence in a major city has been "rejected."

Retros or Retrotechs: People who have rejected high-technology and who prefer to use items of a tech level equal to or below 20th Century Earth, including S.D.C. weapons and materials. It is important to note that these characters don't reject all technology, just high-tech stuff like mega-damage weapons and alloys, genetic engineering, bionics (basic cybernetics may be acceptable), and so on. Many retros are also history buffs and collectors of pre-Rifts artifacts and memorabilia.

Sams or Sam: Another name for the flying SAMAS power armor.

Sludgers or Sludgies: Usually human and D-bee refugees and fugitives who live or hide in the sewers and between the walls of the great fortress super-cities on the lowest levels (1-4 and sub-levels of service, sewer and drainage tunnels).

Sky Kings: Another name for citizens who live on the highest levels of the fortress super-cities; usually reserved for those who live on the top five levels (31-35).

Technocrats: The scientific elite of the Coalition States.

The Coalition Army

By Kevin Siembieda with additional text,
inspiration & concepts by Patrick Nowak

The Military Presence

The government of Chi-Town, and all the Coalition States, is built upon militarism. Human survival in a world filled with alien monsters, supernatural demons, D-bees and magic would have been impossible without a powerful army, whether it drew upon magic or technology. The Coalition Army is the largest and most powerful institution within the Coalition States. It is as important in the lives of its citizens as the government. Everyone in Chi-Town is affected in some way by the military, and everyone has an opinion concerning it.

For the *working class, educated* and *political elite*, the army is the lifeblood of the Coalition States. It provides security in a world filled with extra-dimensional horrors and is a visible symbol of mankind's fight for freedom, at least as its preached by State propaganda. To these people, the CS army is good and its soldiers are heroic warriors dedicated to the preservation of humankind.

The average CS citizen not only enjoys the peace and safety provided by the military, but are employed by companies tied directly to it. In fact, the military and government control, operate and profit from many of the most lucrative areas of business and manufacturing. For example, the Chi-Town military employs over 1.2 million citizens in their factories and facilities alone. This includes everything from the production of military uniforms, medals, munitions, weapons, armor, robots, and armored vehicles to microchips, parts and widgets for just about everything.

Most areas of CS scientific research and development falls under the broad jurisdiction and control of the military including medicine, genetics, cybernetics, bionics, robotics, energy technologies, and engineering. The military also supervises civilian construction and assigns troops to guard and monitor most construction sites around the clock, especially those in the less civilized areas where an enemy attack is most likely. There is no freedom of the press because the military, under the *Department of Public Information* (a.k.a. the propaganda department under the supervision of Colonel Joseph Prosek II), controls the press and the dispensing of all information in all of its forms; television, film, radio, public broadcasting, computer networks, print, and even public assembly and addresses.

The majority of the *working class* population regards the army as a valuable asset and a source of national pride. Many encourage their children to join such a worthy institution — 75% of all enlisted men make the military their career, staying in service for 36 to 48 years (each term of service is six years).

The *poorest residents* of the lowest levels of the fortress super-cities (known as Sludgers or Grundgers), small towns, industrial cities and wilderness, and border communities are usually of a different opinion. For them, the army is a two-edged sword. It provides protection from invaders, but who protects them from the army? The army and police often take liberties with them or treat them as second-class citizens — low priority in the overall scheme of things. The worst of the lot accept pay-offs and bribes to look the other way, so crime is comparatively high in city slums and the poorest sectors of the States. Some police even moonlight for the Black Market or run their own illegal operations, with body-chop-shops, gambling halls, prostitution, saloons, and drug dens being the most common. That having been said, even this is comparatively uncommon in most Coalition cities with less than 8% of the military and/or police involved in illegal activities.

The 'Burbs are another story entirely. Soldiers and the ISS constantly patrol the neighborhoods of "Rejects," squatters, crooks and D-bee riffraff. The inhabitants of the 'Burbs exist in a political no-man's land that has *no* legal rights. Thus, shakedowns and harassment at the hands of the authorities is commonplace, as well as from gangs, criminals, merchants, mercenaries and drifters. For D-bees it is even worse, if the soldiers aren't giving them a beating then somebody else is; nobody worries about what happens to D-bees. For many residents of the 'Burbs, CS soldiers are just uniformed gangsters and the unwitting pawns of a deranged Emperor and his brutal vision of the future. Yet, even here, the Coalition Army and ISS represent some measure of law and order, as well as defenders against supernatural predators, inhuman invaders, creatures of magic, terrorists and madmen. Tragically, even the 'Burbs are a better, safer place to live than many other communities and parts of the world.

The Coalition Army

As Karl Prosek grew in power, so did the size and strength of the army. The military became increasingly important in all facets of Coalition civilization. Rather than an intrusion or threat, the Army is seen as a benefactor and lifeline to the "good life." Consequently, the lowliest grunt is regarded as a dedicated, national hero entrusted with law enforcement, civil defense and the protection of humankind. The military is seen as the hand of justice fighting for freedom and the harbinger of peace, not war. By 53 P.A., the goals and actions of the Coalition Army could not be separated from the government or its people — something Emperor Karl Prosek and Colonel Joseph Prosek II use to their maximum benefit.

The military also oversees most scientific research and development as well as the dissemination of technology, education and information/propaganda. Thus, the military is the first to benefit from new technology and is the power that decides what technology and knowledge is *suitable* for the masses. Consequently, there is no competition from civilian contractors, because the government and the military control technology and industry. They are, in every sense of the word, "the" power in the Coalition States, with Emperor Prosek, his son, and their handpicked and loyal supporters at the top of the heap. The people don't complain (they don't even care) because their lives are so (comparatively) good under the guidance and control of the Emperor and the omnipresent military guardians. Decades of propaganda has created a complacent society who embraces their lifestyle.

CS Hierarchy

The Emperor

Despite some of the outward trappings of democracy and socialism, the Coalition States is a rule by dictatorship. Ultimate authority over the Armed Forces, government and all affairs of the States rests with **Karl Prosek**, the Supreme Commander and Chief of the Army and Emperor of the Coalition States. His son, trusted generals and other Heads of State counsel and advise him as members of the *Coalition States Executive Counsel*, but even they serve to implement his master plan — a vision of conquest and power shared by all participants, from the highest ranking general to the humblest citizen.

Emperor Prosek makes it no secret among his elite, that he has found many of the practices, approaches and world views of the 20th Century Dictator, Adolf Hitler, to be insightful and brilliant. As a result, the Emperor has adopted many of Hitler's methods and practices, particularly the manipulation of the people through a powerful sense of unity, patriotism, purpose and power. Like Hitler, he uses *war* as a vehicle to unite and motivate his people. War helps to make the people believe that they have control over their destiny and gives them a (misguided) sense of empowerment, control, and strength. However, Emperor Prosek also acknowledges that Hitler was a madman with delusions of grandeur and an insane agenda. Regardless of the man's sanity, Prosek has found and borrowed a number of things from the German Chancellor, quickly pointing out that the line between true genius and insanity is often a slender and tenuous one. As is so often the case, Emperor Prosek is confident that while he follows a similar path, he is not insane, will not make the same mistakes, and thus, avoid Hitler's dishonorable fate.

Personally, Karl Prosek, a pre-Rifts historian in his own right, prefers to think of himself as a combination of the best traits of *Genghis Khan, Julius Caesar, Napoleon* and *Hitler*. So far, he has proven to be a strong, charismatic leader and an adept administrator, manipulator, strategist, and politician with a keen eye for long-range planning and setting into motion the things necessary to shape the future to *his* will. He is acutely aware of his strengths and weaknesses, and compensates for the latter by turning to trusted advisors who excel in those areas. In matters of war, military strategies, tactics and operations, he usually defers to the wisdom and judgement of his Generals. Likewise, when it comes to the dissemination of information and the manipulation of the people, the Emperor may make suggestions and insist that certain issues be addressed or policies be implemented, but he leaves the details to his son and the propaganda experts he employs. The Emperor also tries to avoid reacting to anything without due consideration. He is very much like the conductor of an orchestra. He directs and focuses the members of the orchestra while they actually make the music. Like a finely tuned orchestra, each player knows his place and works in concert with the conductor and other members to create the final, triumphant result. Others may make suggestions, but it is ultimately Emperor Prosek who has the final word in all matters regarding the military, government and all things concerning the Coalition States. Those who defy his will or publicly chastise him are removed — and the band plays on.

The Executive Counsel

The Executive Counsel is something like a presidential cabinet composed of the heads of government. Among the executive counsel are the influential people in the Coalition States.

Colonel Joseph Prosek II: Head of propaganda at the Department of Public Information and Chairman of the Executive Counsel; Chi-Town.

General of the Army, Charles Reed Baxter; Five-Star general, Chi-Town.

General Marshal Cabot: Three-Bar General and veteran of numerous CS military campaigns, including General Joseph Prosek the First's "Bloody Campaign" against the Federation of Magic. General Cabot is a long-time friend and confidant to the Prosek family. Chi-Town.

General Loni Kashbrook: Head of Lone Star Operations & Administration; Three-Bar General, Lone Star.

General Apollo Lucitonis: Head of the Military's Department of Special Divisions (DSD), a Two-Bar General; Chi-Town.

General Thomas Lopez: ISS Commander-in-Chief, Four-Bar General; Headquarters is Chi-Town.

Judge Bradley Martindale: Head of the Justice Department, Chi-Town

Tyler Wilpepper: Head of Industry, Chi-Town.

Doctor Matthew Fronval: Head of Medicine, Lone Star.

Doctor Victoria Lansport: Head of Science, Chi-Town.

Doctor Thomas Clinton: Head of Advanced Cybernetics Department, Chi-Town.

Colonel L.J. Klonicki: Head of the Food and Drug Administration, Missouri.

Professor Carla L. Korehira: Head of Foreign Relations, Chi-Town.

It is important to note that the Coalitions' Executive Counsel is a powerful *advisory* board that can (and does) make military suggestions and design entire military campaigns, but cannot implement them without the approval of the Emperor and the General of the Army. Thus, the Coalition Executive Counsel, as a political entity, cannot issue direct commands to the Army unless it is through the General of the Army and his command officers. If the order is coming from one of the lower ranking Generals, even someone like General Cabot, he or she must have cleared the operation with General Charles Reed Baxter at High Command. This is a deliberate fail-safe measure implemented by the Emperor himself. Thus, with the exception of General Baxter, not even his own son can mobilize and command any portion of the Coalition Army without the authorization of the Military High Command or himself.

The Military High Command

Once the Emperor or his Executive Counsel determines the grand strategy for the nation and war, the job of planning and implementing military operations falls to the **Military High Command**. The High Command is a body of 40 highly trained and experienced professional officers and military scientists hand-picked by the Emperor and his Executive Counsel. The bulk (70%) are from within the Chi-Town bureaucracy — men and women who have proven their loyalty to the Emperor and support his vision for the future. The 30% who are from outside the Chi-Town elite include one representative from Missouri and four from Lone Star (many critics of the Emperor consider these two States little more than extensions of Chi-Town). Only three are representatives from Iron Heart and one from the allied territory of Arkansas/Fort El Dorado. Free Quebec has always felt unfairly represented, so three of its four representatives have been absent (an informal boycott) for five years — their point being that their presence had no impact one way or another. The one Quebec leader who remains is *General Sean Oulette*. He is loyal to the Emperor and actively involved in the implementation of the Quebec Campaign.

At the head of the Military High Command is *General of the Army, Charles Reed Baxter*. Currently General Cabot, General Ross Underhill of Special Ops, CSID commander General Ford, and Colonel Carol Black of Psi-Battalion are part of the elite task force coordinating the Tolkeen Campaign.

Working together, the officers of the High Command decide on the strategy of a mission and identify the central objectives. When the High Command determines what the army has to do, they identify what assets are needed to accomplish the job and assign the Army Corps and Divisions to do the job. This includes deciding exactly which forces to send, who to put in command, how to transport them to the combat zone, supply routes, strategic plans, time-tables, and other major considerations. After the High Command has made these decisions the responsibility for putting the plan into action is delegated to subordinate officers in Regular Army units. However, one or more officers of the High Command may join the field of battle to take charge, or suggest strategies and tactics, or simply to observe.

Regional Command

The Regional Command is an important administrative force that functions in a support and logistics capacity as well as an intermediary body between field units and the High Command. Its purpose is to follow orders and implement the decisions and plans of the High Command. Even during combat operations, the Regional Command rarely formulates plans or strategies for *combat* troops. It is the High Command who issues orders and directives to the field commanders who, with their staff officers, devise specific strategies and methods to accomplish their mission. Meanwhile, the important but unremarkable details like logistics, transportation, communications, maintaining supply-lines and internal security are delegated to the Regional Command. This doesn't mean the troops under the direction of Regional Command aren't combat seasoned, quite the contrary,

it's just that fighting is not the primary purpose of these units, keeping lines open and supplies and information flowing so that the war can continue, is.

Each Coalition State has its own Regional Command which handles all the behind the scenes operations described above. Each is also responsible for the command and deployment of Army Corps assigned to service and defend their particular State and strategic locations within the State. Army Corps assigned to defend a State are not called to join a campaign at locations outside the State except under extreme circumstances, and only by order of the High Command, General of the Army, or the Emperor.

Regional State Forces

The overwhelming bulk of Coalition army personnel serve in the *regular army* of the Coalition States. Although each State contributes to the Armed Forces (another area where Free Quebec was remiss), the troops are under the direct command of the Emperor and the Coalition High Command at Chi-Town. The Regular Army is divided into *Army Corps* (typically two divisions or 11,520 troops) and are dispatched to serve and protect each specific allied State. Six or more Army Corps are assigned to the defense of most allied States, with additional uncommitted troops at bases and camps located in the State. An entire Corps is assigned to important and densely populated cites. The City of Chi-Town has six Army Corps assigned for its defense, plus ISS forces and another 30+ Regular Army Corps at its immediate disposal because they are located at bases and training camps throughout the State of Chi-Town. Typically, 50% of the army troops assigned to the defense of a particular State are comprised of local boys and girls — the thought being that natives of the area are more likely to serve with dedication and fiercely defend their homeland than completely detached forces.

Unlike the extremely specialized forces of the High Command, the State Armies are conventional combat, support and service units that are the muscle of the Army. There are large standing armies in each state, relative to local population, that include these elements and have the capacity to war without the aid of other CS states. Bound together by nationalism, ideology and the centralized command of the CS government at Chi-Town, these combined State armies form a massive military powerhouse.

Remember that with the level of high-technology available to the Coalition States, with its mega-damage flying power armor, manned robot vehicles, automated Skelebots, hover tanks, aircraft, cyborgs, Juicers and other resources, a CS Army Company (640 troops) has the armor and firepower of an old 20th Century Army Division (5760 troops)! Each city and town is also protected by the ISS (Internal Security Specialists) who serve as both civilian defenders and law enforcement officers; they are a formidable defense force in and of themselves. Furthermore, there is almost always a substantial force of uncommitted troops located in the State, or neighboring State, and rarely more than an hour from most any place in the State (especially to SAMAS and aircraft). Uncommitted troops are forces located at military bases and training camps that have not yet been assigned to a specific military campaign or operation. Consequently, they are available to be sent to wherever they are needed most.

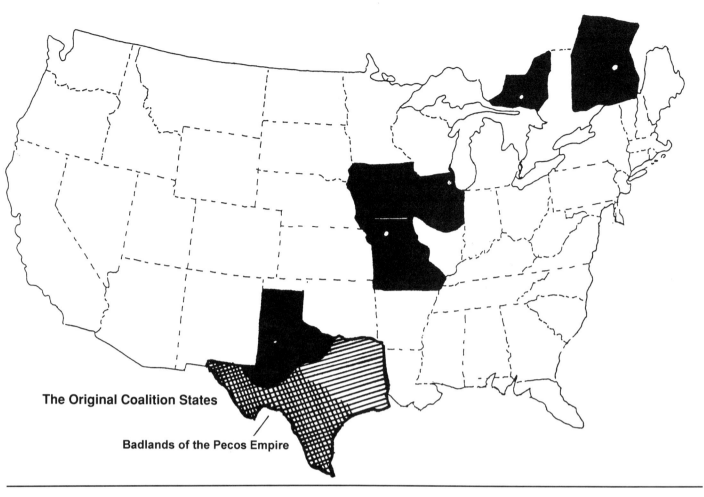

The Original Coalition States

Badlands of the Pecos Empire

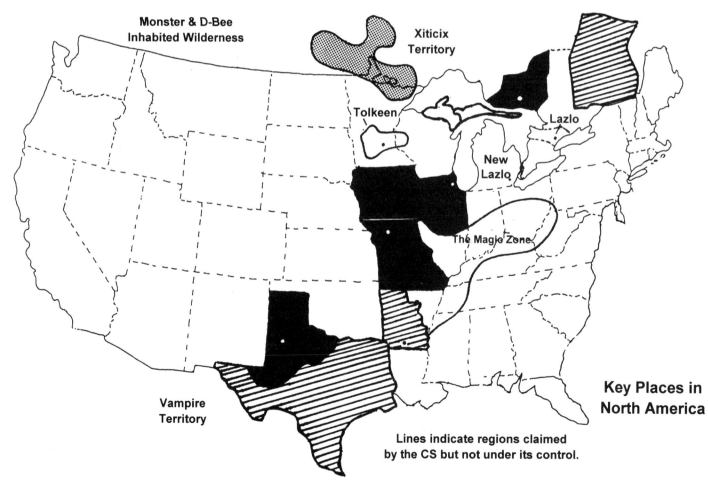

Monster & D-Bee
Inhabited Wilderness

Xiticix
Territory

Tolkeen

Lazlo

New
Lazlo

The Magic Zone

Vampire
Territory

Lines indicate regions claimed
by the CS but not under its control.

**Key Places in
North America**

Other Components of the Coalition Army

20 Year Plan for CS Expansion

There are literally dozens of divisions, regiments and other CS military units in the Regular Army. All are subordinate to the Emperor and the High Command, even when assigned to the Regional Command of specific States as a standing defensive army. In addition to the Regular Army, there are a number of Special Divisions at the *direct* disposal of the Emperor and the Military High Command. They are numerically smaller than those of the individual States or the CS Army as a whole, but they are much more specialized and powerful. They include the **Rapid Deployment Force (RDF), Department of Special Divisions (DSD), Intelligence (CSID), Psi-Battalion (PSI-BAT), Rift Control Study Group (RCSG), Naval Advisory Commission (NAC)** and **Coalition Expeditionary Force (CEF).**

Rapid Deployment Force (RDF)

When the Coalition States go to war, the first force deployed to the area is the **Rapid Deployment Force** (RDF). The RDF is a force of four combat divisions (around 23,000 soldiers) prepared to assemble at a moment's notice and deploy to any spot in North America within 48 hours. From the moment it arrives the RDF is ready to fight without any support from other Coalition units. It is a combined arms force that is equipped with all the equipment necessary to fight a war, including infantry soldiers, tanks, MLRS artillery vehicles and even aircraft! The aggressive Rapid Deployment Force divisions form the Coalition's spearhead which smashes at the enemy while reinforcement divisions are shipped to the front.

Combat units from each of the Coalition States are earmarked for duty in this Force, including a full division from Iron Heart, Missouri, and Lone Star and three from Chi-Town. The RDF has to be ready to fight at any time, so the divisions are given no regular post or assignment and are sent wherever they are needed at a moment's notice. Thus, their location is known to the High Command at all times! Circa 101 P.A., the RDF divisions have begun to prepare for the invasion of Minnesota, but will not deploy until combat is imminent. The troops also receive training in anti-supernatural and anti-magic warfare and attend detailed briefings on alien forces like the Xiticix, Gargoyles, Splugorth, Naruni, and others.

Note: The addition of Juicers and, to a lesser degree, cyborgs, is expected to play a significant role in the Rapid Deployment Force.

Department of Special Divisions (DSD)

Of the forces at the High Command's disposal, the most renowned and intriguing is the **Department of Special Divisions** (DSD). Rather than a single integrated unit, the DSD is just an umbrella structure into which several distinct organizations are grouped for ease of administration. It is under the DSD that the Rift Control Study Group (RCSG), Commandos, spies and all Special Forces operate. Consequently, most CS enemies and some civilians regard the Department of Special Divisions as the *espionage* branch of the Coalition Military. The Special Operations Division is the brainchild of *General Ross Underhill* and *General Cabot*, formed to provide the CS Army with a greater capability to conduct unconventional warfare operations.

In the early days, the civil defense forces now recognized as the ISS (Internal Security Specialists) and its sub-divisions, NTSET and PRP, were all part of Army Operations and functioned under the DSD. It was only 27 years ago that the ISS was removed from the Department of Special Divisions and from the Army entirely, and made into a completely separate organization.

Recently, the *Coalition Cyborg and Juicer Divisions* have been placed under the command and direction of the DSD. Every one of the DSD organizations is a highly specialized force created to accomplish a specific task for the CS military. Each also has its own commanding officer who answers only to the High Command. In fact, the only reason the separate forces were grouped was for the ease of funding, logistical support and direction. The headquarters of the DSD is conveniently found in Chi-Town near the High Command.

CS Intelligence Division (CSID)

The Intelligence Division of the Coalition Army is the organization charged with gathering reliable research and strategic information for the military. CSID works closely with the military and the other DSD divisions on a daily basis. It is constantly involved in reconnaissance operations and assists in most espionage and Special Forces missions, supplying up to the minute information, observations, suspicions and other data relating to military operations and defenses. Intelligence officers are also involved in mission briefings, debriefings, investigations and interrogations.

Psi-Battalion (Psi-Bat)

The Psi-Bat is a Special Forces battalion composed almost entirely of psychic humans (72%), with support by Psi-Hounds (18%), Psi-Stalkers (8%) and non-psionic humans (2%). Psi-Bat is a completely separate force unlike ISS or NTSET or PRP operatives, although human psychics, Psi-Hounds and Psi-Stalkers are members of those operations as well.

Psi-Bat recruits the most powerful and (seemingly) loyal psychics in the Coalition States. All human members of this battalion are given special clearance and registration with the military, but do *NOT* participate in the civilian Psychic Registration Program (PRP) or given Identification Coding (IC). To have them submit to such registration and IC would make them vulnerable to monitoring and assassination by the enemy. Most Psi-Bat operatives function as super-elite spies, assassins and Special Forces operatives that function as a Psi-Bat squad or who are assigned to other Special Division squads and operations.

These soldiers include human Mind Melters, Bursters and other major and master psychics; most are trained for espionage and other areas of military specialty.

Rift Control Study Group (RCSG)

The RCSG group is a brigade of CS troops and military scientists who are charged with the study and containment of the Rifts. Their headquarters and main base of operations is at the East Saint Louis Rift more commonly known as *The Devil's Gate*. A RCSG company is also active in the ruins of Old Chicago where Rift activity is frequent and right in Chi-Town's backyard. In addition to reaching an understanding about how the Rifts and related dimensional phenomena work, they are assigned with controlling the forces unleashed by them. This includes the "containment" of beings that emerge from these dimensional gateways. "Containment" typically means the capture, study and/or extermination of the other-worldly beings, from entities and demons to D-bees and alien invaders. To do this, a giant, mega-damage containment center similar in appearance and construction to the great fortress cities of Chi-Town, except instead of housing humans and keeping them safe from the horrors outside its walls, the *Devil's Gate Containment Center* is intended to hold monsters and inhuman invaders in until they can be destroyed or sent retreating back into the Rifts. Power armor, robots and Psi-Hounds are used extensively by the RCSG.

Naval Advisory Commission

The Naval Advisory Commission (NAC) is becoming an increasingly important organization. Back before the CS planned to build a navy, the NAC existed as a small military department in Chi-Town with the job of fighting piracy and monsters on the Great Lakes (also handled by hiring privateers). Over the last five years, the High Command has been building a more formidable Great Lakes force and a sea-faring Navy operating out of Lone Star. It has already been agreed upon to remove NAC from the Department of Special Divisions and make it a separate military organization soon to be known as the Department of the Navy (DON). *Admiral Travis Fisher* is to head the new Department, with NAC maintaining control over the Great Lakes operations and serving in both an advisory and back-up capacity. The Admiral is competent but has little experience in leading large fleets. He was selected by Emperor Prosek for his unquestionable loyalty and dedication to the building of a CS Navy. Presently, the assets of the NAC include a small fleet of combat ships, patrol boats and power armor based at a handful of military bases along Lake Michigan.

Coalition Expeditionary Force (CEF)

The Coalition Expeditionary Force (CEF) is a military division comprised mostly of volunteers. The CEF serves two functions: 1) To explore unknown or hostile territories and, 2) to monitor and meddle in the affairs of other nations with some m-

inute measure of deniability. The exploration of the other lands is pretty straightforward, although the CEF team is likely to be in disguise. Such expeditions have been used for decades and are currently active in what was once the old American West, Canada, Mexico, and South America. The Expeditionary Force typically functions as an extremely long-range reconnaissance team without the usual support of nearby military bases. The team explores and maps the region, makes note of natural resources, wildlife, potential enemies and trouble, the presence of magic, strategic positions, the occupying population and similar details. To avoid alarming the inhabitants of the region, the CEF team often (79%), but not always, conceals its military and political affiliations with the infamous Coalition States. This often entails using non-CS equipment and dressing in the garments of the region or as is common to adventurers or mercenaries.

The CEF is also involved in covert operations in other nations and hostile territories. The Coalition Expeditionary team rarely engages in acts of sabotage, assassination, the theft of technology or secrets, or seriously meddles in foreign affairs — they leave that for the Intelligence Division — what they do is "observe and report," some might say "spy." Again, however, their spying is very subtle and inoffensive. The CEF operatives in a foreign land study the people, their customs, and society, paying close attention to their view of the world and the Coalition States, expansion/colonization, military operations, technology, magic, nonhumans, and any alliances with D-bees and supernatural beings or people and places beyond a Rift. The CEF team reports their findings to the Intelligence Division. **Note:** The CEF is rarely directly involved in activities that undermine a foreign government or acts of espionage, but they do supply the information that is used for such purposes. They may also assist espionage agents and Special Forces directly or indirectly and establish safe-houses, false identities and map escape routes for them. The CEF currently has operatives in some of the cities and towns of the American West, a few of the Mexican border towns (including El Paso, New Del Rio, and Ciudad Juarez), Whykin, Kingsdale, Tolkeen, Lazlo, Ishpeming, the Manistique Imperium, Iron Heart, the City of Free Quebec (and allied communities) and even abroad in the New German Republic and Poland.

A Note Concerning Modern Warfare on Rifts Earth

The trend in tactics across North America, and much of the world, has been the use of small-sized combat units. Except for massive campaigns and sieges by forces such as the Coalition States, field armies of more than a few thousand are uncommon. In a world where a squad of armored infantrymen with laser rifles could obliterate a company of 20th Century infantrymen, small unit wars and guerilla tactics are the warfare of the day.

In North America, anyone who can assemble a force of fifty robot vehicles and/or several dozen power armor troops, or a couple hundred cyborgs, Crazies or Juicers, is a force to be reckoned with, and one able to bring most small cities and some kingdoms to their knees! Huge battles like those of World War Two are things of the past since the destructive power of magic and human technology makes such a concentration of force un-

desirable. What's more, there are almost no wide scale wars because the world has been divided into thousands of small kingdoms, city-states and nations. The only nations to still amass large forces are the Coalition States, the New German Republic and supernatural and alien invaders, like the Gargoyle Empire and Xiticix, among others.

Most military forces send out combat units of squad (6-10 troops) to platoon size (40 troops) which are perfect for small engagements (and ideal for role-playing). A medium-sized force is typically the size of one or two Companies (160-320 soldiers), while a large force is typically the equivalent to a Brigade (1920 troops) or a Division (5760 troops). Even during the *Juicer Uprising*, one of the largest military forces assembled in the last 20 years, it is believed that less than 30,000 men were involved on the side of the Uprising (**Note:** The war was such that all numbers are estimated; exact figures are not known. At least half the forces were Juicers — perhaps as many as three-quarters). Even the Xiticix and other alien and supernatural invaders who attack in swarms, rarely exceed five thousand. Alien creatures and herds or swarms of animal intelligence predators who attack in waves, are usually slaughtered in large numbers by forces 60-80% smaller than the attacking force!

Everything is about to change in North America. After years of secretly building an expansive, professional army, the Coalition States is ready to march. Except for a few notable exceptions, like Tolkeen and Free Quebec, the nations surrounding the CS have armies of about 5000-15,000, sometimes less — nothing compared to the nearly one million Coalition soldiers ready for combat (and according to some reports, as many as another half million in the process of training)! Soon the skull-faced soldiers and war machines of the Coalition States will march on Tolkeen and Free Quebec, commencing the greatest battle on Earth since the Great Cataclysm. The armies of each side will number well into the hundreds of thousands and the volume of magic and human weaponry released in the conflict will dwarf any battle ever fought in human history! If the Coalition States is successful in these campaigns, the small kingdoms of North America will have to unite and build an army to match the Coalition or perish in the birth of the exploding human Empire.

Some CS Strategies & Tactics

Blitzkrieg: The Coalition military frequently engages in "Blitzkrieg" assaults, also known as lightning and maneuver warfare. A swift, sudden military offensive that utilizes both ground and air forces. In the case of the Coalition, ground forces usually consist of a robot and hover tank attack group, followed by (sometimes led by) swarming *Skelebots* and infantry troops (armored Dog Pack, cyborg, Juicer and human troops). The air forces are predominantly the fast and incredibly mobile SAMAS (light and/or super), supported by Skycycles and other attack aircraft (helicopters, transports, jet fighters, etc.).

Army commanders use surprise whenever possible and always strike rapidly at the enemy with an array of heavy forces to crush them. They are trained to prey on the indecisiveness of the enemy and to exploit its weaknesses. Once a breach has been made in the enemy front-lines, Coalition soldiers push forward and try to divide the enemy while other combat troops encircle and constrict the enemy to contain and destroy it. In the words of Emperor Prosek, the Coalitions troops "fight a war of annihilation." Thus, the Army completely obliterates nonhuman and magic empowered enemies, and fight human combat forces with near equal ruthlessness. Once a human kingdom is conquered, it is the occupying troops' responsibility to remove all active and passive resistance. The officers and soldiers of the Coalition Army are experienced at this style of war and excel at it.

Fanaticism: The Coalition army has the best troops in North America. This is due in part, to the fanatical patriotism and loyalty to human supremacy, the Coalition States, and their Emperor. The Emperor is often quoted as publicly stating, "Fortune smiles on the brave man who takes on the mantle of the hero." Privately, he confides to his son and Executive Counsel that, "I have made the masses fanatical to make them my instrument. With the vision and passion you and I have given them, our people will achieve things they could never have imagined."

Training: Great emphasis is placed on the individual both in his indoctrination and combat training. Every soldier in the Coalition is provided with rigorous, specialized training and some of the best equipment in the world. The Coalition States has also recruited psychics to detect and combat unnatural forces regularly encountered on the field of battle and hidden among the enemy. Thanks to the combination of training, advanced weapons, firepower, psionics and personal dedication, Coalition soldiers can accomplish missions that other armies could not. Their training and commitment has enabled the Coalition Army to successfully spread Karl Prosek's vision of the future across the mid-section of the American continent.

Standard Missions

Over the past couple of decades, the Coalition, under Emperor Karl Prosek, has been content to consolidate its position. Unnoticeable to most, they have quietly secured strategic positions. In some cases, this meant solidifying trade and/or political relationships, establishing friendly, positive and strong lines of communication, cooperation and obligation. In other cases, the position has been increased through the military presence of advisors (Military Specialists and Special Forces), militias organized and often run by the CS Military (and to whom the militia men are loyal), regional defense forces — typically a platoon to company size squad of CS soldiers assigned to duty to protect the community (often with armored or mixed troops), and fly-by patrols (SAMAS, Skycycles, Helicopters, etc.) as well as new and expanded military bases, outposts and fortifications.

Furthermore, Chi-Town and its closest allied States have been very slowly expanding into and conquering strategic territories by invading a small village here, a tiny town there, routing D-bee squatters, chasing mercenaries or bandits out of the area, clearing and securing land areas, and so forth. Again, these subtle tactics have strengthened their strategic positions and opened avenues for further expansion. Most military operations have been fairly low key, nothing resembling the brewing campaign against the Minnesota territory.

In the absence of extended assaults, there have been four standard missions, Reconnaissance, Search and Destroy, Strategic Assault and Pacification. These missions are all short-term operations initiated and completed within a couple of months. The operations in the Campaign of Unity will include these four standard missions with two differences, they are part of an extended military campaign and will be conducted in enemy territory earmarked for invasion and conquest by the Coalition States.

Reconnaissance: Missions of reconnaissance are usually conducted by small teams with light mechanized support, often composed of Special Forces troops and/or Scouts and Psi-Hounds. The objective of a reconnaissance mission is to explore or investigate a particular region. A mission could be conducted inside CS territory or "over the fence" in the territory claimed by another kingdom. A squad can be sent on short-range patrols, working from a nearby base, or on long-range patrols operating hundreds or thousands of miles away from the nearest CS outpost. Whether a reconnaissance patrol is short or long-range, the objectives are always basically the same: locate and identify enemy forces, assess their strengths and weaknesses, determine their numbers and operation/purpose, possible enemy objectives/targets, and return to a CS installation to report what they have learned.

Reconnaissance missions can also be conducted for the purpose of mapping a region, identifying unusual features, resources or dangers such as ruins, indigenous life forms, the presence of ley lines/nexus points, farmlands, potential base sites, rivers, swamps, mountains, forests, traps, and similar features. Once the reconnaissance squad has completed their investigation, they are to report back to their superiors.

In most cases, a reconnaissance team is to avoid engaging the enemy or alerting hostile forces to the presence of the squad. After returning, the information, or intelligence, collected by the team is processed and analyzed by their superiors. Further missions could result from their reconnaissance report. This could include further reconnaissance, surveillance of the enemy, sabotage, search and destroy missions, and so on.

Search and Destroy: A search and destroy mission is an aggressive patrol where the goal of the participating soldiers is to locate, identify and eliminate hostile forces. Infantry units involved in S&D operations can be large or small. Large-scale operations may be supported by power armor troops, cyborgs, robots, tanks and aircraft that number into the dozens or even hundreds of participants. Small-scale search and destroy missions are likely to employ a small, elite team of 6-12 soldiers (not necessarily Special Forces) best suited to the task at hand.

Search and Destroy teams will generally attack forces larger than themselves, if they feel they have military superiority or the element of surprise. Patrols are usually conducted in unsecured CS territories, like the ruins of Chicago, or in hostile regions bordering the Coalition States. Whenever an S&D mission is conducted, there will usually be units stationed nearby, earmarked to give assistance if called upon. These usually include SAMAS (which can get in and out of situations quickly), heavy armored vehicles (tanks, APCs and/or robot vehicles) and/or aircraft.

The CS often conducts covert S&D missions far beyond CS borders and into other countries, including Mexico, Central and South America and even Europe. Special Operations troops or soldiers with espionage training slip in, hit their target, then slip out before their presence is noticed. Often, these seek and destroy missions are top secret and officially denied and operatives

disavowed by the CS government. Soldiers in covert operations may be equipped with captured enemy equipment, body armor and unmarked vehicles, enabling the CS to deny sponsoring the mission should members of the team be killed or captured.

Strategic Assault: A strategic assault mission is an organized raid with specific objectives, usually the elimination of hostile forces or sabotage. Units assigned to such missions are very similar in composition to those sent on search and destroy patrols. Like the S&D patrol, this mission involves an aggressive strike on the enemy; the difference however, lies in the fact that the enemy is already located and identified prior to the planned assault (no "search" is involved). Using the information gathered by reconnaissance missions, the military chiefs identify strategic targets and target them for capture, sabotage or destruction. These can range from a city ruin filled with supernatural beings, a Xiticix hive, a mercenary camp, Black Market hideout, body chop-shop, drug production facility, magic practitioners, cultists, D-bee enclave or enemy base to kidnapping an official(s), assassination, stealing plans, planting false information or evidence, capturing a prototype, rescuing prisoners of war, etc.

Strategic assault teams are generally large and mobile strike forces, the idea being to hit hard and fast, destroy the target or attain the objective and then return to CS territory. As a rule, the Coalition tends to authorize strategic assaults only against targets along or beyond its borders. Small teams (6-12 men) and small strike forces (1-2 platoons/40-80 troops) may conceal their identity, while large-scale assaults are usually pretty straightforward with no attempt to conceal their identity.

Pacification: The term pacification refers to missions where the objective is to subdue, divide, splinter, and dissipate hostile forces within friendly territory. In essence, pacification is extremely aggressive peacekeeping with the goal of rooting out enemy forces who have infiltrated a region of the Coalition States. Soldiers may be sent to cordon off or contain an area and to keep hostile troops from escaping until policing units are sent in to identify and eliminate the enemy.

Generally speaking, pacification missions are conducted in settlements like shanty-towns, border villages or sections of the `Burbs that get out of hand. Psi-Stalkers and Dog Boys are used extensively in *pacification* operations due to their psionic sensing abilities which enable them to identify the nonhumans, practitioners of magic and the supernatural much more easily than regular troops. Once the enemy has been identified and contained, they are eliminated. This can be an orderly removal/deportation or, as is more common with the Coalition States, a bloodbath in which the enemy is slaughtered.

Other pacification actions are more subtle and less bloodthirsty. These include enforcing laws, curfews and conditions on an occupied people that restricts and divides the community. In addition to the limitations and disruption such tactics produce, the pacification force can take its time to identify and eliminate "key" targets such as political and religious leaders, activists, enemy sympathizers, D-bees and troublemakers. Propaganda may also be part of this operation in an attempt to win the hearts and minds of the people.

When a pacification operation is authorized in an area outside the States or a region controlled by D-bees, the methods may more resemble a strategic assault. Such pacification actions or purges are frequently a massacre against less powerful, often defenseless D-Bee settlements, tribes or sections of the `Burbs. In these missions, troops do not distinguish between hostile or friendly but simply kill anyone that doesn't look human or who is carrying a weapon. There have been a couple of instances in recent years where the Coalition has justified raids outside of their territory by declaring them pacification operations. Neighboring kingdoms often protest to no avail and pray they don't become a target of pacification.

Enlistment & Conscription

The enormous armed forces of Chi-Town represent approximately one-tenth of the total population of the Coalition States. Keeping the force at that size has been relatively easy, thanks to the CS propaganda machine and the high regard of the general population for the CS Military. Although there are laws on the books for conscription, there has been no need for it in over 30 years. Every year there are more recruits anxious to replace those soldiers who have retired from the force, deserted or have been killed in the line of duty. Approximately half are career soldiers (36-48 years of service), which also means that the CS possesses many of the most experienced soldiers on the continent; the typical veteran has 12-24 years experience and is 5-9th level!

Approximately seventy-five percent of all soldiers in the Coalition Army enlisted of their own free will. Of the remaining percentage, roughly 20% are mutants "grown" specifically for the task, and the others are special recruits (psychics, headhunters, 'borgs, mutants, mercenaries, and criminals coerced into joining). Youths in all the Coalition cities, but especially those in Chi-Town, Missouri and Lone Star, are constantly bombarded by propaganda that promotes and glorifies the Army, "and the heroic men and women who keep us safe." All their lives they are told that the military is a place to stand up for their families, race and nation against supernatural and demonic invaders. The Army is also perceived as an organization that offers endless adventure and opportunities. Furthermore, a career as a soldier is regarded as a noble and honorable profession. Hundreds of lower and middle class men and women join the army each year as a result of the encouragement or pressure from family, friends, school and State-sponsored propaganda. Many wilderness folk join in hopes of proving their worth and getting their families bumped up on the waiting list to become CS citizens or authorization to live and work in one of the fortified cities or other safe communities. Many of the poor and desperate join, because they have few other options that are attractive. **Note:** Each term of duty is six years.

Indoctrination

From the first moment a recruit joins the Coalition military, they are exposed to propaganda above and beyond that forced on the public. Throughout the recruitment process, training and even during regular service, the soldier is inundated with propaganda which serves to indoctrinate the individual with the Coalition's ideology. Beliefs and doctrines imprinted onto the citizenry of the CS are reinforced on troops since the military is vital in keeping the dreams of Emperor Prosek alive.

Ideals of discipline, loyalty to the military, loyalty to the Prosek family, hatred of magic, and human supremacy are constantly drilled into recruits during boot camp. During the strenuous weeks of basic training the new soldiers are "brainwashed" by the constant assault of propaganda and praise mixed with sleep deprivation. The purpose of indoctrination is to keep the soldiers loyal and motivated, and to maintain their fighting spirit and dedication to the cause. This is achieved and reinforced by constantly praising the soldiers for their patriotism, dedication, and courage — most CS citizens (and the soldiers themselves) consider all soldiers to be *national heroes* and are treated with the respect worthy of such a title. The result is the zealous and fearsome soldiers of the Coalition dreaded throughout North America and dubbed with the fearsome nickname of "Dead Boys."

Not all troops in the Coalition are indoctrinated fanatics dedicated to Emperor Prosek and his vision for the future. In fact, many soldiers retain a strong sense of identity rather than having their own submerged in the propaganda of the State. These soldiers believe in many aspects of the Coalition's ideology. They believe wholeheartedly in the need for discipline, loyalty to fellow troops and the Army at large. Most even believe in human supremacy to a certain extent, thinking it necessary to protect humankind from supernatural and alien invaders, but they are *not* the hard-core zealots who have bought into the system completely. These soldiers are generally left alone by their superiors as long as they continue to perform in the service of their country. As soon as they begin to promote radically different ideas or disrupt the chain of command, steps are taken to send the soldier back for *reorientation*. If the soldier continues to buck the system, defy military law, and spread dangerous ideas, they are dishonorably discharged (and placed under ISS surveillance as a possible dissident) or even imprisoned or executed for treason.

Combat Experience

Soldiers with combat experience are valuable assets to any military organization. Veterans, as a rule, are better troops than those with training but no actual time in the field. A soldier who has been in battle before will be better prepared for combat than one who has never experienced warfare firsthand. In general, veterans are more apt to remain calm in the heat of battle, less likely to break formation or retreat against orders. Furthermore, their resolve to fight is hardened and their fighting skills more finely honed. When pitched against foes with little or no combat experience, veterans can play a vital role and change the course of a battle.

The Coalition States has a huge number of veterans, but almost all soldiers have some combat experience. For most, this field experience will have been in the form of a skirmish or two rather than a large-scale battle or a war. This is a result of the constant raids, reconnaissance patrols, search and destroy operations and other missions into enemy territory.

A recent trend for the Military High Command has been to declare areas prone to conflict as **War Zones**. These so-called War Zones are regions with uncharacteristicly high rates of engagement with hostile forces, although not enough to be considered a direct threat to the CS or a full-fledged war. Rather than send in huge pacification forces and destroy the enemy outright, the Coalition Army contains the area and sends in raw recruits to get some firsthand combat experience in a somewhat controlled environment. Some regions currently declared as War Zones include the Old Chicago Ruins, East St. Louis, the Pecos River territory, the American West, Northern America (Canada), Xiticix Territory and the Magic Zone. Once their tour is over the soldiers move into regular units where their background of field experience helps in active missions for the Coalition. Rookies are also assigned to police actions in the 'Burbs and border duty.

Training

All recruits in the Coalition Armed Forces are sent through a common course of basic training. Rudimentary military skills are taught during the course but it also includes introduction to army life and indoctrination. Recruits become familiar with army language/slang, barracks life and standard procedure. Discipline is another major facet drilled into the trainees during the course of basic training. Their instructor is god, he or she controls every aspect of life and tells recruits how to walk, talk, eat, sleep and so on, the Coalition way.

Physical training is a major part of training to get each character into top fighting form. The recruit is also taught the use of fundamental military weapons, the basics of marksmanship, hand to hand combat, radio communications, operation of military vehicles, and reading electronic and sensory equipment. These "basic" skills are the ones deemed necessary for combat and as such, all soldiers, including officers, must complete the basic course before moving on to specialized training.

Once a recruit has finished the basic course, he is given specialized training to conduct specific tasks. Usually the soldier is allowed to select his training, pending the approval of the instructor based upon the soldier's aptitude and past performance. There are numerous fields in the Coalition Army that troops can select from, including infantry duty, vehicle piloting, robot or power armor piloting, mechanics/engineering, communications, technical skills or officer school. This "individual" training determines the role (O.C.C.) that the soldier will fulfil in the army and will help to determine where the soldier will be stationed.

Game Master Tips

The Coalition Good or Evil?

By Kevin Siembieda

Note: Some of the material in this section is reprinted from **Rifts® Sourcebook One**, with additional comments and updates. Other parts are new or elaborations of past observations.

Circa, 105 P.A.

The evil of the Coalition States lies primarily at its core. Emperor Prosek, his son Joseph II, the Executive Counsel, many of his generals, and virtually the entire power base of the current Coalition States are fundamentally self-serving villains who use and manipulate the people to trust and believe in them for their own personal gain and the greater glory of the allied States. In many cases, this is the classic lust for wealth and power. Emperor Prosek and his son dream of building and ruling the greatest empire on earth. The military, propaganda, patriotism and fanaticism of the people are all weapons in the leadership's arsenal to achieve their goal. They have espoused so incessantly and vigorously about human supremacy, the inhuman threat, the horrors of magic, and the CS being the last hope for humankind, that not only do the majority of the CS citizens believe it, the Emperor and his minions are actually beginning to believe their own hype and lies too. Sadly, they have used such idealistic notions as freedom, peace and heritage as well as the fear of the unknown and inhuman, to corrupt, prejudice and control the citizens of their Empire.

Hate and fear make possible the militarization of a nation

After decades of masterful propaganda, the Emperor and his minions have succeeded in turning Chi-Town and most of the allied States into a militarized nation. War, conflict and the omnipresent military are part of everyday life for the average citizen of the Coalition States. Through the strong leadership of the Emperor and the acceptance of the military, the people of Chi-Town in particular, and the Coalition States in general, are united and given purpose through war. War and aggression (for whatever justification given) are welcomed, accepted and supported — it is their way of life.

The average CS citizen is militant and cold-hearted when it comes to the protection of their race, nation and lifestyle. They have allowed themselves to be convinced that all D-bees and aliens are evil monsters who threaten their existence. In many cases, it is the fear of the unknown that motivates them to destroy what they do not understand. The CS propaganda machine has preyed upon this fear for generations, turning an estimated 85% of the people in the States of Chi-Town, Lone Star, and Missouri into fanatical human supremacists who hate and fear (they are terrified of) all nonhumans and practitioners of magic. For them, these beings are the "evil enemy," end of story — kill them before they kill you. It is as simple as that.

Note: Free Quebec is equally fanatical regarding magic and nonhumans, but it has little to do with the propaganda from Chi-Town. At Iron Heart, 65% are fanatical human supremacists, up 15% in the last six years due to Chi-Town propaganda and increasing fear of the Xiticix and other supernatural horrors. An estimated 75% of the population of Arkansas share Chi-Town's anti-nonhuman sentiments.

The Average Coalition Citizen

Every society is a collection of people all living and working in the same environment. Within that collection there are good, selfish, and evil individuals. In addition, there are the misguided and manipulated, the righteous and the humble, the well meaning and the miscreant.

In game terms, the average citizen of the Coalition States is of a good or selfish alignment. Of course, there is your criminal element and those of evil alignments who prey on others, just as we have in our real world today. However, the majority are well-meaning people who try to eke out fruitful, happy lives without intentionally hurting anybody. Anybody human, that is.

The orientation, beliefs, fears, and morals of the average CS citizen makes them the enemy of men of magic, mutants, nonhumans, and D-Bees. Why? Because they have been taught that these strange people are the enemy and *should be* feared, hated, shunned, enslaved, or destroyed. They genuinely fear nonhumans and believe these creatures will subvert their civilization and destroy humankind. Many humans have experienced or witnessed attacks by supernatural monsters and evil human or D-bee sorcerers, which only substantiates their worst fears and supports the government's propaganda. Consequently, the citizens are not evil when they notify the ISS or NTSET to capture or gun-down a D-bee. Nor are they necessarily evil when an angry or terrified mob traps and kills an invading wizard or mutant who has snuck into the city. After all, by their perception, these characters are *not* feeling people like them, but monsters that threaten their lives. At best, the fiend is an enemy spy or scavenger who probably has the blood of countless humans on his hands (no doubt killed in their sleep).

Is it wrong to lie to the enemy so that he may be apprehended? Is it wrong to kill a murderer or monster? The problem is a matter of perception and degree. The average citizen's perception is simply very different than those who live beyond the protective walls and borders of the Coalition States. They have come to accept the views of isolation and human supremacy. From our point of view as the omnipotent reader who sees the overview of the world in far better perspective, we know they are wrong and unjust. Many D-bees and practitioners of magic are well-meaning, caring people. Many are peace-loving heroes who fight for the rights of all living beings. We see the citizens of the Coalition as frightened, uneducated, misguided, and often fanatical people who fiercely cling to their narrow and self-serving view of life. They see themselves as the last bastion of humankind fighting for their very existence in a world gone mad. All a matter of perception and degree.

The evil that arises from these twisted perceptions and emotions is the cruelty that comes from such inhumane convictions. Nonhumans, mutants, wielders of magic and other beings who possess strange powers have been routinely *dehumanized*, so that they are not perceived as other intelligent life forms with feelings and families, but as monsters and evil incarnate. While the world should not be seen as black and white, the Coalition citizens do see life in that simple spectrum. As a result, it is easy to hate and destroy such a terrible enemy without guilt; "They would have done far worse to us."

A player note about CS characters: The average citizen is not inherently evil, but hate filled, terrified and misguided. While they may be comparatively innocent pawns, the average citizen is still a serious threat to those they perceive as their enemy or as traitors to humankind. However, not all Coalition citizens feel this way. Some are true villains who have no regard for nonhumans (and probably little regard for human life as well). Others believe that the government's policies and treatment of nonhumans is wrong, but they are in the minority (about 5-10% of the overall population). And some don't know what to think, and try to avoid having to take a stand. Of course, Coalition player characters may be in the minority, but their actions will be judged harshly by their peers.

The Average Coalition Soldier

The average soldier is not much different than the average citizen. Their alignments range the full gamut of good, selfish, and evil. As loyal believers in the human supremacist regime of Karl Prosek, these soldiers are, without a doubt, misguided individuals unwittingly serving an evil cause. Many are blinded by what they see as the righteousness of the Coalition States and their heroic Emperor. Furthermore, as combat soldiers locked in war, they are trained to trust in the judgement of their superiors and to follow orders without question. Regardless of individual alignment and convictions, Coalition soldiers are out to do their job, and that job is to destroy all enemies of the States — all nonhumans and practitioners of magic.

Philosophically and historically speaking, the bad guys or evil force in most wars is the loser. Again we are back to perception and degree. In the *American Revolutionary War*, the British Government was perceived by the colonists as the oppressor and the bad guys. The British government of the day viewed the colonies as rebellious citizens and dissidents; i.e. the bad guys. As things would turn out, the colonies won, became Americans, and despite some further conflicts with the British (like the war of 1812), went on to develop ties of friendship and trade. The same is true of most wars. During the conflict the enemy is the bad guy. Afterwards, the winner (and usually self-proclaimed good guy) may make certain overtures to the defeated that will either result in friendly relations in the future or continued bad feelings and unrest. In most wars, both sides believe themselves to be right and just. Nothing has changed.

Stop and think for a minute. Does it matter if the enemy soldier is a bloodthirsty maniac or a person of principled good alignment, a wonderful family man, merciful, and hates war, if he is trying to blow your brains out because he sees *you* as the enemy? That is the tragedy of war. It's kill or be killed.

Like all good soldiers, theirs is not to question why, theirs is just to do or die! In a life and death conflict one tends to try his hardest to defeat the other. There is little time for thoughts of morality when one is wrestling with an opponent who is trying to kill him.

The degree of mercy and cruelty may be a different story. The soldiers are indoctrinated to loathe the enemy. To show no mercy or kindness to the "inhuman monsters." These sentiments are fueled by combat experience against horrific creatures from the Rifts, power hungry sorcerers, and genuine evildoers. The world of **Rifts** is one of savagery and the bizarre. It is a constantly changing environment where there never seems to be an end to would-be-conquerors and malevolent monsters with a taste for human blood. Under the circumstances, it is easy to forget one's compassion and perspective and give in to anger, hatred, and vengeance. After a while, a soldier can become cold and vindictive, honestly seeing all non-human creatures as monsters who must be destroyed without hesitation.

Only CS soldiers sent on special missions, espionage, or deep into the wilderness may have the opportunity to observe and *interact* with the so-called "enemy." An opportunity that may demonstrate that, like humans, not all aliens or mutant life forms are inherently evil. That many are good and loving beings who abhor war and have no desire to enslave or destroy humankind. It is among these soldiers that the highest rate of desertion and traitorous action occurs. Why? Because they are given the chance to learn, firsthand, about other life forms and may come to understand and care about them. Suddenly, the enemy has a face and a name, along with hopes and dreams. Under these circumstances, the CS soldier may begin to question the propaganda and perhaps even his orders. The soldier is likely to faithfully report his findings and make recommendations contrary to the government's policies. This will not be viewed kindly by his superiors. *Reorientation* will be required (after all, it is obvious that the soldier has lost his perspective under the strain of his mission; poor fellow). Emperor Prosek and his human supremacist forces do not want to reach an understanding or develop a tolerance for other races because it will deplete their power base. If a soldier does not comply with reorientation, he may be branded a traitor or a psychopath and become the enemy himself. This means the soldier may have to face the moral dilemma of choosing between what he knows is right (defending nonhumans and promoting *real* knowledge and freedom) or to turn away and stay with the Coalition and follow their doctrines — each injustice meted out by his hands or in front of his eyes, all the more painful. The choice is always a difficult one with bitter consequences either way. To reject the teachings of the human supremacists is to defy the Coalition States and the Emperor. This means losing everything the soldier is likely to hold dear: his CS citizenship, the society he knows and loves, his friends and loved ones, his career and future. Not only does he lose his place in the world, but his own people, even family members, are likely to chastise him and hunt him down like an animal to bring him to justice for his treasonous words and actions. To say and do nothing means to accept and allow the ignorance, fear, cruelty and death to continue.

Some try to find an alternative between the two extremes. This can include holding one's tongue and trying to make a difference within the system in subtle ways. Another is to pretend to be a loyal soldier and human supremacist, while secretly helping D-bee refugees escape the wrath of the Coalition. Others try to teach friends and family about the things they have seen and lived through in hopes that they too may find some enlightenment, and perhaps together make a better, more tolerant world. Any choice other than unquestioningly following the edicts of the Coalition States is flirting with disaster. But then, life is full of hard decisions. It's only the strongest who dare to stand for what they *know* is right and refuse to compromise their morals, regardless of the personal consequences. Perhaps, this is why Erin Tarn has become such a heroic figure, and why the Coalition leadership fears her so.

CS Soldiers as the villain

NPC character tips

The average CS soldier may not be inherently evil, but he is dedicated to crushing the enemy and that includes practitioners of magic, D-bees, other nonhumans, and anybody who opposes the CS (and all too often, those who associate with the enemy)! At least 75-85% of all Coalition troops are anti-human and pro-Coalition fanatics. The bottom line: a CS soldier shoots first and rarely bothers to ask questions. If you are an enemy of the States, you better flee or die. The morality of combat/war is usually lost in the hail of gunfire and emotion.

While we've focused on the general public thus far, there is a frightening percentage of villains and hatemongers among the Coalition Military. At least 20% are so filled with hate, revulsion and fear regarding nonhumans and other CS enemies that there is no reasoning with them (anarchist and evil alignments). Many of these vile characters enjoy killing and torturing the enemy and have no qualms about murdering defenseless D-bee women and children. Likewise, they have zero tolerance for those who talk about trying to accept and live in peace with the different alien races, or most anything that goes against the words of the Emperor and ways of the Coalition. Thus, they will bully, beat, and kill anybody, human or nonhuman, who challenges their values and ideals. Many are career soldiers who have made it their life's work to destroy the enemy; the notions of human supremacy and the power of the CS lending justification to acts of cruelty and depravity.

Others (10%) are opportunists who are primarily concerned with their own careers and self-interest. The military, especially one as aggressive and hate-filled as the CS, is the perfect place for people who might be considered cruel or miscreants in polite society. It is an attractive environment for those who see the military as a means to power, fame, glory and wealth. If others must fall so that they succeed or advance, so be it. They may or may not believe the propaganda; it doesn't really matter because they will do what they must to achieve their goals. If they must adopt a particular doctrine, lick a boot, grease a palm, look the other way, send troops to their death, or slaughter innocent people, they will; and woe to the person(s) who threatens their quest for power or questions their authority. These characters are typically anarchist or evil (any) alignment; many are officers.

Then, there are the acts of CS soldiers who are truly creatures of evil (15%). Men, women and CS mutants who are thrilled by combat and derive pleasure by inflicting pain and suffering. These misanthropes like the power the military gives them and like to prove their superiority by belittling, frightening, hurting and killing others. For them, there is no greater thrill than holding the power of life and death in their hands. These characters typically treat other humans and soldiers of inferior rank with contempt and cruelty as well. They are truly mean and vicious characters who are typically miscreant or diabolic in alignment.

In a strictly game context, the CS military forces pitted against our player character heroes are likely to be predominately evil or self-serving scum, but this is *not* necessarily the *average* CS soldier! The player characters are likely to avoid problems with most fair and reasonable people, but clashes with arrogant, mean, and corrupt characters (who may come to them looking for trouble) is inevitable. It is the evil squad leader or Commander who will ask or put the player characters in a position to compromise their morals. It is the brazen warrior responsible for horrible atrocities and/or has something to prove who will clash with characters not willing to back down to his or her will.

Remember too, that in the basic context of most RPG adventures it is the heroic player characters who fight against evil and struggle for truth and justice. In this sense, the antagonists with whom our heroes are most likely to encounter will be evil ones. However, Game Masters should also include the occasional good, kind!y, and friendly (perhaps even a momentary rescuer or protector) who is also a member of the Coalition military, driving home the point that no group of people is entirely good nor entirely evil.

Coalition Soldiers as Good Guy Player Characters

As a player character, the individual is probably a special field operative or espionage agent placed in the more wild and woolly regions and/or dispatched to spy on or infiltrate the enemy. Or the player character may be assigned to a wilderness outpost that is much more lax in its dealings with nonhumans. Either way, the character is likely to start as a loyal CS soldier who is greatly prejudiced against D-bees and all who oppose the CS or fail to conform. This can be a delightful role-playing element in the playing of the character. However, the CS player character is likely to change his views as the campaign continues and he or she gets to know, like and understand other life forms and people with opposing philosophies. This new perspective should be reflected in the character's attitudes, friendliness, diminishing prejudices, and growing knowledge of the world beyond the narrow and distorted one of the Coalition.

The soldier character may never feel completely comfortable with monstrous or supernatural characters and/or may never completely trust D-bees or practitioners of magic, but he will not be the unquestioning or gullible pawn of the CS that he once was. Of-course, everybody experiences and perceives life differently, so one character may grow against the teachings of the CS while another's, similar experiences, may only serve to reaffirm everything the Coalition fears and fights against.

Role-Playing Officers

Commissioned Officers

A commissioned officer is a character who has earned a *commission* and a rank of lieutenant or higher. One becomes a commissioned officer by rising through the ranks, starting at private, or by finishing *Officer's Training School* with honors.

The elite Military Academy is very similar to pre-Rifts institutions like West Point. These characters must have a minimum I.Q. of 10 and excel in at least one other attribute (mental or physical; 14 or higher), otherwise they "wash out." Most (70%) come from a wealthy, powerful or influential family. The remaining 30% have been selected for academic or military excellence; the latter includes an aptitude for strategy and tactics, staying cool under fire, leadership abilities and a high I.Q., M.A. or M.E. (10 or better). Academy Officers usually start at first or second level even though they are likely to start at the rank of First or Second Lieutenant.

Officers who have risen through the ranks tend to have more field experience, and the characters are usually fairly high level; 5-10th level. But this is not always the case. Characters who are shmoozers and know how to play the system, can engage in politics and earn favors that can get them a commissioned rank with minimal field experience (3rd level).

Special Officer Bonuses: +1 to save vs horror factor, +1 to M.E., and +5% to all communication skills.

Special Officer Skills: In addition to the standard skills available from the various Military O.C.C.s, the character also gets to select one additional skill at levels two, five and ten. All Special Officer Skill selections are limited to the categories of Communication, Espionage, Military, and Weapon Proficiencies; O.C.C. bonuses are applicable.

Non-Player Characters (NPCs) & Player Characters

As a commissioned officer, the character is taught, or learns through experience, how to behave as an officer, lead and command his troops, maintain discipline, military procedure, and strategy and tactics. Of course, leadership is a very personal quality and can vary dramatically from person to person. Some men and women are natural leaders and will rise to the challenge with little or no training. Others are terrible leaders no matter how many hours of training and years of first-hand experience they may attain. Take this into consideration when using officers and the chain of command as non-player characters. Also, give the officer a personality and a goal. Is he friendly or aloof? Is he concerned about his troops or only his career? Is he his own man, willing to express his views to his superiors or a bootlicker? Is he or she a dedicated career soldier or an opportunist? Is he sympathetic to D-bees and mutants or is he a fanatical human supremacist? Then think about his and other officers' positions in the chain of command. Do the player characters have to deal with some weasel or deadbeat at some point? Do their requests or needs get stalled by the weaselly or deadbeat character? Do they have to grease some palms? Is one of the officers jealous of them or just doesn't like them so he or she tries to make their life hell? Does the requisition officer like them and secretly gives them preferential treatment? These and similar questions can only make the setting more fun and interesting.

Some Character Types

Poor Leaders

Being an officer does not mean the character is any better, more experienced, moral, or wiser than anybody else. Some are corrupt and take bribes or show favoritism in exchange for favors and special considerations offered to them by others. Some are outright crooks involved in smuggling, drug dealing, partnerships with the Black Market and other criminals. A tiny handful *may* even sell military secrets and/or supplies to the enemy.

Others are bullies who use the "power" of their command like a weapon. They relish being an "elite" officer and feel it necessary to prove themselves by constantly exerting their power over others, from belittling those beneath them, enforcing the most petty rules, or punishing the tiniest infractions to life and death command decisions. The bullying officer doesn't actually lead, but commands through threats, intimidation, punishment, fear and hatred.

Still others don't care about anything anymore. Maybe they were always self-serving scum or they've become worn out and jaded by the stress of command and the horrors of war. In any case, these officers either want to get through their tour of duty and get out of service, or have resigned themselves to doing only what's absolutely necessary to keep their jobs. These dispassionate leeches and bureaucrats can be just as bad as criminals and bullies, turning a blind eye to the troubles and needs of those under their command. This officer is likely to bury his problems in bureaucracy and paperwork and is surrounded by corruption that he ignores.

A poor officer may be petty, vindictive, "chicken-shit" and/or a "by the book" and "by the rules" leader without consideration of the situation, extenuating circumstances, morale or strong personalities among his men. Another personality that makes a poor officer is one who treats his men like nameless cattle and cannon fodder. This character is likely to have little or no regard for his men and lets them know it by treating them in a condescending or even contemptuous manner.

The glory hound or politically minded officer can make a strong, capable leader and tactician, but is likely to be feared, disliked or hated by his men because they realize that the officer's career comes before anything and anyone else. This character is likely to exhibit a vast range of understanding and behavior that varies with each situation, from compassion to disassociation or cruelty. The bottom line is that the officer does what's best for his career, which will change from moment to moment.

Consequently, winning and looking his best in the eyes of his superiors is of paramount importance, his men are secondary, and often regarded as little more than chess pieces or stepping stones to be manipulated to advance "his" career.

A variation of this type of self-serving officer tends to be cunning, resourceful, and daring, especially with the lives of his men. He typically puts himself above his men and treats even lower officers with cool aloofness. He, or she, is usually respected, at least to some degree, by his troop and highly regarded by his superiors. The self-serving officer is not likely to jeopardize the lives of the soldiers in his charge foolishly or wantonly, but he views them dispassionately and will condemn them to death if the strategy or tactic will win the day or garner him the accolades of his superiors. Likewise, he will follow the orders of his superiors to the letter, digressing only if he can make a deft move that will win him praise without offending the superior who gave him the orders, or if it will win him the favor of a higher ranking superior (and is very likely to get him a promotion or position equal to or higher than the officer with whom he is taking issue or liberty with).

Respected Leaders

Well liked and respected officers are generally characters who genuinely care about the troops under their charge. Again, the style of command will vary greatly.

Generally speaking, the best leaders are characters who show their troops the honor, respect, and appreciation they deserve. The officer may have to remain somewhat aloof, enforce rules, maintain protocol, and make the hard (sometimes terrible) decisions that are unpopular, as well as push his men to the breaking point (when necessary), but the troops know he cares about them and has their welfare at heart. Unfortunately, the military, particularly the CS Military, is a war machine; people die and it's the officer who must bear the burden of life and death decisions. In fact, it is this inevitability of pain and death which entices some officers (good and bad) to keep their distance between themselves and the warriors under their command; it's just too difficult to see friends die.

Some of the most highly regarded officers can be men and women who believe in discipline and live "by the book." Yet they maintain balance and garner respect and loyalty because they expect no less (perhaps more) from fellow officers. He is likely to promote discipline as a virtue, strength, and quality to be proud of; something to strive for. This officer is fair, reasonable and honest, always aware of and responsive to his soldiers' needs, fears, and morale. He shows them *his* appreciation and respect as well as providing rewards in the way of special liberties, food, recreation, and little favors.

Those who lead by example are arguably some of the best leaders. Pre-Rifts General Patton was such a strong and charismatic leader. The troops often love and respect this type of blood and guts leader. The best "in the trenches" leader commands incredible loyalty. His troops will follow him to hell and back, usually without question or hesitation as long as he leads the way. However, sometimes this can lead to tragedy if the leader makes a bad judgement call and leads his soldiers on a foolish campaign, or into a trap, or on a suicide run. Furthermore, this officer is so highly regarded that his men *may* follow any order he gives, even those that defy the Military High Command or takes action against the government; this is where military coups and juntas are born. The worst "in the trenches" commander can turn his troops into an undisciplined and unorganized mess, vulnerable to enemy attacks, raids or infiltration. Since his men follow his example, if he shows no respect to his superiors or the rules of the military, neither will his men. Furthermore, familiarity may breed contempt, meaning that if he and the officers underneath him are "one of the boys," they may ultimately lose their respect for him and may question his orders or resent it when he "bosses" them around (gives necessary orders). This can lead to anarchy, desertion and insurrection.

Coalition Military Chain of Command

By Julius Rosenstein & Kevin Siembieda

Note: The chain of command is listed from the top down. Each term or tour of duty is six years. Career soldiers usually remain in active duty for 32 to 48 years! Some Generals have served their nation for even longer.

Heads of State
Emperor — Commander in Chief
Head of Propaganda
Special Advisors
Military Counselors
Individual Coalition State Governors
Territorial Representatives
High-Mayor of major cities

Military: Commissioned Officers
General of the Army (5 star)
General
Lieutenant General
Major General
Brigadier General
Colonel
Lieutenant Colonel
Major
Captain
1st Lieutenant
2nd Lieutenant

Military: Non-Commissioned Officers
Chief Warrant Officer
Warrant Officer
Command Sergeant Major
Sergeant Major
Master Sergeant
Sergeant 1st Class
Staff Sergeant
Sergeant

Military: Enlisted Personnel
Corporal
Private 1st Class
Private

Service Specialist
Civilian scouts and assistants (see description elsewhere)

Military Salaries by Rank

Commissioned Officers

Rank: General of the Army

Insignia: Five star General — there is only one, five star General and head of the army at any given time.

Base pay: 40,000 credits per month.

Rank: General

Insignia: Four stripes under an upward pointing triangle on sleeve, epaulet with four bars, four gold bars and triangle on collar.

Base pay: 25,000 credits per month.

Rank: Lieutenant General

Insignia: Three stripes under an upward pointing triangle on sleeve, epaulet with three bars, three gold bars and triangle on collar.

Base pay: 20,000 credits per month.

Rank: Major General

Insignia: Two stripes under an upward pointing triangle on sleeve, epaulet with two bars, two gold bars and triangle on collar.

Base pay: 16,000 credits per month.

Rank: Brigadier General

Insignia: One stripe under an upward pointing triangle on sleeve, epaulet with one bar, one gold bar and triangle on collar.

Base pay: 12,000 credits per month.

Rank: Colonel

Insignia: Four stripes above a downward pointing triangle on sleeve, standard epaulets, four silver bars on the collar.

Base pay: 7,000 credits per month.

Rank: Lieutenant Colonel

Insignia: Three and a half stripes above a downward pointing triangle on sleeve, standard epaulets, three bars (two silver and one gold) on the collar.

Base pay: 5,500 credits per month.

Rank: Major

Insignia: Three stripes above a downward pointing triangle on sleeve, standard epaulets, three silver bars on the collar.

Base pay: 4,500 credits per month.

Rank: Captain

Insignia: Two stripes above a downward pointing triangle on sleeve, standard epaulets, two silver bars on the collar.

Base pay: 3,500 credits per month.

Rank: 1st Lieutenant

Insignia: One and a half stripes above a downward pointing triangle on sleeve, standard epaulets, one gold bar on the collar.

Base pay: 2,800 credits per month.

Rank: 2nd Lieutenant

Insignia: One stripe above a downward pointing triangle on sleeve, standard epaulets, one silver bar on the collar.

Base pay: 2500 credits per month.

Note: The lowest commissioned field officer rank in the CS military, CS Military Specialists begin at this rank.

Non-Commissioned Officers

Rank: Chief Warrant Officer

Insignia: One stripe above a diamond on sleeve, standard epaulets, one bronze bar and a diamond on the collar.

Base pay: 2400 credits per month.

Note: The Chief Warrant Officer is primarily an executive administrator. They are seldom found on the frontline.

Rank: Warrant Officer

Insignia: One diamond on the sleeve, standard epaulets, one bronze diamond on the collar.

Base pay: 2200 credits per month.

Note: The Warrant Officer is primarily an administrator and organizer. They are seldom found on the frontline.

Rank: Command Sergeant Major

Insignia: Five stripes under an upward pointing triangle on sleeve.

Base pay: 2300 credits per month.

Note: The highest non-commissioned officer rank in the CS military. The next higher rank would be a Lieutenant.

Rank: Sergeant Major

Insignia: Four stripes under an upward pointing triangle on sleeve.

Base pay: 2200 credits per month.

Rank: Master Sergeant

Insignia: Four stripes above a downward pointing triangle on sleeve.

Base pay: 2100 credits per month.

Rank: Sergeant 1st Class

Insignia: Four stripes on sleeve.

Base pay: 2050 credits per month.

Rank: Staff Sergeant

Insignia: Three and a half stripes on sleeve.

Base pay: 2000 credits per month.

Rank: Sergeant

Insignia: Three stripes on sleeve.

Base pay: 1,900 credits per month.

Enlisted Personnel

Rank: Corporal

Insignia: Two stripes on sleeve.

Base pay: 1,800 credits per month.

Note: The highest enlisted rank in the CS military (short of non-commissioned officer), Technical Officers, Psi-Stalkers, and some Commandos begin at this rank.

Rank: Private 1st Class

Insignia: One stripe on sleeve.

Base pay: 1,750 credits per month.

Note: Nautical Specialists begin at this rank.

Rank: Private

Insignia: Plain sleeve.

Base pay: 1,700 credits per month.

Note: Private is the lowest rank in the CS military. Grunts, Borgs, Dog Boys, and most mercenaries (including Headhunters, Crazies, and Wilderness Scouts) begin at this rank.

Service Specialist (civilian special agent)

Rank: None

Insignia: None

Base pay: 1,000 to 2,000 credits per month depending on the character's level of experience and area of expertise.

CS Rank Reference Chart

Typical Rank Structure of the Coalition States:

Coalition O.C.C.s	Initial Rank	Top Rank
'Borg	Private	Noncom
Crazy	Private	Noncom *
Commando/Special Forces	Corporal	Officer
Dog Pack/Psi-Hound	Private	Noncom
Glitter Boy (Quebec)	Sergeant	Officer *
Headhunter	Private	Noncom *
Infantry: Grunt	Private	Noncom
Infantry: Juicer	PFC	Noncom
Infantry: All Others	Private	Officer
ISS Inspector	SFC	Officer *
Military Specialist	Lieutenant	General
Nautical Specialist	PFC	Officer
Psi-Stalker	Corporal	Officer
RPA Elite: SAMAS Ace	Sergeant	Officer
RPA Elite: PA pilot	Corporal	Officer
Support Staff	Private	Officer
Technical Officer	Corporal	Officer
Wilderness Scout	Private	Officer

* Outside of normal chain of command.

Non-Combat Coalition O.C.C.s

Bio-Cyber Specialist (Cyber-Doc)	Major
Equipment Maintenance Technician (Operator)	Noncom
Medical Doctor	Colonel
Research Scholar	Captain
Research Scientist (Field Scientist)	Colonel

Hazard & Combat Pay

Combat Pay

Any soldier sent into active combat receives combat pay. This is an increase in salary that is typically 10% for enlisted men, 15% for non-commissioned officers and Special Forces, and 20% for commissioned officers. Combat pay is in addition to the soldier's regular salary and any possible hazard pay.

Remember, it is the soldier's job to fight for his country, so there is no additional compensation even for life and death combat missions or espionage operations. Overall pay is based on the soldier's rank, which in turn, is usually reflective of the character's training, area of expertise and experience.

Hazard Pay

Hazard pay is an additional amount of money paid to only two areas of military service, EOD/demolitions and RPA and fighter pilots.

EOD: Characters who specialize in Explosive Ordnance Disposal (demolitions and demolitions disposal) get an additional 15% added to their normal salary because of the dangerous and specialized nature of their work, which includes preparing, checking and arming explosives (including missiles), disposal of explosives, demolitions, and the setting, locating and removing of land mines and the handling of all types of explosives.

RPA pilot: Robot & Power Armor pilots, including SAMAS and other power armor combat pilots, robot vehicle pilots, and Sky cycle and combat helicopter pilots — all aces, dog-fighters and elite robot warriors of the Coalition Armed Forces. They get an additional 20% added to their normal salary.

Rank Ceilings & Notes

Like most armies, the Coalition military tries to promote their most deserving personnel. However, there is a formal policy in the military hierarchy that limits the highest attainable rank by race, social background and performance.

The overall ranking levels can be divided up into: 1) Enlisted men, 2) Non-commissioned officers, 3) Lower rank commissioned officers (Lieutenants & Captains), 4) Middle rank commissioned officers (Majors & Colonels), and 5) Generals.

1. Enlisted men: Most Dog Boys, 'Burb Rejects, and Grungers (the poorest and least educated CS citizen) remain as enlisted personnel throughout their military careers. They may get higher pay rates and other considerations because of seniority and performance but will not rise in the chain of command beyond the rank of Corporal or Sergeant.

2. Non-commissioned officers: A large number of Military O.C.C.s will max out as noncoms. They can rise up to the various ranks of Sergeants but will never gain their full commissions. Juicers, Psi-Stalkers, and 'Borgs as well as uneducated human grunts from a poor background rarely become commissioned officers.

3. Lower rank commissioned officers: Research personnel (Scholar & Scientists), and the occasional 'Borg, Psi-Stalker and uneducated grunt. Most medical personnel max out at these ranks although a few have gone higher than this.

4. Middle rank commissioned officers: RPA Elites (SAMAS), Aces/pilots, Military Specialists, Nautical Specialists, Special Forces/Commandos, Technical Officers, and Medical personnel (primarily Doctors) frequently attain these rankings.

5. Generals: These are typically the elite, educated professional soldiers who have proven themselves through years of service in the military. 80% of all Generals started their careers as commissioned officers and come from wealthy or influential families.

6. ISS Inspectors: Are not part of the Coalition Military but are patterned after it and use military ranks. When working with the military (the two often cooperate, especially in the 'Burbs), the ISS is regarded as outside the normal chain of command and are not given free access to military facilities or military security clearance.

The Internal Security Specialists and the special divisions within the ISS (NTSET and PRP/Psi-Net) also use military ranks to denote experience, authority and position within that branch of service. All ISS inspectors are the equivalent of *Sergeant 1st Class to 1st Lieutenant*. Special Unit Officers and Field Commanders are ranked *Lieutenant through Colonel*. Top ranking officials and administrators are typically *Brigadier General through Lieutenant General*. At the top of the Command structure is one *4-Bar General* known as the ISS Commander-in-Chief, in charge of all ISS Operations.

7. Dog Pack: Most Dog Boys will remain as enlisted personnel. Some of the more intelligent breeds (German Shepherd, Rottweiler, etc.) may work their way up to noncom status, but will only command other Dog Boys. Dog Boys *NEVER* command human troops.

8. Psi-Stalker: Noncoms command Dog Boys. The rare Psi-Stalker officers may have humans and Dog Boys under their command.

9. Nautical Specialists: There are three main types of officers: a) "Landlubbers," Military Specialists assigned to this duty, b) "Converts," ex-Military Specialists turned Nautical Specialists, and c) the true Nautical Specialist, trained from the beginning to serve in the Coalition's Great Lakes Patrol and fledgling Navy in the south.

10. Special Forces: These elite espionage and commando troops rarely attain a rank higher than Colonel.

11. Support Staff & Technical Officers: Medical, Science, Research, Communications, Transportation and Engineering/Construction Officers are generally out of the direct line of command as far as combat troops are concerned; meaning these officers do *not* command the Infantry or any other combat troops except in extreme emergencies. Instead they command their own specific work divisions and units. Maximum rank is typically Major General.

12. Mercenaries: Crazies, Headhunters, Juicers, Wilderness Scouts and other mercenaries may be hired as *Service Specialists*. They are generally considered outside the normal chain of command.

O.C.C. & R.C.C. Notes:

'Borgs are still uncommon in the CS army, although rapidly gaining favor in Chi-Town.

Crazies are rarely hired and only as S-Spec personnel. They will never be included in the CS, except by the ex-State of Free Quebec.

D-bees of any O.C.C. are seldom hired even as S-Spec personnel for any reason.

Glitter Boys are used openly solely by Free Quebec. They are paid equivalent to a Staff Sergeant, although they may not be in the direct chain of command.

Juicers. Until recently, Juicers were illegal to hire. However, since the *Juicer Uprising* and with a war against Tolkeen and Free Quebec imminent, the Coalition States (Chi-Town in particular) has started to create their own Juicers (see **Rifts® World Book 10: Juicer Uprising** for more information).

As for Juicer mercenaries, those Juicers not created by the CS Army are occasionally hired as frontline troops (cannon fodder) used to soften up the enemy, as well as used for spying, assassinationss, and special operations. Juicers were secretly maintained by the Quebec government and represent the equivalent of one full battalion (640+ troops).

Mercenaries are hired only as S-Spec personnel and can be paid anywhere from grunt to captain's pay depending on their level of experience, reputation, and areas of expertise.

Psi-Hounds are most commonly part of the Army and ISS defense forces located in the States of Chi-Town, Lone Star, and Missouri. Only a small division exists in Free Quebec whose leaders always found the *animals* to be disturbing. Rogue Dog Boys are only hired as S-Spec in territories outside the Coalition States.

Practitioners of Magic of any O.C.C. are seldom hired even as S-Spec personnel for any reason.

Psi-Stalkers are found throughout the mid-Western States. Again, Free Quebec was the only State that avoided enlisting these mutants.

Vagabonds are simply the uneducated and unemployed Coalition citizens, 'Burb Rejects, adventurers or wanderers.

Wilderness Scouts are among the most commonly used as S-Spec personnel. The CS Rangers are the military equivalent to Wilderness Scouts.

"Brevet" Rank

In pre-Rifts times, Brevet rank was "A commission promoting a military officer to a higher rank without increase of pay and with limited exercise of the higher rank." This allowed armies which were subject to high casualty rates to quickly replace their leadership.

It was used as a stopgap measure and once hostilities had ended, the brevet officers were restored to their original (lower) ranks. However, officers that remained in active service would find that their actions as brevet officers could affect their normal military careers. It was standard procedure to give priority for promotions to officers with brevet experience on the idea that they had already been exposed to the responsibilities of the higher rank.

In addition to Brevet rank, the Coalition Army has implemented a variation of this procedure. Instead of granting higher rank without increase of pay, certain soldiers are granted higher pay without an increase in rank. A pay hike without rank can be given to soldiers who are highly skilled in one narrow area or who possess a special ability (one or more extraordinary attributes, psionic powers, etc.) but lack the discipline, maturity or leadership abilities to serve effectively as a higher ranking officer. CS Juicers, 'Borgs, young power armor "aces," and Psi-Stalkers frequently fall into this category.

Service Specialists

Support personnel not within the Chain of Command

A Service Specialist not within the chain of command is typically a scout, mercenary, spy, informer, free agent, adventurer, or laborer who has earned special recognition and status with the CS Military. The Service Specialist may be hired to serve the army for special missions, select operations, or for extended duty as part of its *support network*. The exact period of time can be limited to the fulfillment of a particular mission or job, or last for an entire six year tour of military duty. Service Specialists are considered "privileged civilians" allowed to directly serve and affiliate with the military. They do not have military I.D., status, rank, or commission. Nor do they receive combat or hazard pay although they may be employed to work in combat situations and handle deadly materials. CS enemies frequently consider Service Specialists to be spies, sympathizers or mercenaries in collusion with the CS military or government.

Service Specialists are expected to take orders from officers and follow basic military protocol, procedure and the chain of command. However, such Specialists cannot issue commands to even a private, are not acknowledged as military personnel, and are not *required* to salute officers. Consequently, they may be excluded from military meetings, strategy sessions, military administrative offices, officers' clubs and restricted areas.

A Service Specialist will be rated for security clearance, but their inclusion in special meetings or access to restricted areas is left to the officer under which they serve (their military boss and his superiors). All Service Specialists are *human*. Only in remote wilderness areas or in enemy territory far from the Coalition States are D-Bees, mutants and practitioners of magic occasionally retained as Service Specialists — primarily as scouts, native guides and spies (all documents will identify them as humans with an acceptable occupation).

Service Specialists can be employed to perform unskilled, physical labor (typically building/construction, warehouse work, digging ditches, sanitation, etc.), clerical work, medical and science aids, and general assistance. Employment of a more military nature and involving combat includes serving as a scout, native guide, spy, assassin, smuggler (maintain and service supply lines) and frontline warrior (combat as a mercenary). **Note:** "S-Spec" is the abbreviated slang for Service Specialist.

Mercenaries/Combat Personnel: Some of the most common S-Spec O.C.C.s employed by the CS Military include the following:

Wilderness Scout   Juicer
Headhunter   Crazy
Spy (See the *Rifts® Mercenaries* book)
Smuggler (See the *Rifts® Mercenaries* book)
Safe-Cracker (See the *Rifts® Mercenaries* book)

Non-Combat O.C.C.s: Some of the most common S-Spec non-combat personnel include the following:

City Rat, Vagabond, Peasant or any O.C.C. for use as labor.
City Rat or Vagabond as an Urban or wilderness Guide.
City Rat, Rogue Scholar or Operator as a computer hacker.
Operator or Rogue Scientist as an Equipment Maintenance Technician (EMT) or field scientist.
Body Doc or Cyber-Doc for Medical service.

CS military uniforms

Coalition military uniforms stress two things — Practicality and Uniformity. Individual expression is frowned upon and discouraged with two notable exceptions, award medals and shoulder patches. These exceptions are allowed since they are meant to serve as incentives to the rank and file.

Medals and ribbons: These are awarded to soldiers who have demonstrated exceptional courage or otherwise performed notably while in the service of the Coalition military (see separate section for individual awards).

Shoulder patches: These are awarded to military *units*, as opposed to awards for individual achievements. These can be combat units (i.e. the 25th Chi-Town Airborne, "the Jumping Furies") or support units (the 86th Medics, the 4th Engineer Corps "the Busy Builders", etc.). These are not standard issue for Coalition troops and must be earned. When the commander of a newly-formed or existing unit feels that his unit has earned the right to wear a shoulder patch, he may petition the General Staff for that privilege. If the General Staff approves the request, the commander may commission a shoulder patch to be designed at his own discretion and subject to the authorization of the General Staff. **Note:** Authorization is not a given, and it will depend upon circumstances. As a rule, only 45% of general military units (85% of active combat units) are granted permission for this honor.

Rank Placement on Uniforms

On Coalition States military uniforms, the insignias of rank can be found in three places: 1) The right sleeve (the left sleeve has the Death's Head armband), 2) the collar, and 3) the shoulder epaulets.However, the shoulder epaulets and collar insignia are only on the uniforms of officers. Certain uniforms may have a

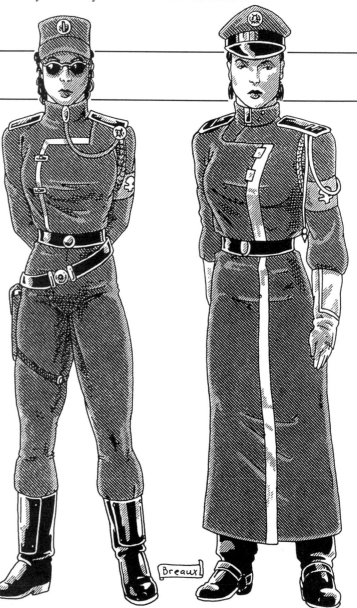

CS Infantry Non-com Officer   **CS Infantry Officer in Dress Coat**

patch on the left shoulder above the armband but these are for specific units and not the standard CS uniform.

Sleeves: Sleeve insignias can range from an empty sleeve to some combination of a triangle and four stripes. The placement of the triangle to the stripes will denote the rank involved.

Collar: Collar insignias will range from one to four bars. Generals will also have a triangle near the bars (other officers will not).

Shoulder epaulets: Shoulder epaulets are basically the standard Death's Head. These will be otherwise plain for officers up to the rank of Colonel and have bars denoting the various ranks of General.

Notes concerning Generals:

1. None of the nonmilitary O.C.C.s can achieve the rank of General. Only the Military Specialist (and, if allowed, the Commando, Inspector, and Nautical Specialist O.C.C.s) can make General. The highest rank that any other O.C.C.s can achieve is that of Colonel.

2. Generals are distinguished by having their triangles on their sleeves above their stripes; the Sergeant Major is the only other rank that shares this distinction.

3. Because of their number of various ranks (four), Generals are sometimes unofficially referred to by the number of their bars, i.e. "2-Bar General," etc.; just as their pre-Rifts counterparts were referred to by their number of stars. Due to this informal practice (and with soldiers being how they are), a number of jokes have arisen dealing with some Generals' decisions being based on a lack of sobriety. Although these comments are neither automatically meant as (or serve as grounds for) insubordination, how they are received is often up to the General in question. For example, Field Marshal Prosek has generally taken these comments in good humor while the staff of General Underhill has quickly learned to avoid such jokes while in earshot of their irascible commander.

CS Infantry Grunt **CS Infantry Officer in Dress Uniform**

4. Only the General of the army, of which there is only one, at any given time, wears five "stars" to distinguish his rank and position.

Medals & Awards
By Julius Rosenstein & Patrick Nowak

The Coalition Military makes extensive use of medals, citations and qualification badges to boost the morale of troops. Badges can be earned by successfully completing training or medals won through acts of valor. For many troops, the number of medals or qualification badges are the measure of skill and success as a soldier. As a result, there are those troops who actively seek medals by engaging in reckless acts of heroism just for the honor of wearing a medal bestowed by a General or Emperor Prosek.

In truth, these decorations are like so many other things in the Coalition States, cleverly devised tools of manipulation. Such awards cost the government little to produce. Even special presentations in military or public ceremonies are comparatively inexpensive affairs which also serve as a means of public relations and propaganda. This all helps to earn the invaluable loyalty of its soldiers. Field officers fully realize this and use the nomination of a medal or citation for select soldiers and squads as a tangible reward. All officers use a mixture of praise and reprimands to push their soldiers to their maximum and to keep morale high. A medal represents the highest form of praise. When a soldier has exhibited heroism beyond the call of duty, he is nominated for such recognition by his commanding officer. The soldier is recommended for a specific medal or citation by the officer, but it's his superiors who decide whether or not the trooper is deserving of the award.

Qualification Badges of Note

Qualification badges are earned for the successful completion of training courses. Depending upon the course signified, a badge will be seen in varying degrees of prestige. Patches are stitched onto dress uniforms for recognition but only the most important qualifications are emblazoned on the Coalition combat armor, including the Field Experience Badge/CS logo on the forehead, the letters PSI on the chest, Airborne badge on the chest, and Marksmanship also on the chest in addition to the regular unit insignia/badge found on the right arm.

Aviation: The "cream of the crop" from the graduates of the RPA course move on for aviator training. Those who complete the pilot training fly the Coalition's jet fighters, combat helicopters, skycycles, Death's Head transports and other aircraft. Aviators are a welcome sight in combat and are considered to be elite troops by the majority of military personnel. On the badge is the silhouette of a skycycle aircraft.

Airborne Qualification Badge: The hardships of parachute training are notorious throughout the military. It is a commonly held belief that one must be of a special breed to complete this elitist training. Airborne troops are treated with great respect and deference by the common soldier. A CS soldier character must have selected the Parachuting skill as an "O.C.C. related" skill to earn this badge. A pair of wings joined by a miniature CS skull design is depicted on the airborne badge.

Field Experience Badge: A soldier earns this badge by participating in combat operations; nearly all CS troops have one from serving in standard missions or in War Zones. It is not a prestigious badge, although a trooper must have one to get any kind of respect from peers. The badge is the stylized Skull and Lightning Bolt logo of the Coalition States military, usually located on the forehead of armor.

Marksmanship: To earn a Marksmanship patch, a CS trooper simply has to meet shooting requirements at a firing range. The badge is fairly common since a character needs to only have the Sniper skill or W.P. energy weapon at 4th level proficiency to meet the requirements. The design on the badge is of crossed C-12 rifles.

Medic: Soldiers with training in the medical field are issued this patch upon graduation. The course is demanding and medics are viewed with high regard for their life-saving skills. The medic badge is a simple red cross on a white background.

PSI: The letters "PSI" on the chest of a CS trooper denotes their having completed psychic training and countermeasures. All those who have completed Psi-Battalion training, including Psi-Stalkers, Dog Boys, Mind Melters, and PRP ISS agents, wear the symbol. While psychic assistance is invaluable in most operations, the badge has somewhat low regard due to lingering prejudice in the officer corps.

RPA Badge: Only those soldiers who manage to finish the rigorous RPA Elite O.C.C. training course have the right to wear the patch. Those who graduate are soldiers of high calibre who are respected by the military at large for their outstanding performance. A clenched robot fist on a plain background is the depiction on the badge.

Medals

Medals are bestowed on soldiers to recognize feats of honor or bravery beyond the call of duty. These awards are far more prestigious than qualification badges, since they are earned through valor in combat operations, not just by simply completing training. For most of these medals, the character must do something extraordinary to earn one, just completing one's job is not enough. A soldier must risk his or her own life, usually to save the lives of comrades, in order to be recognized for a medal. Many times, medals, especially the most prestigious like the Medal of Honor, are issued posthumously since many soldiers die during their acts of heroism.

Imperial Medal of Honor: Death's Head motif on an elaborate medal flanked by a wreath (like the back of Prosek's throne as shown on page 192 of the **Rifts RPG**) with an ornate, metallic gold ribbon.

Loosely based upon the pre-Rifts American Empire's *Congressional Medal of Honor*, this is the highest military decoration that the Coalition Military can bestow. This coveted medal is awarded for "exceptional gallantry and valor above and beyond the call of duty."

In addition to the honor and status accrued, there are some tangible benefits as well. Medal of Honor recipients who are still in active service are given their choice of assignments (within reason) and considered for promotion. The children of the honored veteran, upon reaching enlistment age, become eligible for a scholarship to officer's training school and the soldier's family is provided with a nicer than average place to live at the State's expense (if rejected for citizenship or waiting for CS citizenship and/or entry into one of the fortress super-cities, the character and his immediate family are put at the very top of the list and given special consideration).

Emperor's Medal: A round medal with the profile of the reigning emperor (currently Karl Prosek, but will change when his son succeeds him as Joseph II). The attached ribbon is *red* if awarded for military distinction or white if awarded for civilian distinction (includes ISS operatives) and can have a number of black bands; one for each time the medal is awarded.

Although less prestigious than the Medal of Honor, this medal is unique in being the only Coalition States decoration that is also awarded to civilians. As an award for "Meritorious service to the Coalition States," the Emperor can bestow this award for a variety of reasons, and often does so personally. It is generally considered the highest honor that the Emperor can grant to civilians.

Reasons this medal can be awarded include acts of extreme heroism, exceptional service of some kind, and outstanding dedication to the States. Thus, a civilian who risks his life to uncover a possible enemy of the state, a businessman who donates huge sums of his own wealth or portion of his business to support the war effort, or an individual who spends years as a community leader and aiding Coalition society would all be eligible for this award. The definition of "Meritorious service" is so open to interpretation that the Emperor has a great deal of leeway in awarding this medal (which is just the way he likes it!). A military or political leader must submit a petition for consideration on behalf of the person who merits the award.

Iron Star: A star-shaped iron medal (grey in color) with the imprint of a lightning bolt. The medal is attached to a ribbon that is dark blue with a black border. Strictly for military personnel, this medal is awarded for "Conspicuous gallantry and courage in battle."

The Iron Star is less prestigious than either the Medal of Honor or the Emperor's Medal but is awarded more often. Unlike other CS medals where the ribbon changes with multiple awards (such as the Emperor's Medal and the Crimson Heart), heroic (and lucky) soldiers will simply be given repeated copies of this medal.

Crimson Heart: A heart-shaped iron medal (red in color) with the imprint of a cross (the Red Cross was the pre-Rifts symbol for medicine and healing). The attached ribbon is white with a red border. This medal is awarded for injuries taken in the service of the Coalition States. Although the attached ribbon starts as white with a red border, a gold stripe is added for every third time the medal is awarded.

Minnesota Cross: This award is not yet available but will be issued to all soldiers who participated in the war against Minnesota once that campaign is over. Realistically, all this award will do is identify veterans, it will not be a measure of bravery or heroism since all participants in the war will receive the cross.

Cybernetic Heart: The lucky few who survive serious combat wounds sustained in combat are given the Cybernetic Heart medal. A medal bestowed just for being wounded does not have much prestige in the eyes of many soldiers, other than the recipients.

Awards for Bravery: Soldiers who perform their duty with excellence and risk their lives above and beyond the call of duty are deemed worthy of recognition. Heroic actions that expose these individuals to great personal danger in order to save comrades are rewarded with one of several awards, including the **CS Cross for Bravery**, **Joseph Prosek Medal for Valor**, **Distinguished Service Medallion** or the most prestigious, the **Imperial Medal of Honor**. Officers decide which medal is appropriate depending upon the level of heroism displayed by the soldier through their actions. These could range from the infantryman who rushes across no-man's land to rescue a fallen comrade (who is given the Medal for Valor) to the dying medic who continues to administer first aid to the other wounded soldiers and is awarded the Imperial Medal of Honor posthumously.

G.M. Note: When running a Coalition campaign, the G.M. should be careful not to be too generous in handing out medals for courage. If player characters are given extremely prestigious awards for actions involving little personal danger, then the effect of the reward is greatly diminished. A fair guideline is to hand out the CS Cross for Bravery when the character's actions *might* lead to injury or death but he takes the chance and saves numerous lives or the life of an officer. Also keep in mind that the number of successful missions completed and high kill counts are meaningless, these medals are awarded only for acts of great heroism or valor.

Assorted battle & service ribbons: Campaign ribbons for such things as terms of service (years), good conduct, efficiency, etc., are designed to bolster the morale of the rank and file soldiery, but these ribbons are awarded for the less than heroic (but still necessary) actions. These often unique ribbons can be awarded for (but are not limited to) participating in various military battles and/or campaigns, long-term service (12+ years), for superior quality and efficiency in one's performance of duty, and even for good conduct.

The ribbons for years of service, efficiency, and good conduct tend to be uniform, while the campaign and battle ribbons are more unique and specific. Unlike the more important medals, Emperor Prosek has given his commanding officers much greater leeway in creating and awarding these ribbons. **Note to G.M.'s:** This is your chance to be creative, so knock yourselves out; we're fairly sure that Prosek won't object.

Promotion Notes: The Coalition uses promotion as a reward for superior service, and as a method to inspire and motivate soldiers to perform on a higher level. G.M.s too can use promotion as a reward when running a Coalition campaign. Those player characters who show superior role-playing ability can be rewarded with more than experience points, they can be promoted! Be careful to not be too generous with promotions, otherwise they will become routine and will not be as rewarding for the player characters.

Here are a couple of general rules of thumb to go by when promoting player characters. Unless stated otherwise in the O.C.C. description, a character begins his career as a Private. Upon reaching 2nd level of experience, he is automatically promoted to Private First Class. The rank of Corporal can be attained either through superior role-playing or by reaching 4th level of experience, whichever comes first. For the rank of Sergeant, a character can earn the position through good judgement and role-playing, but should be of at least 4th level, otherwise he will attain the rank once he has reached 7th level of experience. No matter what experience level is achieved, the only way to rise to a higher rank after reaching that of Sergeant, is for the character to display leadership, good judgement and courage through superior role-playing!

Officers, usually Military Specialists and Special Forces, must work even harder than enlisted men to get promoted. To rise higher than 1st Lieutenant, they must show excellent leadership and extreme professionalism. The G.M. has sole discretion in determining whether or not the actions of an officer player character merits promotion. It is suggested that a character be of at least 5th level to be considered for the rank of Captain, 7th for Major and 10th for either Lieutenant Colonel or Colonel. An active player character should *never* be able to achieve a rank higher than Colonel!

Shell-Shock Rules (optional)

Horror Factor on the Battlefield

By Pat Nowak and Kevin Siembieda

All supernatural creatures have a horror factor. The horror factor represents either the hideous appearance of the monster or its overwhelming aura of evil and power, or combination of the two. Whenever a human encounters one of these monstrosities the character must roll a 20 sided die to see whether or not he or she is momentarily stunned by the sheer horror of the thing. This horror factor roll might be thought of as a saving throw or mental parry. Fortunately, the character only needs to roll for the first melee of each encounter, *not* every melee of combat.

There are horrors on the battlefield too. Seeing one's buddy atomized or blown in half by an energy weapon, half the company mowed down in an ambush, a monstrous predator eating somebody alive and countless other things can stun and shock a soldier. In addition, the constant stress of combat and killing can take its toll. This can lead to a character becoming shell-shocked. In this case, the shell-shocked warrior becomes overwhelmed by a panic attack and either cringes in a corner or becomes completely catatonic. In either case, he is incapable of taking any action, even to defend himself.

A character becomes shell-shocked as the result of incredible mental, or mental and physical trauma, usually over a long period of time. We leave the assigning of a shell-shocked condition to the player and Game Master; G.M.s be fair and reasonable, shell-shock is less common than one might think.

To save against the horrors of war (horror factor): A shell-shocked character rolls to save vs the horror every time he is confronted with the source of the shell-shocking trauma. A successful save means, this time, he has managed to suppress his fears and can function relatively unimpaired; penalties are -1 on attacks/actions per melee round and -2 on initiative.

A failed roll means the warrior is so overwhelmed by panic that he cannot take action; no attacks or actions per melee round for the entire period that he is forced to face the object/situation of his horror. He may suffer hallucinations and flashbacks to the original traumatic experience.

If faced with imminent attack or a situation where he must overcome his fears (such as saving himself or comrades), the character can roll again to save vs the shell-shock horror factor. A failed roll means no change. A successful save means he can function at an impaired level. All attacks per melee round and combat bonuses are at half their usual number.

To save against the Horror Factor (H.F.) the player must roll a 20-sided die. Just like a parry, the roll must be equal or higher than the horror factor to successfully save. A failed roll means his character is affected by the horror.

Shell-Shock Sources of Trauma

Battle or the sound of battle: Horror Factor (H.F.) 14
Bombardment of bombs/the sound of explosions: H.F. 14
Close combat/physical violence: H.F. 15
Torture or the threat of torture: H.F. 17
Facing enemy soldier(s): H.F. 16
Facing robots: H.F. 15
Facing individual monsters/nonhumans: H.F. equal to the creature's normal horror factor (if none, H.F. 13).

Complete Alphabetical List of Skills, Old and New by Category

The following is the complete list of skills available to the various Coalition Military O.C.C.s and other men at arms O.C.C.s.

Communications
Cryptography
Electronic Countermeasures (new)
Laser
Optic Systems
Radio: Basic
Radio: Scrambler
Surveillance Systems
T.V. & Video

Domestic
Cook
Dance
Fishing
Play Musical Instrument
Sewing
Sing

Electrical
Basic Electronics
Computer Repair
Electrical Engineer
Robot Electronics

Espionage
Detect Ambush
Detect Concealment
Disguise
Escape Artist
Forgery
Imitate Voices/Impersonation (new)
Intelligence
Interrogation Techniques (new)
Pick Locks
Pick Pockets
Sniper
Tracking
Wilderness Survival

Mechanical

Aircraft Mechanics
Automotive Mechanics
Basic Mechanics (new)
Field Armorer (new)
Locksmith
Mechanical Engineer
Robot Mechanics
Weapons Engineer

Medical

Criminal Science & Forensics
Field Surgery (new)
First Aid
Holistic Medicine
Paramedic
M.D. in Cybernetics
Medical Doctor
Pathology

Military

Armorer (new)
Camouflage (new)
Demolitions
Demolitions Disposal
Find Contraband, Weapons & Cybernetics (new)
Military Etiquette (new)
Military Fortification (new)
Nuclear, Biological, & Chemical Warfare (new)
Parachuting (new)
Recognize Weapon Quality (new)
Trap Construction (new)
Trap/Mine Detection (new)
Underwater Demolitions (new)

Physical

Hand to Hand: Basic
Hand to Hand: Expert
Hand to Hand: Martial Arts
Hand to Hand: Assassin
Hand to Hand: Commando (new)
Acrobatics
Athletics (general)
Body Building & Weight lifting
Boxing
Climbing
Gymnastics
Prowl
Running
S.C.U.B.A.
Swimming
Wrestling

Pilot

Airplane
Automobile
Boat: Motor & Hydrofoils
Boat: Sail Type
Boat: Ship
Boat: Submersibles (new)
Boat: Warships & Patrol Boats (new)
Boat: Water Scooters (new)
Helicopter (Transport & Combat)
Horsemanship
Horsemanship: Exotic Animals (new)
Hover Craft (Ground)
Jet Aircraft
Jet Fighter
Jet Pack
Motorcycle
Robot Combat Basic
Robot Combat Elite
Robots & Power Armor
Tanks & APCs
Truck

Pilot Related

Navigation
Radar/Sonar Operations (new)
Read Sensory Equipment
Weapon System

Rogue

Computer Hacking
Concealment
Find Contraband, Weapons & Cybernetics (new)
Palming
Pick Locks
Pick Pockets
Prowl
Streetwise
Streetwise — Drugs (new)

Science

Anthropology
Archeology
Astronomy
Biology
Botany
Chemistry
Chemistry: Analytical
Mathematics: Advanced
Mathematics: Basic

Technical

Art
Computer Operation
Computer Programming
Language
Literacy
Lore: D-Bee (new)
Lore Demons & Monsters
Lore: Faerie
Lore: Magic (new)
Lore: Psychic (new)
Photography
Writing

Weapon Proficiencies

Ancient Weapon Proficiencies

W.P. Archery & Targeting
W.P. Blunt
W.P. Chain
W.P. Knife
W.P. Sword

Modern Weapon Proficiencies

W.P. Automatic Pistol
W.P. Automatic & Semi-Automatic Rifles
W.P. Bolt Action Rifle
W.P. Energy Pistol
W.P. Energy Rifle
W.P. Heavy Energy Weapons & Rail Guns
W.P. Heavy Weapons
W.P. Revolver
W.P. Sub-Machinegun

Wilderness

Boat Building
Carpentry
Hunting
Identify Plants & Fruits
Land Navigation
Preserve Food
Skin & Prepare Animal Hides
Track Animals
Trap Construction (new)
Trap/Mine Detection (new)

Descriptions of New Skills

Alphabetical List of New Skills by Category

Communications:
Electronic Countermeasures
Espionage:
Imitate Voices/Impersonation
Interrogation Techniques
Mechanical:
Basic Mechanics
Medical:
Field Surgery
Military:
Armorer
Camouflage
Find Contraband, Weapons & Cybernetics
Military Etiquette
Military Fortification
Nuclear, Biological, & Chemical Warfare
Parachuting
Recognize Weapon Quality
Trap Construction
Trap/Mine Detection
Underwater Demolitions
Physical:
Hand to Hand: Commando
Swimming & Fatigue Note
Pilot:
Horsemanship: Exotic Animals
Pilot: Submersibles
Pilot: Warships & Patrol Boats
Pilot: Water Scooters
Power Armor Skill Note
Pilot Related:
Navigation Skill Note
Radar/Sonar Operations (Read Sensor Equipment)
Rogue:
Find Contraband, Weapons & Cybernetics:
Streetwise — Drugs
Technical:
Lore — D-Bee
Lore — Magic
Lore — Psychic
Wilderness:
Trap Construction
Trap/Mine Detection

Skill Note: In most cases, the skills listed in **Coalition War Campaign** are taken from other **Rifts®** titles. They are collected here for your easy reference and convenience. These skills are the most appropriate for Military personnel (CS and mercenaries) in a North American adventure campaign. Skills from other books that have not been included are *optional* and/or remain appropriate to specific O.C.C.s, R.C.C.s or geographic regions. The new skills are listed under *New Skills* and have been *italicized* in the large, complete skill list. The skills on the complete list are not found here but are located in the **Rifts® RPG**).

Communications: Electronic Countermeasures (Jamming): Useful for preventing the enemy's communications from working. Since all armor, power armor and robot vehicles are linked by radio transmissions, jamming can cause unit confusion and disrupt communications. Military organization breaks down, causing a loss of effectiveness for all but the best of units.

Just about any high-powered radio can be used for jamming. Armed with a radio, a small guerrilla unit can completely disrupt the maneuvers of large enemy groups. This skill also enables the radio operator to "follow" the enemy's attempted transmissions over jammed frequencies to trace their general location, a specific building, or direction. This tactic is extremely useful in finding and eliminating lone power-armor troopers. **Base Skill:** 30% +5% per level of experience. **Note:** If the G.M. likes, he can make this part of the *Radio: Scrambler* skill, but still with a base of 30%.

Espionage: Imitate Voices & Impersonation: The ability to imitate the voice, accent and expressions of another person or area. This skill is common among CS spies and espionage agents as well as ninja and the occasional assassin or mercenary. The first number indicates the character's ability to change his voice and imitate accents, inflections and expressions from other regions. A successful roll means he has disguised his normal/true speaking voice and accent, and convincingly sounds like he is from another region or part of the world.

The second number indicates the character's ability to accurately imitate the voice, inflections and attitude of a *specific* person! This is much more difficult, and the character will either need to know the person being imitated very well or have spent hours studying him/her. **Base Skill:** 36%/16% +4% per level of experience.

Note: When combined with the disguise and intelligence skills, the character is able to completely impersonate another person or type of occupation (soldier, ISS Inspector, operator, priest, etc.). This is likely to include a knowledge of the enemy/subject of impersonation, military procedure, dress, command, rank, and will usually require speaking the language fluently. This means the character can convincingly impersonate a general type of person/soldier/occupation by using an accurate disguise, proper actions, and language. **Base Skill:** 16% +4% per level of experience to impersonate a *specific* individual; +12% to impersonate *general* personnel and occupations.

Espionage: Interrogation Techniques: This skill is common among policemen, intelligence officers, and assassins/spies/bounty hunters. The character knows the techniques to get information from (typically unwilling) subjects. This includes such old methods as "good cop, bad cop" (one interrogator is threatening and intimidating, the other is sympathetic and friendly), deceiving and misleading the subject into giving away information, and similar. The character can also judge if the subject is lying (the Game Master might assess bonuses and penalties depending on how good a liar the subject is, and/or on the victim's M.E., M.A. and/or P.B; the higher any or each of these attributes, the more convincing the lies). This skill also includes some basic knowledge on methods of torture, from basic tactics like depriving the subject of sleep, to the use of "medieval" instruments, drugs and psionics. **Note:** Only evil characters will engage in actual torture. **Base Skill:** 20% +5% per level of experience.

Mechanical: Basic Mechanics: A general familiarity and understanding of basic mechanics. This character can fix a toaster, repair a bicycle, replace a belt on a motor, repair or replace a switch, handle or a knob, replace a spark plug, change oil, assist in automobile repairs, maintain machinery, read a schematic and similar fundamental tasks. **Base Skill:** 30% +5% per level of experience.

Medical: Field Surgery (By Pat Nowak): This skill reflects training in emergency, life-saving surgical procedures that can be performed in the field to keep critically wounded characters alive. Given the proper tools, the surgeon character can perform amputations, suture torn arteries, check internal bleeding, cauterize wounds, give blood transfusions and even install cybernetic implants (penalty of -15% except if character has *basic cybernetics* skill). Field expedient surgery is a dangerous proposition that too often results in the death of the patient. Because of the risk involved, field surgery is attempted only when it is the only chance the wounded character has for survival! If the operation is successful, the patient lives and can be evacuated to a hospital, but a failed roll results in the immediate death of the patient. **Base Skill:** 16% + 4% per level of experience.

Optional Guidelines for Fatal Injury Treatment: In the violent world of **Rifts,** regular humans and similar non-mega-damage beings are at an extreme disadvantage. Once a human's body armor is destroyed, a single M.D. blast will usually obliterate him/her. These guidelines are provided to give player characters a chance, however slight, to survive a blast that would normally evaporate the character. If the GM agrees, the character can survive a mega-damage intensity wound if a trained medic makes a successful *field surgery* skill roll.

Unless the attacker made a called shot or rolled an unmodified 19 or higher, the character has the chance to live. The basic idea is that the M.D. blast was partially absorbed by nearby cover or merely sheared off a limb (G.M.s, give some reasonable explanation). Within 1D4 melee rounds after the character's being hit, a medic character must attend to his/her injuries. If the medic makes a successful skill roll, the character is incapacitated but survives the attack, though just barely (reduce S.D.C. to zero and hit points are at 1D6 above zero). A failed roll means the injured character was beyond saving and dies an instant later. Even if the field operation succeeds, the wounded character is in shock, crippled, may require additional extensive surgery and is likely to require cybernetic or bionic reconstruction and a long recovery period before he is able to adventure again. Although crippled, the character lives (it may be appropriate to also determine an insanity and permanent physical side-effects from the injury). **Note:** This optional survival rule is also applicable to Medical and Cyber doctors.

Military: Armorer: This is a somewhat simplistic version of the weapons engineer as it applies to infantry weapons. A competent armorer character can maintain, fix, modify, mount, reload/charge ammunition, and figure out most small arms. They can repair all types of pistols and rifles, repair minor damage to body armor (20 M.D. maximum), adjust targeting sights, use and repair optical enhancements, reload missiles and ammo drums, recharge E-clips, install/mount a rail gun or machinegun on a vehicle, and even fix most simple robot and bionic weapons like forearm blasters and retractable blades. **Base Skill:** 40% +5% per level of experience. **Note:** Automatically gets the basic mechanics skill at +20% as part of this package.

Military: Camouflage: The skill of concealing a fixed base position, vehicle, bot, equipment or individual, using natural or artificial materials. A fair amount of time is involved in the preparation of a larger position. Large cargo nets, cut branches or underbrush are most often used in camouflage. This skill is also used to conceal traps. **Base Skill:** 20% +5% per level of experience.

Military Etiquette: This skill grants a clear understanding of the way the military works, including rules of behavior (when to salute, how to address superiors/subalterns, etc.), military procedures and routines, standard issue of equipment, special ordering procedures, proper display of rank and medals, advancement in rank (and the duties that come with it), proper troop formations, how to deal with military bureaucracy, the chain of command, proper channels, who to contact to get things done, and other useful information on matters of military protocol and bureaucracy. **Base Skill:** 35% +5% per level of experience. **Note:** All soldiers have a fundamental knowledge of military etiquette (base skill 30% with no improvement), but this skill is much more complete, with a strong knowledge of what is expected, correct and the formal approach (e.g. by the book knowledge).

Military & Rogue: Find Contraband, Weapons & Cybernetics: The character with this skill knows where to find arms dealers, smugglers, body chop-shops, cyber-snatchers, M.O.M. and Juicer conversions, criminal cyber-docs and illegal medical treatment, as well as how to spot them. He is also familiar with their practices, hang-outs, gang or criminal ties, general practices, code of conduct, pricing structures and modes of operation. Likewise, the character has a good idea of what black market weapons and cybernetics should cost and what these people pay for contraband items (typically only 20% of the retail market price). The character also knows the penalty for being caught with an illegal weapon, implant or bionics. In all CS cities and most societies, any M.D. weapons, concealed weapons and sidearms are forbidden inside large population centers.

This skill is especially appropriate in the modern cities of the Coalition States, as well as in the large cities of the NGR, Atlantis, Japan, and other large, urban communities. **Base Skill:** 26% +4% per level of experience. **Note:** This skill *should* be considered separate and apart from streetwise.

Military: Fortification: This is the skill of designing and building defensive fortifications suitable for modern mega-damage combat. If provided with the time and materials, the character can greatly increase the defensive value of natural terrain with murderous defenses that include obstacles to impede movement and protective structures to shield friendly forces from enemy fire. The character is trained to prepare mine fields, barbed wire, tank obstacles, tanglefoot wire, booby traps, trenches, tank ditches, foxholes/shell scrapes, reinforced concrete or earthen walls, bunker complexes, rail gun/mortar emplacements, tunnel systems and similar defensive constructions. **Base Skill:** 30% +5% per level of experience.

Even with the advent of mega-damage warfare, the old standby fortifications listed above have useful applications. Obstacles like ditches and mine fields slow the advance of `bots, infantry and tanks, exposing them for longer periods to defender firepower. Earthen walls and foxholes made from S.D.C. materials still afford soldiers some protection and can disperse energy blasts or deflect shrapnel from explosives. If these protective structures are built with mega-damage concrete and alloys, they provide defenders with as much protection as any robot vehicle or tank!

Military: Nuclear, Biological, & Chemical Warfare (NBC): This is the knowledge of safety precautions to protect oneself and others from the effects of nuclear, biological or chemical warfare, waste and contamination. The character is also knowledgeable in the safe handling, and "clean-up" and containment of such hazardous materials. **Base Skill:** 35% +5% per level of experience.

Military: Parachuting: This skill includes the methods, procedures, and techniques of parachuting, packing the chute, skydiving techniques, precision landing, landing without injury, and practice of jumping from a high altitude aircraft. The advantage of parachuting is secrecy, since the troopers' insertion into enemy territory is silent and often goes unnoticed. The following three methods are the ones most commonly used by modern paratroopers:

High-Altitude-High-Opening (HAHO) jumps take place from a height of 25,000 to 30,000 ft. As the paratroopers drop, they travel laterally to the desired drop zone (DZ) where they wish to land. This technique is used to "throw off" enemy units since they will probably search for paratroopers directly beneath the path of the aircraft.

High-Altitude-Low-Opening (HALO) operations also begin at 25,000 to 30,000 ft (7620 to 9144 m) but the paratrooper does not pop the chute until an altitude of 4,000 ft (1220 m), or even less. The jump takes place so rapidly that there is little chance for the paratroopers to be viewed after the chutes open.

The most dangerous method is Low-Altitude-Low-Opening (LALO) drops. The jump is made at the mere height of 300 to 500 ft (91 to 152 m). If there are any complications (a failed roll), the paratrooper is likely to be injured (broken bones) or killed (30% chance)! Even if the jump goes without a hitch, there is a 20% chance of taking 6D6 S.D.C. from an awkward landing, even if wearing M.D. armor.

Failure on a parachuting roll indicates that there are complications somewhere along the jump. This might mean an improperly packed chute, tangling of lines, etc. On a high altitude jump, the character gets a second roll for their reserve chute. If the second roll also fails, then the character falls to his death! There is not enough time on a low altitude drop to use a reserve chute, so a failed roll means the character hits the ground (humans die!) without a second chance. Parachuting can be selected as a Military or Pilot Related skill. **Base Skill:** 40% +5% per level of experience.

Military: Recognize Weapon Quality: The ability to accurately determine a weapon's durability, reliability, and quality by physically examining it. This includes knowing which manufacturers are reputed to make the best weapons, the ability to recognize damage or signs of misuse, modifications/customization or wear and tear, whether the weapon can be made as good as new with a little repair work and/or cleaning, whether it is a cheap (or quality) "knock-off" (copy/imitation), and so on. The character can also recognize if the weapon is stolen (serial numbers filed away, etc.), new, old, and if it has any other special features or properties as well as knowing what the fair price should be. **Base Skill:** 25% +5% per level of experience. **Note:** Reduce the skill ability by half if the item is not actually handled (seen but not touched/examined).

Military and Wilderness: Trap Construction (by Nowak & Siembieda): Training in the design and application of traps and mines used in anti-personnel and defense tactics. With readily available materials and simple tools, including shovels, knives, sticks, wire and rope, the character can build fiendish traps. Any who would scoff at the effectiveness of traps in modern mega-damage combat should reconsider. It is true that traps cannot be made to destroy or even damage M.D. equipment, unless explosives and the demolitions skill are used, but these traps can hamper or disable enemy robots and vehicles, and injure or kill unarmored or lightly armored soldiers! Traps can also be used as an alarm to alert the trap maker to the presence of intruders or the enemy (fires a flare, activates a video camera and transmission, makes noise, etc.).

The greatest drawback of traps lies in the amount of time required to prepare them — it can take hours to prepare rock slides, large pits and similar traps — but, even this time can be shortened with help from others since only one character needs the skill to successfully direct workers. Ingeniously prepared traps can, and often do, shift the advantage of a battle to the side that prepared the field for combat. **Base Skill:** 20% +4% per level of experience.

The following are some examples of traps, complete with their effects; a character can include using the *trap construction* skill. All damage, penalties and considerations are based on a human-sized victim unless stated otherwise.

Pit, Man-Sized: Typically a simple pit/hole 7-14 feet (2.1 to 4.2 m) deep and concealed with twigs and leaves. Pits can slow an enemy advance by delaying troop movement (must pause to climb out of pit or to help comrade out of the pit), injuring the victim (typically twist, pull or bruise and sometimes break a leg or arm), damaging light (S.D.C.) equipment, trapping unfortunate soldiers and disabling robots (at least temporarily).

A person blundering into a pit trap falls, taking 1D6 S.D.C./hit point damage per every seven feet (2.1 m) of depth, even if wearing M.D. body armor (the impact has an effect on the person inside; no damage to power armor or robot pilots)! The same damage is applied to fragile S.D.C. items that tumble into the pit. The character also loses one melee attack/action in that act of falling and 1D4 melee actions gathering his wits and getting back on his feet; stun affect.

To climb out of the hole unassisted requires 1D6 melee actions. An especially deep pit will require a *climbing* skill roll or somebody to give the character a hand. Robot vehicles that step into the hole have a 01-70% likelihood of tripping and falling. Crew members suffer 1D4 S.D.C. damage and must spend 1D4 melee rounds to right the vehicle. While trapped and/or while the victim(s) are attempting to recover, the trap maker and his allies usually launch a vicious attack or surround the victim. The pit trap is very common in the wilds of North America.

Monster Pit: In some instances, the trap designer will place a small (or large), vicious creature inside the pit. The creature will be terrified and/or angry and attacks anything that falls into the pit. These creatures typically fight until slain. Lasae, worms of Taut and M.D. monsters of similar size are often used in this capacity, as well as wild canines, felines, bears and snakes.

Snake Pit: A shallow pit, 4 or 5 feet deep (1.2 to 1.5 m), filled with poisonous snakes or small worms of Taut. Characters who fall or stumble into the pit receive 1D4 bites. Regular snake bites inflict 1D4 S.D.C. damage plus 3D6 S.D.C. from poison if the creatures bite unprotected flesh. Creatures like worms of Taut and other alien "crawly things" may inflict mega-damage. The trap is rarely used in North American and Europe, but is frequently used in the jungles of South America and Asia.

Tank Trap/Giant Pit: Basically the same as a man-sized pit but dug to a depth of 18 to 30 feet (5.4 to 9 m). Infantry ground troops who blunder into the hole suffer 1D6 S.D.C. for every seven feet (2.1 m) of depth from falling and need 2D4+2 melee attacks/actions to climb out, unless helped out by people outside the pit with rope and such.

Robot vehicles and tanks can also fall victim to these deep and often wide pits. The crew suffers 2D4 S.D.C. damage from getting jostled around. Humanoid robots and power armor suits can climb or pull themselves out of the pit with relative ease; must spend one or two full melee rounds (15-30 seconds) unless the vehicle or power armor can fly or leap out (counts as one melee action).

Tanks, trucks and other ground vehicles may have part or all of the vehicle stuck or wedged in the pit and require a crane or giant robot(s) or several power armor troops to pull it out. Just how stuck and immobilized the vehicle is will depend on the size and depth of the pit.

Mined Pit: A pit with land mines or other explosive device(s) dug into or placed on the floor of the pit. It detonates when one or more victims hit the bottom.

Punji Stake Pit: Typically a pit 8-10 feet (2.4 to 3 m) deep, concealed with twigs and leaves. The bottom of the pit is lined with a bed of sharp wooden stakes. Roll 1D6 to see how many stakes the falling character lands on; each inflicts 1D6 S.D.C. damage plus damage and penalties from the fall (see the *man-sized pit* description). Vibro-blades and special M.D.C. materials can be used to inflict mega-damage; roll 1D6 to see how many stakes the falling character lands on; each inflicts 1D6 M.D. plus possible damage and penalties from the fall.

Punji pits are extraordinarily effective against vampires and are found throughout Mexico! They are often used (camouflaged and open) as countermeasures along defensive perimeters and dug-in fortifications.

Punji Sticks: Sharp wooden stakes stuck into the base of trees, in tree branches, or on the ground at strategic locations, near settlements, defensive perimeters, off to the sides of paths and so on. People who stray off the path or go where they don't belong, may step on, stumble, trip, fall or lean into 1D4 stakes/spikes.

Each stake inflicts 1D6 points of S.D.C. damage. Wood and S.D.C. material punji stakes do no damage to characters in M.D. body armor and are rarely used for that reason.

As noted previously, vibro-blades and other mega-damage materials may be used, but are not as effective; vibro-blades tend to hum, tipping off their location, and M.D.C. materials scrape but seldom puncture M.D.C. armor unless the victim falls on or drives across them with some force. Punji sticks are a form of guerilla warfare designed for use against humanoid enemies. Travelling slowly and carefully, they are easy to detect and avoid, but if reckless or running, the character is likely to run into them headlong.

Punji-Stick Drop-Fall Trap: A large weight bristling with sharp, wood stakes is suspended in a tree. It is released by a trip wire and either drops down or swings across the target area. Characters can try to dodge but are -3 to do so. This trap inflicts 6D6 S.D.C. damage to unarmored victims. Those wearing M.D. body armor suffer 2D4 S.D.C. damage from the impact and are knocked off their feet; lose initiative and one melee action!

Swinging Log: A huge log or piece of debris (cannon barrels and the legs from a giant robot are also used) is suspended in a tree. When released by a trip wire or pressure plate, it swings across the target area. All characters in the path of its swing are struck and suffer damage unless they successfully dodge at a -3 penalty. Characters wearing M.D. body armor suffer 6D6 S.D.C. damage from impact, unarmored victims suffer 2D6×10 S.D.C. (or one M.D. point)! Individuals struck by the log are knocked out cold by the tremendous impact for 3D4 melee rounds. The trap is a favorite for attacking groups of soldiers walking in single file, as well as against power armor.

Robot vehicles struck by the huge weight have a 01-50% likelihood of being knocked off their feet; vehicles knocked off their path. The vehicle crew suffers 1D4 S.D.C. damage from being thrown around the cockpit.

Barbed Wire Barrier: Cords or rolls of barbed wire are laid across a pathway, entrance or particular area (concealed or not) to bar its path. While the wire will not hurt mega-damage body armor, it still hooks and entangles the feet and snags any fabric, thus impairing movement (the wire must be cut or pulled away) and makes noise. Power armor units and bots can often tear right thorough it or stomp it down with no penalties, but their passage will still make some noise.

Rock Slide/Log Fall: Rocks or massive logs or debris piled at the top of an incline are released to tumble into the target area. Every foot soldier, bot or vehicle in the area suffers 1D4 M.D. from the impact of rocks or M.D. debris or 1D6×10 S.D.C. from logs. Unless the victims make a successful dodge at -8 and are able to dive for cover, they are struck and carried away by the tumbling rocks, logs or debris. Most will become pinned in or trapped beneath the fallen materials until rescued by companions.

Even those individuals who dodged successfully are trapped at the edge of the pile and need 3D4 melee rounds to work themselves free. Robots and vehicles, who are often targeted by this trap, have no chance to dodge and a 01-90% likelihood of getting knocked down or pushed 1D6×10 feet off the path. Furthermore, they are struck by more of the falling debris, suffer triple damage and are likely (01-75%) to need a crane, giant robot or several power armor troops to pull them free. The crew of the vehicle suffers 2D6 S.D.C. damage. During this time, the designers of the trap typically swarm the helpless vehicles, bots or soldiers, attacking or taking prisoners. In addition, the debris covered road/area is more difficult to travel over. This trap is very popular in hilly and mountainous regions.

Crossbow Trap: A crossbow attached to a tree or in a pit that shoots when a trip wire is pressed or broken. The bolt strikes the target on a 1D20 roll of 14 or higher. Damage from an ordinary bow and arrow is 2D6 S.D.C., but any of the high-tech types can be used. Often the crossbow will be loaded with an explosive high-tech bolt that inflicts 3D6 M.D. rather than a conventional projectile. Fairly common.

A variation can use an S.D.C. or energy pistol typically fires only a single shot) by having the wire depress the trigger on the gun. However, this is a rarity because of the waste and cost of using a more sophisticated and high-tech weapon.

Trip Snare: Causes the character to trip. No damage, but the fall is embarrassing, the character loses initiative, two melee actions, and makes a loud noise that will alert nearby enemies and predators to the character's location. Usually the snare is set as part of an ambush, leaving the fallen character vulnerable to the opening volley of an attack. This type of trap is extremely common.

Variations include trip flares, which in addition to the above, a rocket flare is shot into the sky and explodes. The flare indicates the exact location of the intrusion and, at night, illuminates the immediate area of the snare.

Animal Snare: A simple snare designed to catch or lasso the animal's foot or head. This is typically used to capture small animals.

Rope Snare: This is a concealed, lasso-style snare tied to a tree. When the snare is triggered, the lasso snares the foot or feet and whips the character or animal up and suspends it, dangling from a tree, usually 5-10 feet (1.5 to 3 m) above the ground. No damage, but the character loses two melee actions and needs another melee action or two to cut himself down. It is most effective in forested areas.

Net Trap: Rather than using a lasso-style snare, a net can be used in the above rope snare trap. The net is spread on the ground and camouflaged, but wraps around the target when triggered. The character or animal is whipped up and suspended from the tree 10 feet (3 m) above the ground. There is no damage caused by the trap but the character loses two melee actions and needs a further three melee actions to cut himself loose.

Bear Trap: A pair of large, clamping metal jaws that snap shut when the prey steps on the pressure plate. The metal jaws are typically chained to a tree or stake and require a combined P.S. of 24 to pry them open; a hand activated release switch will also open and reset the trap. Damage is 4D6 S.D.C., but holds its prey in place until the jaws are opened or the prey literally tears itself free; animals often bleed to death. This trap is effective against animals and unarmored humanoid prey. It is sometimes combined with a snare to trigger flares or drop a grenade.

Naruni Bullet Mine: A crippling trap design which employs a Naruni plasma cartridge or small explosive. The cartridge is placed in a small hole in the ground atop a nail or firing pin, then covered by a camouflaged wooden slat. When someone steps on the slat, the cartridge is pressed down on the firing pin, trigger-

64

ing a plasma blast that inflicts 1D4×10 M.D. to the victim's foot. Uncommon, due to the generally poor availability of Naruni ammunition. Hand grenades and other explosives are sometimes substituted.

Grenade Trap: A regular grenade, with its pin removed, is attached to a trip wire and placed in a can hanging from a tree. When the trip wire is pulled, the grenade falls from the can and explodes on or near the unfortunate victim. The explosion causes regular damage by grenade type, fragmentation (2D6 M.D.) and plasma grenades (5D6 M.D) are typically used. This is a fairly common trap.

Variations include the use of riot control flash/stun grenades, tear gas and smoke grenades.

Mini-Missile Trap: Typically a snare that triggers the launch mechanism of a mini-missile! Fairly uncommon; another guerilla tactic.

Fusion blocks, plastique charges and land mines are all frequently used in booby traps throughout the world. However, the character must have the demolitions skill to use them.

Military and Wilderness: Trap/Mine Detection: Knowledge of the strategic placement of booby traps and mines, the tell-tale trademarks and indications of traps and mines, how to avoid them, and the use of mine and explosive detection equipment. The character has been trained to watch for suspicious objects, dirt mounds, trip wires and camouflaging materials that may denote the presence of a trap. Simple snare traps and trip wires can be easily disarmed by the character, but the demolitions disposal skill is required to disarm mines, explosives or complex traps. **Base Skill:** 20% +5% per level of experience on visuals alone. Add +50% when using special detection equipment to locate mines/explosives or +10% to locate other types of traps with detection equipment.

Note: Psi-hounds/Dog Boys who are of the Bloodhound and German Shepherd/Alsatian breeds have a base skill of 35% +5% per level of experience to literally "sniff-out" explosives, magic traps, and "sense" other types of traps without benefit of special equipment! However, these "Sniffers" must undergo special training, and this special focus reduces their other sensing abilities by -10%. The ordinary Bloodhound or Shepherd Dog Boy does not get any special bonus or ability and must use mechanical equipment and his ordinary senses to locate mines and traps.

Military: Underwater Demolitions: Fundamentally the same basic skills and training as demolitions, but with an emphasis on using explosives in an underwater environment, including underwater techniques, area affect, sound wave damage, different types of explosives, as well as arming, disarming and repairing torpedoes and depth charges. **Base skill:** 56% +4% per level of experience. **Note:** Any character with the demolitions skill can use explosives underwater, but is -10%.

Physical: Hand to Hand Commando: See the Special Forces/Commando O.C.C. description for details.

Physical: Swimming & Fatigue Note: For humans and similar surface dwelling D-bees, the act of swimming on the surface of the water has the same fatigue rate as running and medium to heavy exertion, especially at great speed or very long periods of time. Swimming underwater with S.C.U.B.A. equipment or other underwater equipment is considered to be light activity, unless extremely active, involved in combat or fast swimming (in which case it is considered strenuous or heavy activity).

For most aquatic life forms, including D-bees and mutants, underwater activities such as fast swimming, diving, playing and underwater acrobatics are considered light activities and can be conducted for hours without fatigue. Pulling a heavy load and engaging in combat is considered medium to heavy activity.

The buoyancy of water *reduces the weight of most items by 30% when used/carried underwater.* This means the fatigue rate for carrying a heavy load is reduced by 30% — meaning 30% more can be carried at the normal fatigue rate. Characters can also lift 30% heavier weights.

Pilot: Horsemanship: Exotic Animals: This skill is basically the same as the original horsemanship skill, except that the character is experienced in riding other types of "tame" animals. This can include elephants, camels, lamas, pegasus, dragondactyls, gryphons, demon hounds, fury beetles, giant insects, Wormwood parasites, and other alien or monstrous beasts trained to be riding animals. Wild, untamed creatures cannot be ridden (except by the likes of the Simvan monster riders). **Base Skill:** 30%+4% per level of experience. **Skill Note:** Characters with the traditional "horsemanship" skill for riding Earth horses and other very horse-like animals can quickly figure out how to ride exotic and alien riding animals, but at a skill penalty of -12% to ride ground/running animals and -14% to ride flying or tree climbing and leaping animals. Similarly, D-bees not familiar with riding the fast and sleek Earth horse are -10% to ride them. **CS Note:** Except for the *CS Espionage Agent* and *CS Commando*, both highly specialized military operatives given great flexibility to perform their missions and to use disguises, no other Coalition States soldier (not even the Military Specialist) is allowed to ride "unnatural, alien creatures." This skill is available to all non-CS O.C.C.s.

Pilot Submersibles: The knowledge and skill of piloting all types of submersibles, including underwater sleds, mini-subs and most types of submarines, including military submersibles. **Base Skill:** 40% +4% per level of experience. **Note:** -20% when using alien or unusual submarines. Does not include power armor or deep sea diving suits.

Pilot: Warships/Patrol Boats: Special training in the use of military warships, combat hydrofoils, patrol boats and amphibious beachcraft/transports. Includes a basic idea of how to use sonar and targeting equipment, depth charges, torpedoes, and other common weapon systems, as well as evasive maneuvers and piloting. **Base skill:** 40% +4% level. **Note:** Characters with the motor boat or ship skill can also pilot these vessels but at a -12% penalty.

Pilot Water Scooters: The knowledge and skill of piloting all types of one and two-man water sleds (underwater) and jet skis (surface sleds). **Base Skill:** 50% +5% per level of experience.

Pilot Related: Navigation Note: The basic navigation skill described in the **Rifts RPG**, page 30, will enable characters to pilot water vessels that ride on the surface of the water by charting the stars and landmarks and using instruments. Likewise, the character can navigate *submersibles* using instruments and other data. Navigating marine vessels is an aspect of the standard *navigation skill*.

Pilot: Power Armor Skill Note: The skill described in the **Rifts RPG**, page 30, includes non-combat models of light, medium and heavy power armor as well as diving suits and experimental and light combat underwater power armor. *Robot Combat Elite* is required to pilot heavy combat power armor, underwater robots and advanced robot vehicles.

Most types of power armor, including airborne types like the SAMAS, are suitable for use underwater, although flight/propulsion speed is reduced by 80%. Power armor without jet propulsion can travel underwater (swim or walk along the bottom), but also at -80% their normal land speed. The CS is developing a modest Navy that is deployed in the Great Lakes and the Gulf of Mexico. However, their expertise and current watercraft are very restricted, so they often use their conventional ground and air power armor and bots for limited underwater operations.

Pilot Related: Radar/Sonar Operations (Read Sensor Equipment): The ability to use radar (radio echo bounces) and sonar (underwater sound echo bounces) equipment and correctly read the information to precisely locate and follow aircraft, ships and submarines. This is all included in the skill ability to *read sensor equipment*. **Base Skill:** 30% +5% per level of experience.

A note about sonar: In submarines, there are two methods or types of sonar operations, passive and active. To use active sonar, the sub must give a pulse of sound to bounce off any nearby ships or objects. This is very dangerous since it immediately gives away the position of the ship; most subs will not use active sonar unless absolutely necessary.

Most submersibles will rely on *passive sonar* systems. This is much more difficult since the sonar operator must sift through the background noise to find any enemy ships. Sometimes they will not be able to distinguish the location of a ship from the background static. Despite this fact, passive sonar is used because it does not give away the location of the sub. **Skill Penalty:** -15% on read sensor equipment skill.

Rogue: Streetwise — Drugs: The following additional street knowledge can be included as part of the regular streetwise skill or used as an additional rogue skill; G.M.'s choice. If used as a separate skill the **Base Skill** proficiency is 25%+5% per level of experience.

The streetwise: drug skill gives the character the ability to recognize characters addicted to drugs, street corner pushers, big time dealers, drug smugglers, juicers, Japes, and undercover agents looking to bust dealers. Similarly, the character has a good idea what drugs cost, how to use them and where to buy them (even if he doesn't use them himself). The character also knows most of the "street names" of common drugs, recognizes the drug when he sees it and knows the general effects and dangers it represents. He can also recognize the symptoms in others and can guess what drug a user may be high on with reasonable accuracy (roll under skill ability).

Technical: Lore — D-bee: Most D-bees (the slang for Dimensional Beings) are just alien humanoids from another dimension or planet. To be classified as a D-bee, the creature must be remotely humanoid in appearance, usually a biped, have a human-like intelligence and not possess supernatural powers. Creatures who are not humanoid in appearance and have extremely monstrous or demonic appearances and/or powers, are usually considered to be monsters rather than D-bees.

D-bee lore is the general study of alien humanoids. This area of study will include culture shock, common types, common behavioral patterns, the distinction between instinctive predators and social oriented beings, myths and legends. The skill is often limited to those living in a specific geographic region where the skill is being taught; i.e. beings commonly known to live in North America will be known by the CS. The region may be limited further, such as D-bees of Western America (or Canada, etc.), Midwest, East, Coalition States and so on. D-bee lore is not a science. Consequently, it is *not* always accurate, complete or in-depth. See the anthropology skill for an in-depth approach to behavioral science. **Base Skill:** 25%+5% per level of experience.

Technical: Lore — Magic: This area of study does *not* give the character any magic powers, the ability to use Techno-Wizard devices, or the ability to read magic symbols. What it provides is general information about magic, magic creatures, the Federation of Magic, and myths about magic. For example, a character with this skill knows about the general powers and abilities of infamous magic creatures such as the various types of dragons, sphinxes, unicorn, and so on. He'd know what are the main types of magic (on Earth or at least his geographic area), such as spell casting/Line Walkers, summoning/Shifters, Rifting/Shifters, Techno-Wizardry, Stone Magic, Bio-Wizardry, Necromancy, and so on. Likewise, the character is likely to know legends about powerful magic items, places, curses and notorious practitioners of magic. Although the character cannot read runes or mystic symbols, he is likely to be able to recognize whether the symbol is a real magic ward, rune or warning. The following abilities come with this layman's skill: **Base Skill (general knowledge):** 25% +5% per level of experience. **Recognize wards, runes and circles:** 15% +5% per level of experience. **Recognized Enchantment**: i.e. magic items, people under the influence of magic charms, possession, curses, mind control and similar: 10% +5% per level of experience.

Technical: Lore — Psychic: Knowledge about psionic powers, how they are believed to work, how they affect people, their limitations, and who possesses them. This skill also provides a rudimentary knowledge about people and beings who possess psionic powers such as minor and major psychics, healers, Psi-Stalkers, Psi-Hounds, Bursters, Mind Melters, Mind Benders, Cyber-Knights and the most infamous supernatural creatures (vampires, possessing entities, Goquas, Mindolars, Raksashas, etc.). The character may also have a passing knowledge about some of the psionic weapons and symbiotes of Atlantis, famous psychics in the region, mind control (via drugs, psychology, hypnosis, magic and psionics) and myths and legends about such places as the Astral Plane, Dreamstream, The Enclave and Psyscape. The character does not have to be a psychic himself, but he should believe that psychic powers really exist. **Base Skill:** 25% +5% per level of experience.

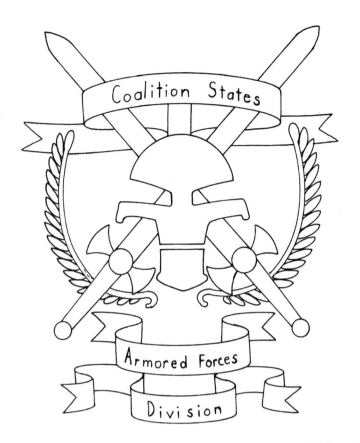

Coalition States
Armored Forces
Division

Coalition Military O.C.C.s

By Kevin Siembieda with suggestions and some text by Julius Rosenstein and Patrick Nowak.

CS O.C.C.s
CS Cyborg Strike Trooper
CS Commando
CS Psi-Hounds/Dog Pack (see *Rifts® RPG*)
CS EOD Specialist
CS Grunt (see *Rifts® RPG*)
CS Juicer
CS Military Specialist (see *Rifts® RPG*)
CS Nautical Specialist
CS Psi-Stalker (see *Rifts® RPG*)
CS Ranger/Wilderness Scout
CS RCSG Scientist
CS RPA Elite/SAMAS Pilot (see *Rifts® RPG*)
CS RPA "Fly Boy" Ace
CS Technical Officer (see *Rifts® RPG*)
CS Special Forces

Note: Also see special division and the Internal Security Specialists (ISS).

Success at war depends on the actions of the thousands of men and women serving in the CS forces. Their degree of loyalty, professionalism, training, and dedication to the cause will all have an impact on their effectiveness. As a rule, the soldiers of the Coalition States are highly motivated, professional troops.

They are especially excited about the siege on Tolkeen and other D-bee communities rumored to be targets. Even those assigned to the Free Quebec front are positive and prepare to bring the rogues and traitors of that territory back into the fold.

Each one of these men and women has the benefit of extensive training, access to specialized equipment and the support of the most powerful nation in North America. They are the greatest military force on the continent.

The original **Rifts® RPG** presented the most common and fundamental Coalition Military Occupational Character Classes (O.C.C.s). The following pages present several *specialized* O.C.C.s of the Coalition States such as the Demolitions (EOD) Specialist, Commando, Special Forces, Cyborg and others; many of which have only been recently included in the *new* Coalition Army. Comparable Military O.C.C.s exist in the Free State of Quebec and among a handful of other high-tech armies and mercenary bands of North America, but they are comparatively uncommon; the Coalition Army is very specialized.

Note: In addition to a base salary and being outfitted with uniforms and equipment, all soldiers get a roof over their head, food, clothing, medical care and all other basic needs provided free as part of his/her pay. Once out of boot camp, a soldier's quarters is a nice dormitory style barracks. Six soldiers share one dormitory quarters. Each gets a private bedroom with a desk and chair, video game system and stereo. All share one bathroom, a sitting room, living room area and television. The soldier can opt to live off base but at his own expense. The character also has access to most military bases, hospitals and facilities (low security clearance unless an officer). In the field, the character will have to rough it in a tent or crude barracks or even under the stars with or without a sleeping bag. Likewise, equipment and facilities may be very limited.

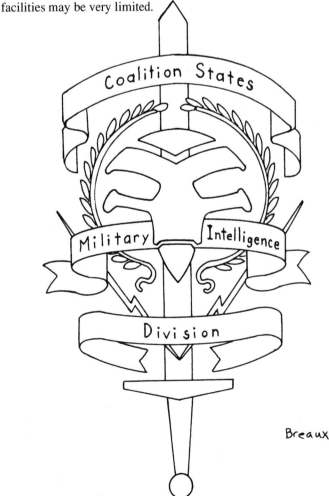

Coalition States
Military   Intelligence
Division

Breaux

Coalition Cyborg Strike Trooper

The official use of partial reconstruction and full conversion cyborgs in the Coalition Army is a new addition. The CS military had done field tests with cyborg troops along hostile borders and preemptive strikes and seek and destroy missions against Tolkeen for nearly five years. They were also deployed as a countermeasure against Juicers and mercenaries during the Juicer Uprising with great effectiveness. The Emperor was hesitant to use bionic augmentation to create a super-soldier for fear that it would dehumanize the soldier. However, close studies over the five year period show that 96.7% of the 1500 test subjects responded well to their mechanical transformation and did not exhibit any of the disassociation with other humans or the psychological trauma that was anticipated. Of course, the long-term effects are yet to be seen. Still, the results were so overwhelmingly positive that the Emperor and General of the Army have agreed to create an official cyborg division (5760 troops nicknamed the CC division) under the auspices of the DSD (Department of Special Divisions). Actually, General Charles Reed Baxter and other officers would like to see an entire cyborg army corps, but the Emperor is hesitant. He prefers the use of the power armor and robots rather than bionic aumentation that permanently alters and disfigures the human body.

There are some advantages to being a cyborg rather than using power armor or bots. For one, there is no feeling of claustrophobia — being stuck in a "tin can" for 24 hours or longer, or a need to get out and stretch one's legs. Nor does the cyborg need to worry about getting caught outside his armor; a cyborg is a mega-damage war machine 24 hours a day. The bionic conversion feels natural and responds at the speed of thought as if it were a natural, living part of the body.

All candidates for full bionic conversion are subjected to a thorough screening process in which a battery of psychological evaluations and stress tests are conducted. A Coalition cyborg soldier must be either a partial or full conversion cyborg. The same basic type of 'borg is created, although weapon systems are often modular so they can be changed to best fit their mission, and there are special operatives, variants and exceptions.

To prevent the enemy from easily identifying and targeting Coalition cyborgs from regular troops, most 'Borgs wear a heavy version of the new "Dead Boy" armor which makes them indistinguishable from the other troops until they take action. The only physical telltale signs are that the cyborgs tend to be extra-bulky (broader than the average soldier) and an extra six inches to a foot in height (typically 7 to 8 feet/2.1 to 2.4 m tall). However, these details are difficult to spot in a crowd of other soldiers, and virtually impossible in a combat situation. Another tip-off is the fact that the CS cyborgs frequently arm themselves with rail guns and other heavy weapons, but with the enhanced exoskeleton body armor and the CS Juicer, even this is no guarantee that one's opponent is a 'Borg.

Attribute Requirements: M.E. 15 or higher, a good I.Q. and P.E. are desirable but not necessary. Any human with the spirit to fight and good mental health can become a Coalition Cyborg.

Typical Full Conversion Features:

Light CS Cyborg: Emphasis is on speed and agility and use for espionage and seek and destroy missions. Typically comparable to human in size (6.6 to 7 feet/1.95 to 2.1 m), P.S. 22, P.P. 22, Spd 176 (120 mph/192 km) and can leap 12 feet (3.6 m) high or lengthwise from a standing position or 4x that distance with a running start.

Standard features include built-in language translator, built-in radio receiver and transmitter, headjack, molecular analyzer, modulating voice synthesizer, bionic lung, multi-optic eyes, garrote wrist wire, climb cord, retractable vibro-blade (1), concealed ion rod in one leg, and one large secret compartment in the other leg.

Additional special skills include:
Climbing (+15%)
Gymnastics (+10%)
Acrobatics (+5%)
Swimming (+15%)
Escape Artist (+10%)
Intelligence (+10%)
Find contraband, Weapons & Cybernetics (+10%)
Pilot Jet Pack (+20%)

Heavy CS Cyborg: Emphasis is on strength and firepower and use for espionage and seek and destroy missions. Typically 7 to 8 feet (2.1 to 2.4 m) tall, P.S. 26, P.P. 24, Spd 132 (90 mph/144 km) and can leap 10 feet (3.6 m) high or lengthwise from a standing position or 2x that distance with a running start.

Standard features include built-in language translator, built-in radio receiver and transmitter, headjack, bionic lung, multi-optic eyes, energy-clip hand or arm port (both), one forearm blaster (typically plasma or particle beam), retractable vibro-blade (1) or concealed arm laser rod, concealed ion rod in one leg, and one large secret compartment in the other leg. 10% have an extra appendage and attack per melee round.

Additional special skills include:
Boxing
Climbing (+10%)
Gymnastics (+5%)
Swimming (+10%)
Intelligence (+10%)
Tracking (humanoids; +10%)
Demon & Monster Lore (+10%)
W.P.: Another one of choice.

Basic O.C.C. skills for all CS Cyborgs: See additional skills by Cyborg type; light or heavy, described above:
Math: Basic (+10%)
Language: American 98% (see built-in language translator)
Radio: Basic (+10%)
Pilot skill of choice (+20%)
Land Navigation (+10%)
W.P. Energy Rifle
W.P. Heavy Energy Weapons
W.P. One of choice.
Hand to Hand: Expert
Hand to hand: expert can be changed to martial arts or assassin at the cost of one "O.C.C. Related Skill."

O.C.C. Related Skills: Select five "other" skills, plus select one additional skill at levels four, eight, and twelve. All new skills start at level one proficiency.

Communications: Any (+10%)

Domestic: Any

Electrical: Basic Electronics only.

Espionage: Intelligence and detect concealment only.

Mechanical: Basic Mechanics only.

Medical: First Aid only (+5%)

Military: Any (+10%), except Demolitions (any).

Physical: Any that are still appropriate.

Pilot: Any (+5%); except robot, power armor, tank, APCs and combat aircraft skills.

Pilot Related: Any (+5%)

Rogue: Any (+2%)

Science: None

Technical: Any (+10%)

W.P.: Any

Wilderness: Any

Secondary Skills: The character also gets to select two secondary skills from the list, excluding those marked "None," at levels two, five, eight and thirteen. These are additional areas of knowledge that do not get the advantage of the bonus listed in parentheses. All secondary skills start at the base skill level.

Standard Military issue for Cyborg Soldiers: All the appropriate ammunition and equipment for the 'Borg's body styling and weapon systems, energy rifle of choice, four extra E-clips, four grenades, utility belt, backpack, walkie-talkie (for back-up), "Dead Boy" body armor and regular maintenance and repairs.

Equipment Available Upon Assignment: Jet pack, hover vehicle or transportation, rail gun, additional weapons, and equipment. The character also has access to most military bases (medium security clearance), hospitals and facilities. **Note:** Availability of equipment and resources may be dependent upon the local commander, supply stock, location, causalities and combat conditions.

Money: The character also receives a monthly salary of 2000 credits (the savings of a first level character is 1D6x1000 credits). All soldiers get a roof over their head, food, clothing, medical care and all other basic needs provided free as part of his/her pay.

Rank: Standard military; private to general.

Bionic Conversion: Described previously. Additional bionic and cybernetics may be added as a reward and/or for special missions. Any of the bionics and cybernetics described in the **Rifts® RPG** are available. In addition, the Game Master *may* consider and allow any of the systems described in **Rifts® Japan, Rifts® Underseas** and **Rifts® Triax and the NGR.** The availability of bionic systems from other World Books is left entirely to the discretion of the Game Master. Note that the cyborg soldier cannot purchase *unauthorized* bionic systems.

Special Term of Duty: The CS requires all candidates for partial and full bionic conversion to agree to a 12 year tour of duty, with the standard six year extensions available after the initial years of service. 'Borgs that go AWOL are considered dangerous rogues and are hunted down and destroyed!

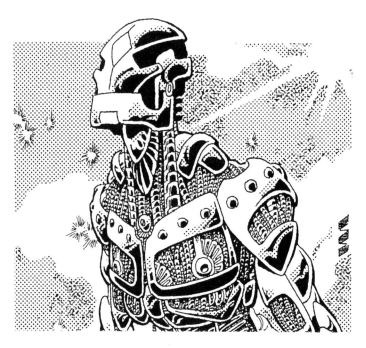

Decommissioned Cyborgs

When a borg leaves military service he or she has a few different options:

1. Keep basic bionics and remain a citizen: All external weapons such as rail guns, vibro-blades and forearm blasters are removed. Spy systems like cyber-disguises will also be removed, although cameras and enhanced hearing are usually left untouched. Physical attributes are also to be reduced by 20%. The character must then register with the *Cyborg Civilian Commission* which helps the character adjust to civilian life, find employment and keeps tabs on his conduct. As long as the cyborg does not abuse his superhuman abilities, break the law and functions well within society, he can life out his live in peace. In all honesty, because the cyborg is a new addition to the CS Army, they have only been in service five years, so there have been no retired or decommissioned soldiers who have entered the civilian population.

2. Special Consideration for Service: Military cyborgs with long (48-72 years of service) or distinguished careers (a hero) may be allowed to keep the majority of their bionic systems, including light or medium body armor and basic bionic weapons, like vibro-blades and forearm weapons. This is only possible if the government has approved and authorized the character's moving into the private sector as a security operative (ISS or corporate or private business), or if the cyborg is moving out of the Coalition States to pursue a career as an adventurer or mercenary. In the latter case, the character relinquishes his CS citizenship and although he can visit the States as an *authorized* foreign visitor (if approved by the immigration department), he or she cannot live within the borders of the nation.

3. Retro-conversion: "Retro-conversion" or "retro-fitting" of cyborgs means the majority of their bionic components/body are replaced with flesh and blood bio-systems! Partial reconstruction 'borgs will see their bionic limbs and special bionic implants, like lungs, molecular analyzers, weapons and the like, replaced with life-like bio-systems. The bio-system limbs are genetically encoded from the character's own DNA to prevent rejection and to be as lifelike as possible.

Full conversion borgs can undergo a similar process in which the vast majority of their bionic systems are replaced with bio-systems, but the basic body (spine, chest, skull, skeleton and internal organs) remains an artificial, bionic construct. The big difference is that a certain portion has been replaced with bio-systems and what bionics remain are downgraded to a basic level to be as close to human as possible. P.S., P.P, and Spd attributes are 18 for those who retire honorably, but 10 for those dishonorably discharged from service. In some cases, those scheduled for a dishonorable discharge go AWOL, fleeing to other kingdoms or becoming mercenaries. Cyborgs who go AWOL or convicted of treason or crimes are destroyed!

Cyborg Life Expectancy

Bio-system retro-fitting: 50+2D4 years from the date of being refitted. Including the person's early years of development and his years as a cyborg, this should provide the character with the approximate equivalent life expectancy of the *average human* living in the Coalition States, which is 80 to 90 years; with modern medicine and artificial bio-systems, some people may live healthy, productive lives to 125!

Partial reconstructed 'borg: Roughly equal to the normal Republic human, 80 to 100 years.

Full conversion 'borgs: With regular maintenance and replacement of old or defective parts, and avoiding brain damage, trauma or mental deterioration, the 'Borg can remain active for 200+ years.

Note: These numbers are roughly the same for the New German Republic as well. Only Japan, unknown to the CS, NGR and most of the world, has superior bionic and medical technology that prolongs life even greater. Of course, the life of a soldier is a dangerous one. 33% of all cyborgs are expected to perish in combat and 8% to go AWOL within their first 24 years of duty.

CS Commando O.C.C.

The Coalition Commando is a highly trained, combat-oriented specialist whose job is to act as part of an elite strike force as well as a member of counter-insurgent and counter-terrorist teams. They engage in surgical strikes, seek and destroy, sabotage, rescue, and reconnaissance missions. The nature of their training is such that commandoes are not generally used as front-line troops. However, if the need arises, they can be pressed into service at the front. The commandoes are trained in the use of most CS power armor, including the SAMAS suit (although they lack the expertise and experience of the Elite RPA "Sams") and can give a good accounting of themselves in a straight up fire-fight. All commandoes begin at the rank of either corporal or sergeant depending upon their performance during training.

These soldiers are deployed under the command of Coalition military specialists, and are often used as members of long-range patrols and for strikes outside the borders of the Coalition States. However, they are also deployed as members of reactionary units within the Coalition States to quell uprisings or other threats to the internal security of the Coalition Military and States.

Attribute Requirements: I.Q. 10, M.E. 10, P.S. 12, P.P. 14, P.E. 12 or higher.

O.C.C. Skills:

Math: Basic (+20%)
Radio: Basic (+15%)
Radio: Scrambler (+10%)
Language: American and one of Choice (+20%)
Land Navigation (+10%)
Intelligence (+10%)
Parachuting (+20%)
Pilot: One of choice (+10%)
Pilot: Robots & Power Armor (+10%)
Recognize Weapon Quality (+12%)
Wilderness Survival (+15%)
Climbing (+10%)
Running
W.P. Energy Pistol
W.P. Energy Rifle   W.P.: Two of Choice

Hand to Hand: Commando; this skill cannot be changed.

O.C.C. Related Skills: Select four skills from one of the following areas of special training: Espionage, Mechanical, Military (typically demolitions and traps), Piloting or Wilderness — all of these special MOS skills get a +10% skill bonus. Two other skills can also be selected from any of the available categories at levels two, five, nine and twelve.

Communications: any (+10%)
Domestic: Any
Electrical: Basic only (+5%)
Espionage: Any (+15%)
Mechanical: Automotive, Basic Mechanics, or Locksmith only
Medical: First Aid only (+10%)
Military: Any (+10%)
Physical: Any
Pilot: Any (+5%)
Pilot Related: Any (+5%)
Rogue: Any (+4%)
Science: Any
Technical: Any (+5%; +10% to Literacy and Language skills)
W.P.: Any
Wilderness: Any (+5%)

Secondary Skills: The character gets two secondary skills at levels one, four, seven, and ten (normal restrictions apply).

Standard Equipment: Standard Coalition "Dead Boy" body armor, energy rifle and energy sidearm of choice, 4 extra E-clips for each, four explosive grenades, two smoke grenades, two flares, vibro-knife or saber, survival knife, distancing binoculars, robot medical kit, pocket computer, utility belt, air filter & gas mask, walkie-talkie, uniform, dress uniform, combat boots, canteen, and an additional non-energy weapon of choice (typically S.D.C. automatic weapon, or bow and arrow). Conventional military vehicle of choice (motorcycle, jeep, hovercycle, etc.) for daily use.

Equipment Available Upon Assignment: Any type of body armor, 2D4 hand grenades, 1D4 smoke grenades, 1D4 flares, access to explosives if demolitions is a known skill and necessary for the mission, any types of weapon, extra ammunition, optical enhancements, camera or surveillance equipment, and food rations for weeks. Non-regulation weapons, armor, equipment and vehicles may also be issued to Commando squads, mainly for the purpose of disguise and infiltration. In addition, the character has access to military facilities.

Vehicles can include a simple hover cycle, car, conventional military vehicles, or jet pack to SAMAS power armor (old style or light assault types only), Spider-Skull Walker, and robot vehicles.

The exact type of equipment will depend on the Commando's mission, the commanding officer and availability of items at the command base. Most Commandos have medium level security clearance while experienced and trusted veterans will have top clearance.

Money: The commando gets a roof over his head, food, clothing, and all other basics provided free as part of his pay, as well as access to military facilities. His monthly salary is 2000 credits, plus combat pay. He starts off with one month's pay. The commando's quarters are the same as those for the Elite RPA.

Cybernetics: None to start with, but implantation of cybernetic and bionics is not restricted and may be awarded for exemplary service and heroics. Most (60%) Commandos eventually acquire 1D4+2 implants, some (25%) have systems equal to the Headhunter.

Hand to Hand: Commando

The commando hand to hand combat skill is exclusive to the commando and Special Forces O.C.C.s and is a form of martial arts.

Commando O.C.C. Bonuses: +2D6 S.D.C. and +1 to M.E. (focus and concentration).

Descriptions of Special Combat Moves

Automatic Body Flip/Throw: Commando training means the character can do a body flip/throw *in place of a parry*. This means that instead of blocking or deflecting the blow, the character attempts to leverage the attacker's own force into a flip. Success requires beating the attacker's roll to strike, just like a parry, but using the bonuses for body flip (not parry). Failure means taking full damage from the attack, without a chance to roll with punch/fall/impact. A successful roll means the character has grabbed his opponent and sent him flying in a judo-style throw. Damage is 1D6 points but the victim also loses initiative (if he had it) and one melee attack. The P.S. damage bonus should be added to the damage inflicted.

Automatic Dodge: The character must roll to dodge as usual, but the dodge maneuver does *not* use up a melee attack/action, it functions just like a parry. This is purely a defensive move. **Note:** This is how the automatic dodge is always supposed to function.

Body Block/Tackle: This is a combination of a damage causing body block and a knockdown attack. A successful attack does 1D4 damage (P.S. damage bonuses apply) and the opponent is knocked down. The victim can do only one of the following two defensive moves: a dodge or maintain balance. A successful dodge means no damage and no knockdown, but failure means damage, knockdown and loss of one attack that melee round.

A successful maintain balance means the victim is not knocked down but loses an attack and takes full damage.

Body Flip/Throw: A judo style throw or flip that uses an attacker's own momentum and leverage to "flip" or "throw" him off his feet and onto the ground. Damage is 1D6 points but the victim also loses initiative (if he had it) and one melee attack. The P.S. damage bonus should be added to the damage inflicted. A victim of a throw can try to *roll with impact/fall* to diminish the damage (half if successful), but other penalties are unchanged.

Body Flip/Throw: Critical: Characters with this attack inflict double damage; typically 2D6 + P.S. and damage bonuses by rolling a certain "natural" die roll (a high number not modified with bonuses). The victim of a critical body throw loses initiative and *two* melee actions/attacks as a result of being thrown.

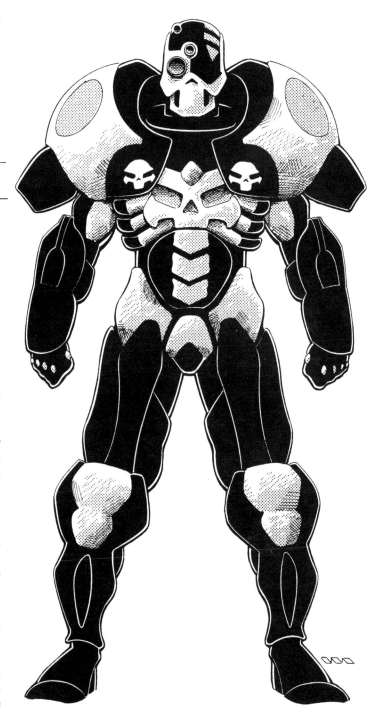

This move cannot be done with an automatic body flip/throw because it is an attack, while the other is a defensive move.

Death Blow (revised): A special attack designed to kill an opponent in one or two strikes! This attack is often limited in hand to hand combat to the roll of a "natural" high strike number; i.e. death blow on a natural 18-20. Whenever the words "death blow" are presented without limitation, the character can use a death strike whenever he desires; however, such a devastating attack counts as two melee attacks/actions.

Human vs Human: Against humans and S.D.C. creatures, the attack does double the normal damage, plus P.S. bonuses direct to hit points. This attack can be used with punches and kicks or hand-held weapons such as swords, clubs, etc. It is not applicable to guns and does not work through armor; the armor must be removed or penetrated.

Mega-damage creature vs Mega-damage creature: The attack does double normal damage, plus P.S. bonuses, and it is so devastating to the creature's body that it cannot *bio-regenerate* injury from a death blow for 1D4 hours! This attack is not applicable against M.D.C. robots, borgs and power armor, unless the M.D.C. attacker is making a *called shot* to the head or power supply, in which case double damage is inflicted to that part of the bot, 'borg or armor.

Disarm: The act of disarming is simply getting rid of the opponent's weapon; it does no damage. It can be used as a defensive move in place of a dodge or parry, or can be done as an attack/strike.

The disarm move is a strike, hold or grappling maneuver that causes an opponent to drop his weapon or whatever he's holding. The move counts as one melee attack/action. Disarm does not give the weapon to the character making the disarm move. True, the item is forced out of the victim's grasp, but it is either knocked away or falls to the ground.

Using disarm as a defensive move typically requires the attacker to roll a natural 19 or 20.

Using disarm as an attack requires the character to roll to strike as usual, and the high roll wins.

A failed disarming attack does no damage, uses up on melee action (even as a defensive move) and means the character's opponent remains armed, is probably mad, and ready to strike.

Paired Weapons: Certain kinds of weapons, such as sais, nunchaku, daisho, knives, clubs and swords, can be used as paired weapons. Users of paired weapons can strike and parry simultaneously, can do twin strikes against a single target or against a pair of targets, and can parry two different opponents at the same time. In other words, warriors skilled in paired weapons often can do two actions for every one of their melee attacks (i.e. strike and parry). However, a twin, simultaneous strike with both weapons means losing the automatic parry and leaves the character open to his opponent's next attack without benefit of a parry (dodge is optional but uses up a melee action).

Hand to Hand: Commando

Level

1   Starts with two attacks per melee round, paired weapons, body flip/throw, body block/tackle and +2 to save vs horror factor.

2   +1 on initiative, +1 to strike, +2 to parry and dodge, +3 to roll with punch/fall/impact, and +3 to pull punch. Backward sweep kick: Used only against opponents coming up behind the character. Does no damage; it is purely a knock-down attack (same penalties as body flip) but cannot be parried (an opponent can try to dodge it but is -2 to do so).

3   Disarm, +1 to automatic body flip.

4   + One additional attack per melee and Karate kick attack. This is a conventional, karate-style, kick. It starts with bringing the knee, folded, up to chest level, then the foot is completely extended. Does 2D6 damage.

5   Automatic dodge and critical body flip/throw.

6   +2 on initiative, +1 to strike, parry and dodge, and +1 to body flip/throw.

7   +2 to damage, +1 to save vs horror factor, +1 to disarm, +1 to automatic dodge and +2 to pull punch.

8   + One additional attack per melee, jump kick, +1 to body flip/throw, and +1 to roll with punch/fall/impact.

9   Death blow on a natural 18-20!

10 +2 to save vs horror factor, +1 on initiative and +1 to strike.

11 +1 to disarm, +1 to pull punch and +1 to body flip/throw.

12 +2 to damage, +1 to parry and dodge, +2 to automatic dodge.

13 + One additional attack per melee.

14 Automatic body flip/throw

15 Critical strike on a natural 17-20.

EOD Specialist

By Kevin Siembieda and Pat Nowak

The Explosive Ordnance Disposal (EOD) Specialist is a highly trained soldier in the use, handling and disposal of explosives and other dangerous substances. This is one of the few areas of military training that requires the teaching of reading, writing and arithmetic. Individuals in this program are taught to understand and use a number of different explosive substances, fuses, primers, blasting caps, timers, and triggering devices, along with basic electronics. The soldier learns the best techniques and methods to deploy explosives in combat operations, and improvisation techniques in the manufacture of homemade explosives as well as simple but effective traps.

Many EOD Specialists in the Coalition Army are also taught a number of basic espionage skills because they are often members of Special Forces teams and engage in acts of espionage, sabotage, and strategic strikes. These characters tend to be daring souls with a knack for tinkering, steady hands and nerves of steel. Most are resourceful and inventive.

Special Skills Exclusive to the EOD Specialist:

Homemade Explosives Skill: A base skill of 40% +4% per level of experience to manufacture *homemade* explosives. With the proper amount of time and equipment the character can make explosive substances, increase the killing power of existing explosives and set booby traps. The following is a list of the different types of homemade explosives the Specialist can create.

Molatov Cocktail: A flammable substance in a glass jar or bottle that is lit and thrown. The container shatters upon impact and the flaming liquid covers the area. Effective Range: Thrown 50 feet (15.2 m); -3 to strike man-sized targets. Damage: 1D4×10 S.D.C. Effective Casualty Radius: 6 feet (1.8 m); plus may set surrounding combustible materials on fire. Cost to Make: 5 credits each.

Exploding Canister: A nonlethal device in which a simple, small explosion "pops" open a canister and sprays its victim with its contents; typically a fluid like paint, perfume, rotten eggs, beans, etc., when used as a prank, or gasoline, acid, poison, skin irritant, paint (blinds or marks victim), and similar when used as a weapon. Effective Range: About 5 feet (1.5 m); -2 to strike man-sized targets. Damage: Depends on the substance released. Effective Casualty Radius: 3 feet (0.9 m). Cost to Make: 8 credits each.

Homemade Flash Bomb/Grenade: Typically a mixture of materials that ignites in a brilliant flash, often accompanied by a popping sound and a puff of smoke. Range: Thrown about 50 feet (15.2 m). Damage: None; creates a flash that distracts and may temporarily blind those within 20 feet (6 m) of the flash. Everybody in the radius of affect loses one melee action/attack and must roll a 16 or higher to save vs momentary blindness when used in the dark (only needs a 12 or higher in light). A fail roll means blindness for one melee round (15 seconds); -9 to strike, parry and dodge. Radius of Affect: 10 feet (3 m). Cost to Make: 15 credits each.

Homemade Tear Gas: This device is most typically used in traps or to create a distraction. It often uses ammonia mixed with other chemicals to create a cloud of smoke or vapors that burns the eyes and irritates the nose and throat. Range: Thrown about 50 feet (15.2 m). Damage: None; releases noxious gas and may temporally blind those within the radius of affect. Everybody in the radius of affect must roll a 16 or higher to save vs momentary blindness and coughing. Duration: The homemade vapors last for 1D6 minutes. The effects of the vapors lasts 1D4 minutes after the character leaves the area of affect. Penalties: Blindness, coughing and irritation: -2 on initiative, -5 to strike, parry and dodge and -1 melee action/attack per melee affected. Radius of Affect: 6 feet (1.8 m). Cost to Make: 25 credits each.

Homemade Smoke Bomb/Grenade: Typically a mix of saltpeter and other common components in a homemade package. Range: Thrown about 100 feet (30 m). Damage: None; creates a smoke-filled area to provide protective cover (opponents cannot see into or through smoke) or as a signal. Opponents whose vision is obscured by the smoke are -6 to strike, parry and dodge. Color range: Black, grey, red or yellow. Radius of Affect: 20 feet (6 m). Cost to Make: 25 credits each.

Homemade S.D.C. Grenade: A weak grenade using a homemade explosive mixture created from readily available materials. The package will either be of improvised design or a refurbished military grenade. Range: Thrown about 100 feet (30 m). Damage: 1D4×10 S.D.C. Effective Casualty Radius: 10 feet (3 m). Cost to Make: 40 credits each.

High-Powered Homemade Grenade (light M.D.): Similar to a regular S.D.C. grenade but made from a higher grade explosive substance, yet still inferior to typical military grade mixtures. The grenade can be a refurbished military grenade casing or pipe casing. Range: 100 feet (30 m). Damage: 1D4 M.D. (or 1D4×100 S.D.C.). Effective Casualty Radius: 20 feet (6 m). Cost to Make: 100 credits each.

Homemade Explosive Charge: Explosive substances of varying strengths can be manufactured from readily available materials. All that is required is a propellant substance and a booster or accelerant. Nitrogen rich fertilizer combined with a flammable substance as a booster is one example of a homemade charge which in a large enough quantity can cause extreme devastation. A homemade explosive charge is less effective than military grade counterparts and is usually huge by comparison. Damage: 1D6 S.D.C. per six ounces (0.25 kg) or 1D4 M.D. (1D4×100 S.D.C.) per ten pounds (4.5 kg). Effective Casualty Radius: 10 feet (3 m) for small bombs (under 50 lbs/22.6 kg) or 20 feet for large bombs (100 lbs/45 kg or more). Cost to Make: 10-20 credits per half pound (0.25 kg).

Homemade Mine: An improvised mine consists of a quantity of homemade explosive packed into a refurbished land mine casing or a container of homemade design. To improve the damaging capability of the mine, the designer can "shape" the charge to increase power at the expense of area effect. Such a mine is fairly weak and not suited for use against modern mega-damage combat vehicles, but can be devastating to S.D.C. equivalents. Damage: 5D6 M.D. or 1D4×10 M.D. for a shaped charge. Effective Casualty Radius: 15 feet (4.5 m), or 3 feet (0.9 m) for a shaped charge. Cost to Make: 300 credits each.

Military Grade Grenade: Rather than using a homemade explosive substance, a demolitions expert character can recover the military grade explosives from an unexploded bomb or missile. Since the grenade canister/package is typically of homemade design, the grenade is not quite as powerful as a military equivalent. Range: Thrown about 100 feet (30 m). Damage: 1D6+2 or 2D4+2 M.D. Effective Casualty Radius: 10 feet (3 m). Cost to Make: 12 credits each if the majority of the parts and materials are all salvaged from existing items; 400 credits to construct a military grade M.D. grenade with military grade materials, but from scratch.

Military Grade Mine: Basically a quantity of military grade explosives recovered from dud bombs or missiles packed into a mine casing complete with a pressure detonator. The charge is quite powerful and is usually shaped to increase damage potential but is still slightly inferior to military issue land mines. Regardless this explosive device is extremely effective. Damage: 1D4×10 M.D. for anti-personnel or 2D4×10 M.D. for anti-armor mines. Effective Casualty Radius: 50 feet (15 m) for anti-personnel, 10 feet (3 m) for anti-armor mines. Cost to Make: 750 credits for anti-personnel, 3,100 credits for anti-armor mines.

Retooled Military Explosives: A demolitions specialist character can use his knowledge of explosives to increase the destructive power of a military explosive by 25%. For example, a fragmentation grenade normally inflicting 2D6 M.D. can be augmented to cause 4D4 M.D. or 2D6+4 M.D. A retooled plasma

74

mini-missiles inflicts 2D4×10 M.D. instead of the usual 1D6×10 M.D. It takes the character at least an hour to alter an explosive device and typically he or she will only have the chance to retool a dozen or so explosives before a combat operation.

Attribute Requirements: I.Q. 9, M.E. 14, P.P. 14 or higher.
O.C.C. Skills:
Literacy: American (+20%)
Basic Math (+25%)
Radio: Basic (10%)
Computer Operations (+10%)
Basic Electronics (+15%)
Mechanical Engineer (10%)
Demolitions (+20%)
Demolitions Disposal (+20%)
Underwater Demolitions (+10%)
Nuclear, Biological, & Chemical Warfare (+10%)
Trap Construction (+15% only when explosives are involved)
Trap/Mine Detection (14%)
Pilot Hovercraft (+10%)
W.P.: Energy Rifle
Hand to Hand: Basic
 Hand to Hand: Basic can be changed to expert at the cost of two "O.C.C. Related Skills" or martial arts for the cost of three skill selections.

O.C.C. Related Skills: Select six other skills. Plus select two additional skills at level three, and one at levels six, nine, and twelve. All new skills start at level one proficiency.

Communications: Any (+5%)
Domestic: Any
Electrical: Any (+10%)
Espionage: Any (+10%), except Sniper and Tracking.
Mechanical: Any (+10%)
Medical: First aid only.
Military: Any (+10%)
Physical: Any, except acrobatics and wrestling.
Pilot: Any (+5%); except robot, power armor, tank, APC and most combat aircraft skills.
Pilot Related: Any (+5%)
Rogue: Any
Science: Any (+10%)
Technical: Any (+5%; +10% for literacy and language skills)
W.P.: Any
Wilderness: Land Navigation and Hunting only.

Secondary Skills: The character also gets to select five secondary skills from the previous list. These are additional areas of knowledge that do not get the advantage of the bonus listed in parentheses. All secondary skills start at the base skill level. Also, skills are limited (any, only, none) as previously indicated in the list.

Standard Equipment: A suit of light or heavy "Dead Boy" body armor, a set of black clothing with ski-mask, uniform, dress uniform, fine leather gloves, a box of disposable surgical gloves (100 per box), tinted goggles, a doctor's stethoscope, PC-3000 hand-held computer, PDD pocket audio recorder, pocket laser distancer, pocket flashlight, portable tool kit, laser scalpel (equivalent to Wilk's model), survival knife, CP-40 or C-12 energy rifle, four additional E-clips for the weapon, knapsack, backpack, two satchels, utility belt, utility/combat harness, air filter, and canteen.

Equipment Available Upon Assignment: 1D6+6 hand grenades of choice, 4 smoke grenades, 1D4 shape charges, 2D4 flares, and access to virtually any type of explosives and EOD equipment necessary for the mission, from plastique/shape charges to fusion blocks! The character may also be given access to rocket launchers, mini-missiles, optical enhancements, camera equipment, mine detection equipment, EOD equipment, radiation suit (remember the "Dead Boy" body armor is not an environmental suit), hovercycle or other vehicle, food rations and so on. In addition, the character has access to military facilities. Most EOD Specialists have mid-level security clearance, while top officers may have highest security clearance.

Money: Base pay is a salary of 1800 credits a month, plus hazard pay and combat pay. Starts with one month's basic salary.

Cybernetics: None to start, but augmented hearing, sight and sensor hands are common. Any of the bionics and cybernetics described in the **Rifts® RPG** *may* be available. In addition, the Game Master *may* consider and allow any of the systems described in **Rifts® Japan, Rifts® Underseas** and **Rifts® Triax and the NGR.** The availability of bionic systems from other World Books is left entirely to the discretion of the Game Master. Note that soldiers cannot purchase *unauthorized* bionic systems.

Coalition Juicers

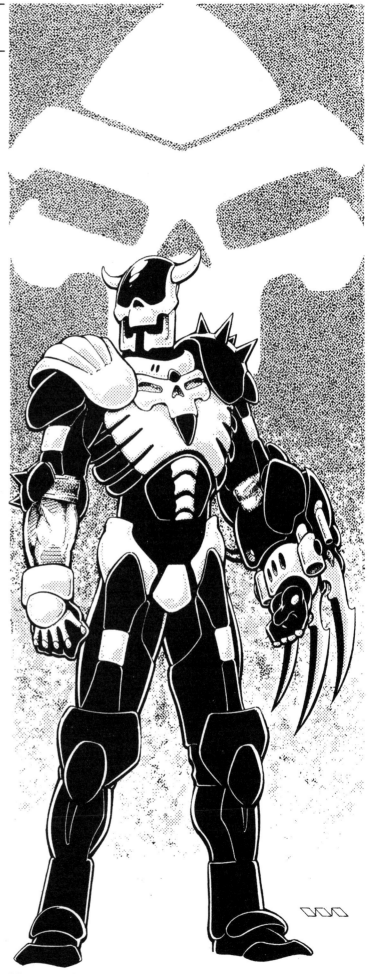

Note: Reprinted from Juicer Uprising with additional data and up-dates by Kevin Siembieda.

The Coalition States have long been vocal opponents of the Juicer process and all its implications. CS Propaganda has made it a point to show how stupid and dangerous tampering with one's body through chemicals can be, and how counterproductive it is to condemn a healthy man or woman to an early grave by cursing him with this chemical addiction. In most cases, these beliefs are shared by the common people and most government officials. The Coalition has long adopted an official policy of exclusion of Juicers from their armies and declared the very process to be *illegal*. For decades, the creation of Juicers in the Coalition States was punishable by death.

However, supporters of Juicers for military use have existed in the CS military and government since the inception of the CS. Government leaders have sat on pre-Rifts Juicer technology for almost a hundred years while military analysts argued the virtues of these augmented warriors. Juicers are 2-3 times stronger and faster than the average human, need far less sleep, possess increased endurance, a low fatigue ratio, and other factors which give these enhanced warriors a much greater chance of surviving actual combat than non-augmented soldiers. As the Coalition began to gear up for its campaign for expansion and prepares to fight nations that rely on magic, Juicers, and D-Bees (many of whom have superhuman attributes and powers), CS strategists predicted that some front-line combat units would suffer in excess of 80% casualties in the first few weeks of fighting. The same studies indicate that if such units were composed of Juicers, the casualties might be reduced to an astonishing 30% or even 20%. One often quoted study showed that the average suit of power armor costs 1-5 million credits, while a fully outfitted Juicer, including the cost of his military training, body armor, weapons, equipment, and Juicer augmentation process, costs no more than 250,000 credits, possibly less (remember the CS produces its equipment at cost). Thus, *four* fully equipped Juicers could be created for the cost of one basic suit of power armor, or *20* Juicers for the cost of one five million dollar power armor suit like the Super SAMAS!

For years, these studies failed to sway the leading minds of the Coalition States. To Emperor Prosek, Juicers are an abomination. In the tradition of his father and grandfather, he had vowed that he would not sacrifice precious "human" life foolishly. Power armor, robots, and other alternatives (Psi-Hounds/Dog Boys, Skelebots, etc.) were the ideal alternatives despite their costs in credits and resources. General Cabot's protege, the decorated war hero *General Ross Underhill*, concurs. To him, Juicers are overrated and certainly not equal to a well-trained human in power armor, or so he insists. He'd much rather see money and effort spent in the development of advanced suits of power armor like the long-heralded "Super SAMAS" and others.

Joseph Prosek II, took a more pragmatic view and was able to win over his father. He agreed that he would have problems condemning full citizens to the almost certain death that is the fate of most Juicers, but he has no qualms in doing so to would-be citizens in the 'Burbs and wastelands, whom he sees as useless rabble anyway. This suggestion prompted a three year study of 400 Juicers under the command of Colonel Lyboc and the supervision of General Cabot. The study seems to confirm the value of the Juicers as part of the Coalition Army. After the Juicer Uprising, the Emperor reluctantly agreed to add Juicers to the military. Thus, the Coalition States passed a law making the use of Juicers and Juicer technology legal under the *exclusive* jurisdiction of the military. Furthermore, he has limited the deployment of Juicers to two Army Divisions (11,520 troops) under the supervision and command of General Cabot (who has lobbied for a Juicer Division for years) and has forbidden the use and creation of the Psycho-Juicer (see *Rifts® Juicer Uprising* for details).

As per the young Prosek's plan, human volunteers can earn citizenship for themselves and two family members, by submitting to Juicer augmentation and faithfully serving in the Coalition Military for a two year tour of duty, after which the soldier undergoes detox. Some volunteer for a second tour of duty, accepting the greater risk of death in return for another few years as a Juicer powerhouse. A few remain in service for the full six years, abandoning all hope in return for the chance to build a stronger human empire and destroy the enemies of mankind. The CS also offers a five year tour of service to begin with. This earns the character his citizenship and gives five family members CS citizenship and/or entry into one of the cities. The long tour of duty condemns the volunteer to death, but many of these impoverished and downtrodden people are so desperate that they jump at the chance of getting loved ones into the safety of a Coalition city.

These Special Forces Troopers were outfitted with a highly stylized Death's Head pattern armor, decorated with spikes and equipped with a Forearm Integral Weapon System (FIWS) and other heavy weapons. The typical CS Juicer is a highly dedicated and motivated soldier who has already undergone basic training before receiving the bio-comp augmentation. Most stay loyal for the welfare of their families. Joseph Prosek's plan may be heartless, but it is effective.

Note: Colonel Lyboc still maintains a small secret force of 50 Juicers and 50 Psycho-Juicers (see *Juicer Uprising*) who are loyal to him and help maintain his various illegal operations in the Chi-Town 'Burbs. He also possesses the knowledge and resources to create the outlawed Psycho-Juicer.

Coalition Juicer Special Operative

Attribute Requirements: None.
O.C.C. Abilities and Bonuses:

1. Super Endurance: Add 1D4×100 to S.D.C., 1D4×10 to hit points, and 2D6 to P.E. attribute. Can lift and carry four times more than a normal person of equivalent strength, and can last five times longer before feeling the effects of exhaustion. Can remain alert and operate at full efficiency for up to five days without sleep. Normally needs only three hours of sleep per day.

2. Super Strength: Add 2D6 to P.S. attribute. Note: Minimum P.S. is 22, if lower adjust to 22.

3. Super Speed: Add 2D4×10 to Speed attribute. Can leap 30 feet (9.1 m) across after a short run (half that from a dead stop) and 20 feet (6 m) high (half without a short run).

4. Super Reflexes and Reaction Time: Bonuses: +4 on initiative, +4 to roll with punch, fall or impact, automatic parry or dodge on all attacks, even from behind/surprise; add two extra attacks per melee round, and add 2D4 to P.P. attribute. Minimum P.P. attribute is 20, if lower adjust it to 20. **Penalties:** Same as normal Juicers (insomnia, restlessness, impatience, etc.).

5. Bionic Implants: Unlike normal Juicers, the Coalition Juicer has a handful of bionic and cybernetic implants designed to make a better warrior, and also to better control him. The implants include *cyber-armor* (A.R. 16, 50 M.D.C.), *a bionic hand* (12 M.D.C.) with a *laser finger blaster* for assassination missions (1D4 M.D.; 300 foot/91 m range) and *climb cord* (30 ft/9 m length; wrist). Finally, a small *explosive device* is secretly implanted in their skulls. If the character goes AWOL, the device is detonated, automatically killing the Juicer. Removing the device requires a roll on Medical Doctor (at -20%) or M.D. in Cybernetics skill (no penalty) and requires surgical facilities. A failure on the roll causes the device to detonate, killing the patient and inflicting 1D6 M.D. to a 10 foot (3 m) radius!

6. Saving Throw Bonuses: +4 to save versus psionics, +4 to save vs mind control (psionic and chemical), +6 to save vs toxic gases, poisons, and other drugs, and +3 to save vs horror factor.

7. Enhanced Healing: Standard: Heals four times faster than normal, +20% to save versus coma/death. Virtually impervious to pain, as per the normal Juicer.

8. Low Life Span: Standard for Juicers: 5 years plus 4D6 months.

O.C.C. Skills:
Speaks American 98%
Basic Math (+12%)
Radio: Basic (+10%)
Pilot Hovercraft (+15%)
Pilot Tank & APC (+15%)
Read Sensory Equipment (+10%)
Intelligence (+10%)
W.P. Energy Pistol
W.P. Energy Rifle
W.P. Knife
Hand to Hand: Expert
Hand to Hand: Expert can be changed to Hand to Hand: Martial Arts at the cost of one "other" skill, or assassin, if evil.

O.C.C. Related Skills: Select seven other skills. Plus select one additional skill and a W.P. at level three, two at level six, and one at levels nine and twelve. All new skills start at level one proficiency.
Communications: Any (+5%)
Domestic: Any
Electrical: Basic Electronics only.
Espionage: Any (+10%)
Mechanical: Automotive only (+5%)
Medical: Paramedic only.
Military: Any (+15%)
Physical: Any
Pilot: Any (+10%); except robots, power armor, tanks, APCs and combat aircraft skills.
Pilot Related: Any (+5%)
Rogue: Any
Science: Math and chemistry only.
Technical: Any (+5%)
W.P.: Any
Wilderness: Any.

Secondary Skills: The character also gets to select five secondary skills from the list. These are additional areas of knowledge that do not get the benefit of the bonuses listed in parentheses. All secondary skills start at the base skill level. Secondary skills are limited (any, only, none) as previously indicated on the list.

Standard Equipment: Coalition Special Trooper Armor with FIWS weapon built into forearm (-5% prowl penalty, 115 M.D.C., 25 lbs with Forearm Integral Weapon System, very expensive, using special M.D.C. alloys; has all standard features).

Standard issued weapons include a choice of the new CP-40 laser rifle, C-50 "Dragonfire", C-29 "Hellfire" or the old C-14 "Fire-Breather" or C-27 Heavy plasma cannon, plus vibro-knife, energy pistol sidearm (typically the old C-18 pistol), 8-10 E-Clips per weapon, 4 reloads for the grenade launcher (48 grenades), three signal flares, survival knife, distancing binoculars, robot medical kit, utility belt, uniform, dress uniform, bio-comp and bio-monitor implants, drug harness (drugs must be added every 6-12 months), and food rations for two weeks.

Equipment available upon Assignment: Troopers on missions may be assigned a vehicle (usually something that's light and fast) and additional food and special equipment. They may even be given non-military issue for special missions. However, CS Juicers are *never* given access to power armor, robot vehicles, tanks, jet fighters or Death' Head transports. Most Juicers have a low security clearance.

Money: Food, clothing and basic services are provided for free, plus a monthly salary of 3,000 credits. Starts with one month's pay.

Cybernetics: In addition to the ones provided above, the character may have 1-3 additional cybernetic or bionic implants, although very few do, as a result of Juicer pride ("I ain't no 'Borg!"). Many feel the addition of cybernetics demeans being a Juicer.

Coalition Juicer Special Operative Cost: The military's cost to create a Coalition Juicer is approximately half a million, including bionics, body armor, weapons and equipment.

Juicers in Free Quebec

When Free Quebec became a Coalition State, it was forced by treaty to abandon the creation of Juicers and to discharge those serving in its army. It took five years for Quebec to comply and dismantle its four Juicer Battalions, some 8,000+ Juicers. By 40 P.A. there were no Juicers in Quebec's Armed Forces — at least not on the official rosters and tables of organization.

In reality, the Quebec government secretly moved several augmentation facilities to the trader's town of Old Bones, in the ruins of the pre-Rifts city of Quebec. Old Bones is allegedly an independent town, but is secretly under the control of the Free Quebec government, which uses the town both as an intelligence-gathering resource (enemies of the Coalition often foolishly talk freely in Old Bones), and to maintain a small covert army of Juicers, Crazies and other special operatives. The code name for this secret operation is the **Liberty Reserve**.

The Liberty Reserve is an unofficial army covertly trained, assembled and maintained without the knowledge of the other Coalition States, especially Chi-Town. As its code name implies, the operation is meant to preserve Quebec's freedom, both from the enemies of humankind and, if necessary, from the Coalition itself! The plan was drafted years ago, when Free Quebec was being pressured to abandon its Glitter Boy armed forces. The Quebecoi leaders feared that civil war might erupt within the Coalition one day, and that their state must be prepared. Since such a war has been declared, the Juicers in the Liberty Reserve have been reinstated as part of the Free Quebec Armed Forces and includes roughly 10,000 Juicers. An estimated two battalions (1280 troops), volunteers from the Army, are expected to under go Juicer conversion within the next 60 days! In addition, Free Quebec expects to bolster its ranks with at least 1500 to 3000 mercenary Juicers and Crazies. **Note:** Chi-Town Intelligence Division knows that Quebec has secretly maintained a Juicer force, but believes it to be less than 2000 strong; they too estimate an additional 1500 to 3000 mercenary Juicers and Crazies to join their forces. However, this grossly underestimates their real numbers which should top out at around 15,000 augmented troops (most of which are Juicers)!

The leader of the Liberty Reserve, renamed the **Liberty Army Corps**, is *General Maurice LeNoir,* an 8th level CS Military Specialist. General LeNoir is a patriot who puts Free Quebec's interests above all other things, including the rest of the Coalition States and even humanity at large. General LeNoir continues to operate from a hidden base built under Old Bones. At this base, a small army of 1000 Juicers and about 500 other augmented soldiers, including 'Borgs and Crazies, are constantly maintained. These are the General's elite troops (1D4+5 average level of experience). They are sent out on missions of reconnaissance, sabotage, seek and destroy and other covert operation against the encroaching enemy. These soldiers do not wear the standard uniforms and pretend to be independent adventurers or mercenaries. The Juicers are supposed to serve for a period of two years and then accept the detox process and partial or full bionic reconstruction as a reward and continue to operate in the service of their country. However, with the war against the Coalition States, as many as 60% of these dedicated fanatics are likely to refuse detox and fight as Juicers to the bitter end!

Free Quebec's Juicers use the standard augmentation, but their training is usually more extensive and includes the *Juicer Assassin* and *Juicer Scout O.C.C.s* among their forces.

CS Nautical Specialist

By Julius Rosenstein with material by Siembieda

There are several waterways and large bodies of water in the proximity of the Coalition States. The most notable include the Great Lakes, particularly Lake Michigan (near Chi-Town), and Lake Superior (near Iron Heart), the Missouri river (going through CS Missouri), the Mississippi River and the Gulf of Mexico (near Lone Star). This led to the creation of the Naval Advisory Commission (NAC), a special branch of the Coalition Army. Originally it dealt with trouble on the Great Lakes which are as large and deep as many seas and alive with ley line activity and supernatural menaces. However, as Emperor Prosek looks toward territorial expansion and increasing the strength of his military, the NAC will soon branch off from the Army to become its own separate military force.

Although officially designated as "Sea Devils," the Nautical Specialists are better known by their nickname "Naughty Boys," much to their chagrin. Service as a Naughty Boy is somewhat different than their land-based Dead Boy counterparts. The men and women of the Nautical Specialist Service (NSS) are specifically trained for nautical operations and are quite expert in sea operations, particularly on the Great Lakes, and coastal maneuvers. They are skilled in the piloting, strategy and tactics of small boats and warships, SCUBA, underwater demolitions and underwater operations. They are not as formidable on dry land, but handle themselves well in an emergency.

It is only a matter of a few years before the NAC becomes the CS Navy, but until the Coalition States formally establishes its Navy (with posts on the Great Lakes and in the Gulf of Mexico), the Nautical Specialist is regarded as part of the army. Thus, Naughty Boys currently have ranks like sergeant, major, and generals, instead of their naval equivalents of chief petty officer, commander, and admirals. At present, the NSS is still considered somewhat of a "stepchild" by the General Staff and is often given lower priority for equipment. Many of its senior officers are transplanted "landlubbers" who regard this assignment as a sort of punishment duty. However, there are increasingly more Naughty Boys (especially among the noncoms and junior officers) who started with the NSS and can see the potential of their service. Emperor Prosek has been quietly building a naval base and headquarters at Lone Star.

Most NAC operations utilize small, close-knit units of Nautical Specialists and RPA power armor troops assigned to patrol boats and small warships. Consequently, these forces have considerably more freedom then the average CS soldier when it comes to the manner in which they apply themselves to their assignments. These sailors have begun to build a reputation for being tough lone-wolves who are independent, strong and resourceful. This, and word beginning to spread about the Emperor's turning NAC into a separate branch of the military, has attracted an increasing number of talented and dedicated recruits looking forward to an exciting career in the Coalition Navy!

Attribute Requirements: P.E. and P.P. 12 or higher.

O.C.C. Skills:

Basic Math (+10%)
Radio: Basic (+10%)
Navigation (+10%)
Read Sensory Equipment (+10%)
Weapon Systems (+10%)
Pilot Boat: Sail Type
Pilot Boat: Motor & Hydrofoils
Pilot Boat: Of Choice
Swimming (+20%)
SCUBA (+15%)
Underwater Demolitions (+10%)
Wilderness Survival (+10%)
W.P. Knife
W.P. Energy Rifle
Hand to Hand: Expert
Hand to hand: expert can be changed to martial arts at the cost of one "O.C.C. Related Skills."

O.C.C. Related Skills: Select eight other skills. Select two additional skills at levels three, six, ten and fourteen.

Communications: Any (+10%)
Domestic: Any (+5%; +10% to fishing)
Electrical: Basic electronics only.
Espionage: Intelligence and interrogation only.
Mechanical: Basic mechanics only.
Medical: Paramedic only.
Military: Any (+5)
Physical: Any
Pilot: Any, except robots, power armor, tanks, APCs and combat aircraft (+10% water vehicles only).
Pilot Related: Any
Rogue: None
Science: Math and astronomy only (+10%)
Technical: Any (+10%)
W.P.: Any
Wilderness: Any (+5%)

Secondary Skills: The character also gets to select six secondary skills from the list. These are additional areas of knowledge that do not get the benefit of the bonuses listed in parentheses. All secondary skills start at the base skill level. Secondary skills are limited (any, only, none) as previously indicated in the list.

Standard Equipment: Standard Coalition "Dead Boy" body armor, energy sidearm of choice, CP-40 or C-12 energy rifle, four additional E-clips for the rifle, survival knife, robot medical kit, pocket computer, portable language translator, pocket compass, flashlight, pocket laser distancer, uniform, dress uniform, backpack, utility belt, air filter, and canteen. Most are assigned as crew members to a particular patrol boat or warship.

Equipment Available Upon Assignment: Water, air, and ground vehicles, including nautical robot vehicles, power armor and conventional military vehicles. Most weapon types, harpoons, depth charges, torpedoes, extra ammunition, equipment (camera, sensory), and food rations for weeks. Also has access to other equipment on an as needed basis, with the commanding officer deciding if the item(s) are really necessary (If the officer doesn't like the character(s), the availability of items may be very limited).

Money: The Nautical Specialist gets a roof over his head, food, clothing, and all other basics provided free as a soldier, as well as access to military facilities. Monthly salary of 1800 credits and the character starts off with one month's pay.

Cybernetics: None to start with, but implantation can be authorized. Any of the bionics and cybernetics described in the **Rifts® RPG** *may* be approved. In addition, the Game Master *may* consider and allow any of the systems described in **Rifts® Japan, Rifts® Underseas** and **Rifts® Triax and the NGR.** The availability of bionic systems from other World Books is left entirely to the discretion of the Game Master. Note that soldiers cannot purchase *unauthorized* bionic systems.

Note: All NSS officers are literate in American (a requirement).

CS Ranger

Coalition Military version of a *Wilderness Scout.*

The Coalition Ranger is the military version of the Wilderness Scout O.C.C., Like the adventurer O.C.C. they are knowledgeable about nature and wilderness survival (although not quite as skilled), but much of their training focuses on tracking human prey, and guerilla warfare. Rangers are frequently deployed on reconnaissance, seek and destroy, and guerilla warfare missions against the enemy. They are also skilled at hunting down and capturing or destroying AWOL troops, escaped prisoners, refugees, monsters, Psi-Stalkers and other Wilderness Scouts. They are resourceful, cunning and expert in setting traps and utilizing hit and run tactics.

Also like their adventurer counterpart, the CS Ranger is typically a rough and tumble character who enjoys tests of skill and physical prowess. Of all the CS operatives, the Ranger and Special Forces are most likely to be sent on long-range missions into the hostile wilderness for extended periods of time. They are also one of the few military O.C.C.s that may be dispatched on a mission as an individual, pair, or a small group of 4-6 rather than a squad of 6-10 or a platoon of 40 troops. This also means the Ranger is among the most likely to fraternize with the enemy. Rangers are notorious for temporarily joining forces with (and befriending) D-bees, dragons, mercs and practitioners of magic while on assignment in the wilderness. Without question, they are the most tolerant soldiers in the Coalition Army in regard to nonhumans, so-called monsters and sorcerers! Even more amazing, their tolerance and association with undesirables rarely interferes with their mission or loyalty to the Coalition States. In fact, their association with nonhuman adventurers and mercenaries often helps to assure the success of the mission. Most experienced Rangers (3rd level and higher) will have several connections and "associates" among mercenary organizations and "outlaws."

A typical Ranger reconnaissance squad or long-range patrol consists of 2-4 Rangers, 1-2 Commandos or Special Forces, 2-3 Dog Boys and one Psi-Stalker. Sometimes one or two Juicers or cyborgs replace the commando or Special Forces.

A typical Ranger Guerilla squad is basically the same, but will usually have a total of ten troops and is more likely to include a Juicer or two and an EOD Specialist.

Attribute Requirements: I.Q. 9, P.E. 12 or higher. A high P.S., P.P. and M.E. are also suggested but are not requirements.

O.C.C. Skills:
Radio: Basic (10%)
Camouflage (+10%)
Climb (+15%)
Hunting
Prowl (+10%)
Identify Plants (20%)
Land Navigation (+20%)
Wilderness Survival (+20%)
Track Animals (+10%)
Track Humanoids (+15%)
Trap Construction (+15%)
Trap/Mine Detection (10%)
Language: Speaks American at 98% and one additional language of choice (+25%)
Pilot: One of choice (+15%)
W.P.: Energy Rifle
Hand to Hand: Basic
  Hand to Hand: Basic can be changed to expert at the cost of two "O.C.C. related skills" or martial arts for the cost of three skill selections.

O.C.C. Related Skills: Select seven other skills. Plus select two additional skills at level three, and one at level six, nine, and twelve. All new skills start at level one proficiency.
Communications: Any (+5%)
Domestic: Any (+10%)
Electrical: None
Espionage: Any (+5%)
Mechanical: None
Medical: First aid or holistic medicine only.
Military: Any (+10%), except demolition (any).
Physical: Any, except acrobatics and wrestling.
Pilot: Any (+5%), except robots, power armor and combat aircraft.
Pilot Related: Any
Rogue: Any
Science: Any
Technical: Any (+10%)
W.P.: Any
Wilderness: Any (+15%)

Secondary Skills: The character also gets to select six secondary skills from the previous list. These are additional areas of knowledge that do not get the advantage of the bonus listed in parentheses. All secondary skills start at the base skill level. Also, skills are limited (any, only, none) as previously indicated in the list.

Standard Equipment: A suit of light or heavy, camouflage "Dead Boy" body armor, uniform, dress uniform, tinted goggles, PDD pocket audio recorder, pocket laser distancer, flashlight, pocket mirror, cigarette lighter, 100 ft (30.5 m) of lightweight rope, small hammer, four spikes, 1D6 animal snares, infrared distancing binoculars, survival knife, vibro-knife or saber, choice of a CP-40, CP-50 or any old style CS energy rifle with telescopic sight, four additional E-clips for the weapon, knapsack, backpack, utility belt, air filter, gas mask, and canteen.

Equipment Available Upon Assignment: 1D4 hand grenades, 1D4 smoke grenades and/or 1D4 signal flares, heavy weapons, optical enhancements, camera equipment, light vehicle, food rations and non-regulation weapons and armor (mainly

for the purpose of disguise and infiltration into enemy territory).

Money: Base pay is a salary of 1700 credits a month. Starts with one month's salary.

Cybernetics: None to start, but augmented hearing, optics, clock calendar and gyro-compass are common implants. Also see **Rifts® : Triax & the NGR** and **Rifts® Japan** for additional types of cybernetics.

main base of operations is at the East Saint Louis Rift more commonly known as *The Devil's Gate*. A RCSG company is also active in the ruins of Old Chicago where Rift activity is frequent and right in Chi-Town's backyard. It is their mission to study and learn about how the Rifts and related dimensional phenomena work and how they might be controlled. In addition, these troops are charged with the "containment" of alien forces and beings that emerge from these dimensional gateways. "Containment" typically means the capture, study and/or extermination of the things that emerge. To accomplish this, mega-damage containment and research stations are constructed at some of the most well-known ley line nexuses where Rift activity is frequent. A huge complex is nearing completion at the Devil's Gate in East St. Louis. **Note:** RPA power armor and robot troops and

Elite RPA Pilot

Officer's Uniform

RCSG Scientist

Rift Control Study Group (RCSG)

The RCSG group is a highly specialized branch of the service composed primarily of combat scientists who are charged with the study and containment of the Rifts. Their headquarters and

their mecha, as well as Psi-Hounds and the occasional Commando or Special Forces troops, are used extensively by the RCSG as a combat support and "containment" force at these outposts.

The research of the *Rift Control Study Group (RCSG)* often takes the scientists into such no-man's lands as the Magic Zone, Chi-Town Ruins, Old Detroit, Calgary and other locations where ley lines, magic and Rift activity is strong. Furthermore, as scientific experts on ley lines and magic (as opposed to practitioners of magic who have a superior metaphysical understanding of how Rifts and magic works), the RCSG scientists are also assigned to special mission teams and posts where the supernatural, magic and/or Rifts may be a factor, or where their skills in math, computers, information gathering, and other areas may make them ideal for missions of sabotage, rescue and spying. Remember, while these are men of science, they are also trained soldiers. They are clever, inventive, observant, and can handle themselves in combat.

Special O.C.C. Abilities:

1. Lore — Geomancy or Ley Lines (exclusive to the RCSG scientist): A study of ley lines, burial mounds, places of magic power, megaliths, and geomantic beliefs and practices (past and present). Geomancy and ley lines are the belief that certain places on earth are polarized with an unknown energy or forces that can heal, cause paranormal phenomena, attract supernatural forces, or open dimensional gateways. The study includes "known" locations of such places, as well as the many theories behind them and the legacy of legends, mysteries, disappearances and dangers linked to each. The skill will provide the character with insight about the areas and enable him/her to recognize specific, known places of power, as well as to recognize unknown megalithic markers of these revered or feared places. **Base Skill:** 30% +5% per level of experience.

2. Ley line Drifting: The character can open himself to the ley line's energies and walk or float through the air along the length of a ley line. The maximum speed is a mere Spd 10, but it is relaxing and does not cause exertion or fatigue. Best of all, the scientist does not need any personal P.P.E. to do this, but draws on the ambient P.P.E. of the ley line. Applicable only to the RCSG soldier; he cannot magically enable others to float along with him.

3. Ley Line Rejuvenation: When standing on a ley line or nexus, the RCSG scientist can absorb ley line energy and use it to heal himself! The natural rate of healing is doubled. To do this, the character must concentrate on healing while relaxing on a ley line. In addition, the character can use a ley line or nexus to perform an instant rejuvenation as often as once every 24 hours. After about 10 minutes of concentration, 2D6 hit points and 2D6 S.D.C. are magically restored; no personal P.P.E. is needed to do this. Effective only on oneself.

4. Recognize enchantment: Just as a doctor can recognize flu symptoms and disease, the RCSG scientist can recognize the influence of magic that charms, hypnotizes, or otherwise causes mind control (including trances, domination, compulsion, quest, etc.). This ability also includes identifying magic sickness, curses, and supernatural or magic possession. Illusions, metamorphosis, and psionic powers do not count as enchantment. **Base Skill:** 35% +5% per level of experience

5. Recognize magic: The scientist has a certain percentage chance to recognize a magic item by shape, inscription, magic symbols or intuition (gut feeling). It's important to understand that while the character may know something has magical properties, he does not know what powers the item may have or how to use it. **Base Skill:** 10% +3% per level of experience.

6. Bonuses: +2 to save vs horror factor at levels 2, 4, 8 and 12, +1 to save vs magic at levels 3 and 8, +1 to save vs possession.

Attribute Requirements: I.Q. 10 and M.E. 10 or higher. A high P.E. and P.P. are also helpful but not required.

O.C.C. Skills:
Math: Basic (+20%)
Math: Advanced (+20%)
Literacy: America (+30%)
Language: American at 98% and one of Choice (+20%)
Chemistry (+20%)
Computer Operation (+20%)
Computer Programming (+15%)
Computer Hacking (+10%)
Radio: Basic (+15%)
Intelligence (+10%)
Lore: Demon/Monster (+20%)
Lore: Magic (+20%)
Pilot: One of choice (+10%)
Climbing (+15%)
Running
W.P. Energy Rifle
W.P.: One of Choice
Hand to Hand: Basic
 Hand to Hand: Basic can be changed to expert at the cost of two "O.C.C. related skills" or martial arts for the cost of three skill selections.

O.C.C. Related Skills: Select four skills from one of the following areas of special training: Communications, Electrical, Mechanical, Medical, Military (typically field armorer, demolitions, and nuclear/biological/chemical warfare), Science or Technical — all of these special MOS skills get a +15% skill bonus. Three other skills can also be selected from any of the available categories at level one, and two skills at levels four, eight and twelve.

Communications: Any (+10%)
Domestic: Any
Electrical: Any (+10%)
Espionage: Intelligence and Wilderness Survival (+10%)
Mechanical: Any (+10%)
 Medical: Any (+10%)
Military: Any (+15%)
 Physical: Any, except boxing and acrobatics.
Pilot: Any (+10%), except robots, power armor, tanks, APCs and combat aircraft.
Pilot Related: Any (+10%)
Rogue: None
Science: Any (+15%)
Technical: Any (+10%; +20% to Literacy and Language skills)
W.P.: Any
Wilderness: Any

Secondary Skills: The character gets three secondary skills at level one, and two additional skills at levels three, six, nine and twelve from the previous list. These are additional areas of knowledge that do not get the advantage of the bonus listed in parentheses. All secondary skills start at the base skill level. Also, skills are limited (any, only, none) as previously indicated in the list.

Standard Equipment: Light Coalition "Dead Boy" body armor, choice of energy rifle and energy sidearm, four extra E-clips for the rifle, vibro-knife, survival knife, dress uniform, fine leather gloves, a box of disposable surgical gloves (100 per box), 2D4 specimen containers, 20 medium-size plastic bags, PC-3000 hand-held computer, PDD pocket audio recorder, portable video camera, portable language translator, pocket laser distancer, pocket flashlight, portable tool kit, laser scalpel (equivalent to Wilk's model), RMK robot medical kit, IRMSS Internal Robot Medical Surgeon System, first-aid kit, portable laboratory, backpack, two satchels, utility belt, utility/combat harness, air filter & gas mask, lab coat, uniform, dress uniform, and canteen.

Equipment Available Upon Assignment: Explosives, heavy weapons, sensory equipment, camera/film and recording equipment, medical equipment, communications and surveillance equipment, optical enhancements, camera equipment, mine detection equipment, EOD equipment, experimental weapons and equipment, radiation suit (remember, the "Dead Boy" body armor is not an environmental suit), hovercycle or other vehicle, food rations and so on. In addition, the character has access to most military medical, laboratory and computer facilities. A RCSG scientist typically has mid to high level security clearance depending on the character's level of experience and history in the military.

Money: The character gets a roof over his head, food, clothing, and all other basics provided free as part of his pay, as well as access to military facilities. His monthly salary is 1900 credits, plus combat pay. Starts off with 1D4×1000 credits.

Cybernetics: Start with clock calendar, gyro-compass, molecular analyzer and headjack with basic ear amplification. Additional cybernetics and bionics *may* be authorized.

RPA "Fly Boy" Ace

The Coalition Army includes a branch that specializes in piloting combat aircraft, power armor and robots, the 53rd Group. Like the RPA elite SAMAS power armor and robot pilot, the RPA Aces (also known as "Fly Boys") are adept at piloting power armor but specialize in flying aircraft, particularly the many different *skycycles*.

Pilots of the 53rd Group are required to complete a rigorous training course that hones skills taught in RPA school and introduces new techniques. Training includes the operation of various vehicle types, night-flying by instrumentation, Special Ops fire support procedures and radar-avoidance techniques. Hopeful Aces spend countless hours mastering these skills in simulators and the cockpit before flying their first mission. At the end of the course, those who pass are issued the 53rd combat patch and begin to fly missions to drop off, resupply, drop and extract troops and provide cover and support fire. They also engage in rescue missions, surgical strikes, air patrols, strafing runs, fly-bys and full scale, frontline power armor assaults.

"Fly Boys" tend to be brazen, wisecracking and arrogant, but no matter how annoying they can be during the quiet times, they are always reliable in a firefight and renowned for their daring and courage.

Special O.C.C. Abilities:

1. Pilot Skycycles: Base skill is 60% +3% per level of experience. This skill enables the "Fly Boys" to expertly pilot any type of skycycle or small, one to four man aircraft with astounding proficiency, grace and speed.

2. Pilot Death's Head Transports: Base skill is 67% +3% per level of experience. The RPA Ace is the only O.C.C. authorized and specially trained to pilot the Death's Head transports and similar huge flying vehicles. Characters with aircraft or fighter jet skills can attempt to pilot the vehicle but suffer a -30% skill penalty and -25% maximum speed and other capabilities.

3. Bonuses: +2 on initiative, +2 to save vs horror factor, and +2D6 to physical S.D.C.

Attribute Requirements: I.Q. 10, P.P. 12 or higher. A high P.E. and M.E. is also suggested but are not requirements.

O.C.C. Skills:
Literacy: American (+30%)
Math: Basic (+20%)
Radio: Basic (+20%)
Computer Operation (+15%)
Land Navigation (+10%)
Navigation (+10%)
Wilderness Survival (+10%)
Read Sensory Equipment (+10%)
Weapon Systems (+10%)
Parachuting (+20%)
Pilot: Robots & Power Armor (+20%)
Pilot: Robot Combat Elite (two of choice)
Pilot: Jet Fighter (+15%)
Pilot: Combat Helicopter (+20%)
Pilot: Hovercycles/Motorcycles (+12%)
Pilot: One of Choice (+15%)
W.P.: Energy Rifle
Hand to Hand: Basic
Hand to Hand: Basic can be changed to expert at the cost of two "O.C.C. related skills" or martial arts for the cost of three skill selections.

O.C.C. Related Skills: Select six other skills. Plus select one additional skill at levels two, five, eight, and twelve. All new skills start at level one proficiency.
Communications: Any (+10%)
Domestic: Any
Electrical: Basic only.
Espionage: None.
Mechanical: Basic only.
Medical: First aid only.
Military: Any (+10%), except any demolitions.
Physical: Any, except acrobatics and wrestling.
Pilot: Any, except warships (+10%, but +15% on all aircraft and modes of flying)
Pilot Related: Any (+10%)
Rogue: Streetwise only.
Science: Any (+10%)
Technical: Any (+10%)
W.P.: Any   Wilderness: Land Navigation and Hunting only.

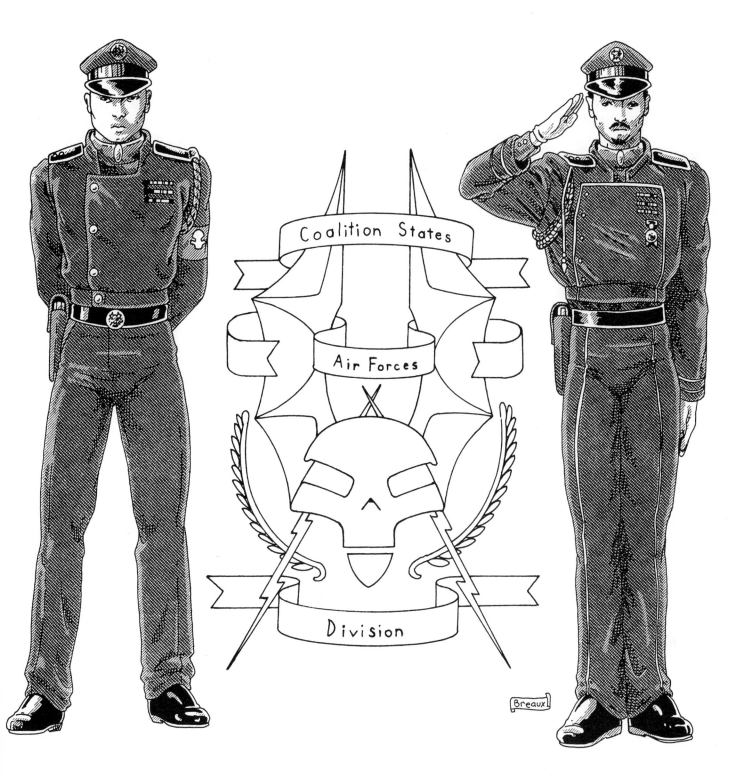

Secondary Skills: The character also gets to select five secondary skills from the previous list. These are additional areas of knowledge that do not get the advantage of the bonus listed in parentheses. All secondary skills start at the base skill level. Also, skills are limited (any, only, none) as previously indicated in the list.

Standard Equipment: Choice of light or heavy "Dead Boy" body armor, a flight suit, uniform, dress uniform, fine leather gloves, tinted goggles, oxygen mask, PC-3000 hand-held computer, portable translator, robot medical kit, pocket flashlight, portable tool kit, survival knife, CP-40 or C-50 energy rifle, CP-30 Officer's pistol, four additional E-clips for rifle, one for the pistol, backpack, utility belt, canteen and hovercycle or jeep.

Equipment Available Upon Assignment: Hand grenades, explosives, any weapon appropriate for the mission, optical enhancements, camera and surveillance equipment, food rations and any vehicle, power armor (including all SAMAS) and robot vehicles appropriate for the mission and which the ace is skilled at piloting, as well as access to military facilities. Most RPA "Fly Boys" have mid-level to top security clearance.

Money: Typically start as a Sergeant 1st Class and a base salary of 2050 credits a month. Starts with 1D6×1000 credits.

Cybernetics: Starts with a clock calendar, gyro-compass and universal headjack and basic ear implant. Most avoid other implants other than bio-systems to restore injured limbs and organs. Any additional cyber augmentation must be authorized by the Army.

Special Forces

The Special Forces of the Coalition Military is the elite of the elite fighting troops. While some would argue that they are simply glorified commandos, the troops in Special Forces are among the toughest, smartest, meanest special operatives in the CS. Unlike the commando, their training does not only focus on espionage, surgical strikes, sabotage, anti-terrorist measures and guerilla combat, but a special MOS specialty in communications, mechanical engineering, rogue skills and other areas. This unique area of study provides a Special Forces team with an incredible range and versatility to handle anything that is thrown their way. They are also deployed as members of reactionary units within the Coalition States to quell uprisings or other threats to the internal security of the Coalition Military and States.

These resourceful, cunning and patient soldiers are often used as members of long-range patrols and covert teams outside the borders of the Coalition States for extended periods of time, and deep within enemy territory. Special Forces troops are frequently expected to operate with very little support from the rest of the army and engage in covert operations that are so secret that there may be no official record of it. They are also one of the few military O.C.C.s that may be dispatched on a mission as an individual, pair, or a small group of 4-6 rather than a squad of 6-10 or a platoon of 40 troops. Likewise, one or two Special Forces soldiers are frequently assigned to other teams, squads or companies (sometimes without being identified as Special Ops) for special missions and outposts.

This also means the Special Forces operative, like the Ranger, is among the most likely to fraternize with the enemy. They may temporarily join forces with (and befriend) D-bees, mercenaries, bandits and practitioners of magic while on assignment in the wilderness or enemy territory. However, they are far less tolerant of the enemy than the Ranger, especially D-bees, the supernatural and practitioners of magic. Such "associations" are usually arrangements of convenience that are severed as soon as the soldier's mission is completed. In fact, the Special Forces character may betray, turn in, or even kill his one-time comrades if it seems appropriate and the opportunity makes itself available. However, such dirty tricks are usually reserved for someone who has gotten on the character's bad side or someone who is completely despicable. The Special Forces operative, like any good secret agent, understands the value of having good connections. Consequently, many Special Operations agents maintain loose associations with select nonhuman adventurers, mercenaries, nonhumans and outlaws.

Special Forces is such an elite division that it even has its own uniforms, insignia/patch, and special "Dead Boy" body armor — roughly equivalent to the new heavy body armor in M.D.C. protection and features, but with its own unique, Death's head and armor styling, with a more sinister skull face plate and helmet. They even get their own, black, Special Forces SAMAS with the same skull styling and special weapon features (see the equipment section for details). The IAR-Hellraiser was also designed with Special Forces, Commandos and RPA Aces in mind.

Attribute Requirements: I.Q. 10, M.E. 10, P.S. 12, P.P. 14, P.E. 12 or higher.

O.C.C. Skills:
Math: Basic (+20%)
Radio: Basic (+15%)
Radio: Scrambler (+10%)
Language: American at 98% and one of Choice (+20%)
Land Navigation (+10%)
Intelligence (+10%)
Streetwise (+16%)
Lore: Demon/Monster (+10%)
Pilot: One of choice (+10%)
Pilot: Robots & Power Armor (+10%)
Pilot: Robot Combat Elite: Special Forces SAMAS
Wilderness Survival (+15%)
Climbing (+15%)
Prowl (+15%)
Running
Boxing
W.P. Energy Pistol
W.P. Energy Rifle
W.P.: Two of Choice
Hand to Hand: Commando; this skill cannot be changed.

O.C.C. Related Skills: Select four skills from one of the following areas of special training: Communications, Espionage, Mechanical, Military, Piloting, Rogue, Weapon Proficiencies, or Wilderness —all of these special MOS skills get a +15% skill bonus. Two other skills can also be selected from any of the available categories at levels one, four, eight and twelve.

Communications: Any (+10%)
Domestic: Any
Electrical: Any (+5%)
Espionage: Any (+15%)
Mechanical: Any (+5%)
Medical: Any (+10%)
Military: Any (+15%)
Physical: Any
Pilot: Any (+10%)
Pilot Related: Any (+5%)
Rogue: Any (+4%)
Science: Any
Technical: Any (+10%; +15% to Literacy and Language skills)
W.P.: Any
Wilderness: Any (+5%)

Secondary Skills: The character gets four secondary skills at level one, and two additional skills at levels three, seven, eleven and fifteen from the previous list. These are additional areas of knowledge that do not get the advantage of the bonus listed in parentheses. All secondary skills start at the base skill level. Also, skills are limited (any, only, none) as previously indicated in the list.

Standard Equipment: Special Forces "Dead Boy" body armor, choice of energy rifle and energy sidearm, four extra E-clips for each, four explosive grenades, two smoke grenades, two flares, vibro-knife, survival knife, RMK robot medical kit, IRMSS Internal Robot Medical Surgeon System, utility belt, air filter & gas mask, uniform, dress uniform, canteen, and an additional non-energy weapon of choice (typically S.D.C. automatic weapon, or bow and arrow). Conventional military vehicle of choice (motorcycle, jeep, hovercycle, etc.) for daily use.

Equipment Available Upon Assignment: Any type of body armor, explosives if demolitions is a known skill and necessary for the mission, any type of weapon, extra ammunition, optical enhancements, camera or surveillance equipment, sensory equipment and food rations for weeks. Non-regulation weapons, armor, equipment and vehicles may also be issued to Special Forces operatives, mainly for the purpose of disguise and infiltration. In addition, the character has access to military facilities. Most Special Forces operatives have mid to high level security clearance, with the highest clearance for top ranked and trusted officers.

Vehicles can include a simple hovercycle, car, conventional military vehicles, or jet pack to Special Forces SAMAS, IAR-Hellraiser, Spider-Skull Walker, tanks, APC and so on. The exact type of equipment will depend on the mission, the commanding officer and availability of items at base.

Money: The character gets a roof over his head, food, clothing, and all other basics provided free as part of his pay, as well as access to military facilities. His monthly salary starts at 1900 credits, plus combat pay. Starts off with 1D6×1000 credits. All Special Forces troops begin at the rank of either corporal or sergeant depending upon their performance during training.

Cybernetics: Typically starts with clock calendar, gyro-compass, radar detector, oxygen storage cell (lung implant), and either a multi-optic eye or type AA-1 cyber-disguise. Additional cyber-systems may be awarded for exemplary service, heroics and special missions. Many (50%) Special Forces eventually acquire 1D4 additional implants, some (20%) have systems equal to the Headhunter.

Coalition War Machine

Intro by Kevin Siembieda
with additional text by Patrick Nowak

From the fragments of the American Empire, the single most powerful force established in North America since the Great Cataclysm is the Coalition States. As far back as most beings can remember, the skull-faced symbol of the Coalition borne by its fanatical power armored soldiers and robots have inspired terror and hatred throughout the Americas. The power of the army is so awesome that a CS diplomat just hinting at the possibility of invasion by "Dead Boy" soldiers has been known to make independent city-states and kingdoms crumble to the will of the Coalition States. Depending on one's point of view, the Coalition army is an unstoppable juggernaut that is either the greatest hope for the survival of humankind, or a constant source of danger and fear.

One on one, the Coalition Armed Forces can dismantle any other military force on the continent, but because such a victory would be pyrrhic and self-defeating, the government has refrained from doing so, at least until now. Even on the international level, the CS army is formidable, only slightly less so than the New German Republic and the Splugorth of Atlantis. The Gargoyle Empire would have the comparative upper hand only because of sheer numbers and supernatural power. The strength of Coalition forces comes not only from their powerful war machines and high technology, but from the spirit and commitment of its millions of fierce, fanatical soldiers and brilliant officers who embody the fighting spirit of the Coalition States. These elements combined with the universal support of the population and the charismatic leadership of Emperor Prosek, makes the Coalition Military a powerhouse with few peers.

The Military Machine

The Prosek family has skillfully built the national character of their nation around the ideal that it is the last bastion of humanity in North America. To protect humankind from supernatural creatures, alien invaders and magic, the citizens have been convinced of the need for a strong and ruthless military force —as characterized by their fearsome skull logos and designs. As the size of the army and weapon stockpiles grew, the military became increasingly active in all facets of CS civilization and society. The lowliest grunt was regarded as a dedicated, national hero entrusted with law enforcement, civil defense and the protection of humankind. The military not only engaged in all aspects of defense but also oversaw most scientific research and development, as well as the dissemination of technology, education and propaganda. By 53 P.A., the goals and actions of the army could not be separated from the governing body of the Coalition States or its people. Decades of aggressive military expansion followed and the CS grew into a world power.

The last six years have been comparatively quiet. The States remain threatening and omnipresent in the Old American Empire, but past decades of aggressive military expansion seem to be at an end. Everybody acknowledge that the Coalition States remained a power to be feared, but some wondered if their glory days were behind them. The CS military made threats and placed sanctions against such enemies as Tolkeen and the Federation of Magic, but no major offensives were launched. The Coalition government seemed mired in their own internal affairs. Overcrowding in the great cities, stalled expansion, growing dissension among member states (particularly Quebec) and other things led some to believe that the CS had overextended itself. During these years, the mighty Coalition Army seemed content to swallow tiny, neighboring communities and to lash out at helpless nonhumans. Opponents of the Coalition States were happy to see the Coalition war machine grind to a crawl. Some observers speculated that the power of the CS had peaked and was on a slow decline. Others believed the CS remained strong, but that future growth would come at a slower pace. Others, the Counsel of Learning at Lazlo and Erin Tarn among them, feared that this was the calm before the storm. They were right.

For approximately the last five years, the Coalition military has been engaged in a secret campaign to refit and improve their forces. The CS managed to make sweeping changes and dramatic improvements in an astonishingly short amount of time — adding an array of new power armor, bots, vehicles and weapons to their already formidable equipment. The greatest military power on the continent has reached new pinnacles of power and diversification. A huge standing army, representing over 10% of the population, armed with an arsenal of new high-tech weapons, experimental combat systems, and the resources of arguably the most powerful nation on Earth, is poised to strike. Brainwashed by State propaganda, the highly motivated "Dead Boys" are eager for war. Even the average citizens are amenable to the expansion of the empire through military actions. The Coalition war machine is ready to march.

CS Weapons & Equipment
By Kevin Siembieda

The following pages present the *new* weapons and equipment of the Coalition Armed Forces.

Many of the old designs like the UAR-1 Enforcer and IAR-2 Abolisher are being phased out, but will be used in some capacity for at least the next decade. Items like the old CA-1 and CA-2 Dead Boy body armor, PA-060A SAMAS and AFC-023 Skycycle have become the standard dress and equipment of the **Internal Security Specialists (ISS)**, thus giving the city defenders/police the distinctive and familiar old icons recognized by the civilian population, while the Army adopts its new, more frightening appearance.

Only the old style *FASSAR-20 Skelebots, AFC-050 Death's Head Transports* and *CR-003 Spider-Skull Walkers* remain in active military service.

Military Equipment Classifications:
C = Denotes hand-held military weapons.
CA = Denotes body armor classifications.
CR = Walker style robot vehicles.
PA = Power armor
AFC = Aircraft
APC = Armored Personnel Carrier/troop transport
IAR = Infantry Assault Robot
UAR = Urban Assault Robot
SAMAS = Strategic Armor Military Assault Suit; aka "Sam."

The Coalition States (CS) have a standardized army with standard weapons and equipment. Generally, the new CS weapons and equipment are standard issue to the soldiers of its new army. However, distant outposts will remain equipped with the old weapons and armor for several (1D4+2) years. Old weapons and equipment may also be issued for special assignments or in case of supply shortages of the new equipment. The old weapons (see the **Rifts® RPG**) are good, reliable items that have been in use for 15-40 years. They just aren't quite as powerful or versatile as many of the new models. Yet some veterans may prefer the old models.

Only Coalition Juicers, Scouts, Special Forces operatives and commissioned officers are allowed to use the old style CS weapons and equipment not of CS manufacture (Northern Gun, Triax, etc.) without special permission.

Likewise, the ISS, NTSET and PRP also continue to use a mix of old and new weapons. In many instances, these city defenders and law enforcement officers don't need weapons that have superior range, and heavy weapons are frequently inappropriate for urban combat (too destructive, putting civilians at risk). They often need light precision weapons and riot control items (stun, flash, smoke).

Note about Uranium Rounds: The Coalition government and military have both agreed to ban the use of Uranium Rounds for environmental reasons. Northern Gun, the Manistique Imperium and most other arms and munitions manufacturers also avoided the creation of U-Rounds for the same reason. As part of its agreement with the CS, Triax does not export U-Rounds to the Americas.

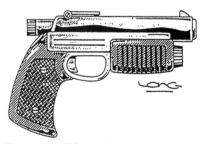

C-5 Pump Pistol

The C-5 pump pistol is an authorized knock-off of the Triax TX-5. The weapon fires high explosive cartridges/rounds which are much smaller than the conventional grenade, but packs a wallop. These explosive rounds are fired at a high velocity, have good range, and contain a powerful explosive charge. The blast is very concentrated, about one foot (0.3 m), unlike the larger grenades which affect an area 5-20 times larger. It is used primarily by CS commandos, Special Forces, and the occasional field officer. It is widely used by the ISS urban forces and even the occasional ISS Psi-Hound.

Weight: 5 lbs (2.25 kg)
Mega-Damage: 4D6 M.D.
Rate of Fire: Standard, see Modern Weapon Proficiency Section.

Maximum Effective Range: 800 feet (224 m)
Payload: 5 rounds, loaded manually one round at a time. A speed loader will load all five rounds in four seconds (one melee action) and costs 1200 credits.
Market Cost: 10,000 credits for the gun and 400 credits per round. Fair availability.

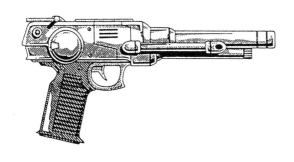

C-18 Laser Pistol — Old Style

This *was* the standard issue sidearm of the Coalition Army, but it is being replaced by the C-20 and CP-30 laser pistols.

Weight: 4 lbs (1.8 kg)
Mega-Damage: 2D4 M.D.
Rate of Fire: Standard, see Modern Weapon Proficiency Section.
Effective Range: 800 feet (244 m)
Payload: 10 shots (less efficient energy delivery system).
Black Market Cost: 12,000 credits.

C-20 Laser Pistol (New!)

This is the new, standard issue sidearm of the Coalition Army. It is primarily issued to officers, military police, guards and special operatives as well as ISS law enforcement officers. Its advantage is a heavier damage capacity without sacrificing its light weight, excellent balance, or range.

Weight: 3.5 lbs (1.57 kg)
Mega-Damage: 2D6 M.D.
Rate of Fire: Standard, see Modern Weapon Proficiency Section.
Effective Range: 800 feet (244 m)
Payload: 21 shots standard short clip or 30 with a long E-clip.
Black Market Cost: 16,000 credits.

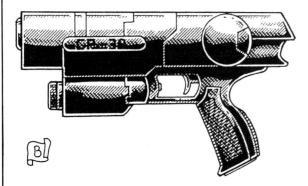

CP-30 Laser Pulse Pistol (New!)

This is the standard issue "officer's" sidearm of the Coalition Army. It is also used by Special Forces as well as NTSET law enforcement officers (monster hunters). It comes standard with laser targeting (+1 to strike). The multi-pulse firing capability provides heavy firepower in close combat.

Weight: 4 lbs (1.8 kg)

Mega-Damage: 2D4 M.D. per single blast or 4D6 M.D. per multiple pulse burst (three simultaneous shots).
Rate of Fire: Equal to the number of combined hand to hand attacks of its user (usually 3-6).
Effective Range: 600 feet (183 m)
Payload: 21 single shots (7 pulse blasts) per standard short E-clip, or 30 single shots (10 pulse blasts) with a long E-clip.
Special Payload: The standard E-Clip of the CP-30 can be replaced with a clip connected to an energy cable that connects to a portable hip or backpack carried energy canister (both are the same small size). The energy canister provides 72 single blasts or 24 triple blasts. The weight of the energy canister, pack included, is four pounds (1.8 kg). A dual backpack is also available, but is typically reserved for use with energy rifles. It has two energy canisters; when one is used up, the connector cable is removed and reattached to the second, full canister (takes one full melee round/15 seconds).
Laser Targeting: Add +1 to strike on an aimed shot.
Black Market Cost: 26,000 credits for the weapon; 90,000 for the portable generator.

C-10 Light Assault Laser Rifle — Old Style

The C-10 light laser rifle is an old, earlier version of the C-12 and greatly resembles the old C-12 heavy laser. It remains a favorite sniper rifle and is known for its accuracy and durability in the field.

Weight: 5 lbs (2.3 kg)
Mega-Damage: 2D6 M.D., no variable settings.
Rate of Fire: Aimed, burst, wild; see Modern Weapon Proficiencies.

Effective Range: 2000 feet (610 m)
Payload: 20 blasts from a standard E-Clip or 30 from a long E-Clip.
Laser Targeting: Add +3 to strike on an aimed shot, but only when the laser targeting system is functioning. No bonus when on the blink.
Black Market Cost: 16,000 credits for the rifle. Standard clip and recharge costs. An E-Clip canister cannot be used with this weapon.

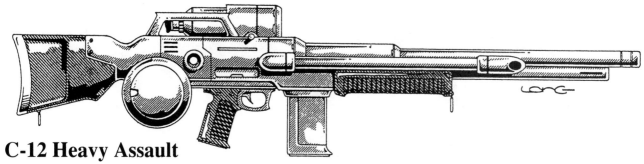

C-12 Heavy Assault Laser Rifle — Old Style

This was the standard weapon of the infantry, a sturdy and reliable rifle that can survive a great amount of combat abuse and activity without mechanical failure. The rifle has three settings, one S.D.C. and two M.D.C. The rifle can also be set to fire a single shot or a burst of five. Comes standard with a passive nightvision scope and laser targeting. It remains a favorite infantry workhorse and will remain in service for at least another decade.

Weight: 7 lbs (3.2 kg)
Mega-Damage: Setting one: 4D6 M.D. or Setting Two: 2D6 M.D.

S.D.C. Damage: Setting Three: 6D6 S.D.C.
Rate of Fire: Equal to the number of combined hand to hand attacks of its user (usually 3-6).
Effective Range: 2000 feet (610 m)
Payload: 20 M.D. blasts from standard E-Clip or 30 from a long E-Clip, plus another 30 can be added with one E-clip *canister*. Note that six S.D.C. shots equals one mega-damage blast.
Laser Targeting: Add +1 to strike on an aimed shot.
Black Market Cost: 20,000 credits for the rifle, 6000 credits for a new, fully charged, standard E-clip; 1500 for a recharge. An E-Clip canister costs 10,000 new and fully charged. A canister recharge costs 2000 credits.

C-14 "Fire Breather"

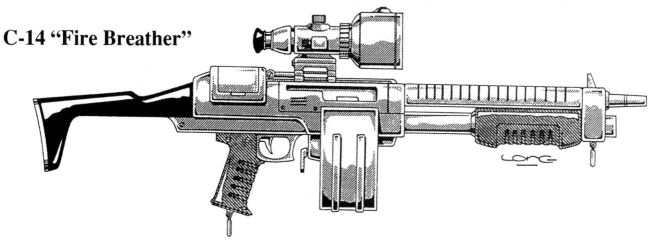

Assault Laser & Grenade Launcher — Old Style

A popular over and under heavy infantry weapon with high marks for durability and reliability in action. A laser comprises the top portion of the weapon and a pump action grenade launch-er is built-in under the laser barrel. Standard issue includes a passive nightvision scope. The CP-50 laser pulse rifle is intended to replace this weapon, but the C-14 will remain in service for at least another 5-10 years.

Weight: 10 lbs (4.5 kg)

Mega-Damage: Laser is 3D6 M.D., Grenades 2D6 M.D. to a blast area of 12 feet (3.6 m)

Rate of Fire: Laser: Equal to the number of combined hand to hand attacks of its user (usually 3-6).

Grenades: One aimed per each melee attack/action of the user or four fired in rapid succession (burst if all at same target, wild if sprayed into an area).

Effective Range: Laser is 2000 feet (610 m).

 Grenade Launcher is 1200 feet (365 m)

Payload: Laser is 20 blasts, Grenade Launcher is 12.

Reloading the Launcher: Requires one full melee, 15 seconds, to manually reload the grenade launcher. As always, reloading an E-Clip takes about five seconds or equal to one melee action/attack.

Black Market Cost: 30,000 credits and a hot commodity not commonly available. Grenades cost 550 credits apiece or 4500 a dozen. An E-Clip canister can not be added to this weapon.

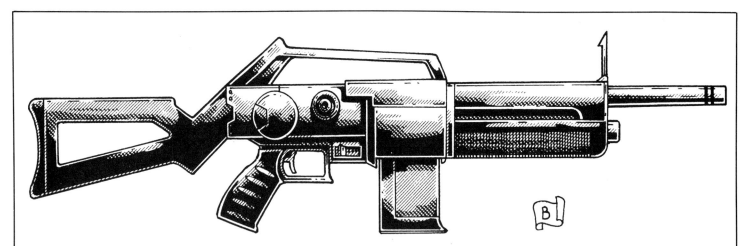

CP-40 Pulse Laser Rifle (New!)

The new Coalition infantry assault rifles are the CP-40 and CP-50. The advantage to both is increased firepower, rapid pulse firing action and durability. The CP-40 has four settings, two S.D.C. and two M.D. The rifle can also be set to fire a single shot or a pulse of three nearly simultaneous blasts. It comes standard with a passive nightvision scope and laser targeting.

Weight: 9 lbs (4.1 kg)

Mega-Damage: 2D6 M.D. per single laser blast or 6D6 M.D. per rapid-fire pulse (three simultaneous blasts fired one micro-second after the other).

S.D.C. Damage: The weapon can also be set to fire a single S.D.C. blast that does 3D6 S.D.C. damage or a rapid-fire pulse that does 1D6x10 S.D.C. Thirty single S.D.C. blasts use up the equivalent energy of a single M.D. blast, while six S.D.C. pulse blasts count as one M.D. blast.

Rate of Fire: Equal to the number of combined hand to hand attacks of its user (usually 3-6); each single shot or pulse counts as one of the user's melee attacks.

Effective Range: 2000 feet (610 m).

Payload: 21 blasts (7 shots) per standard E-Clip, 30 blasts (10 shots) per long E-Clip. In the alternative, the CP-40 can be connected with an energy cable to a portable hip or backpack carried energy canister (both are the same small size). The energy canister provides 60 single blasts or 20 triple blasts. The weight of the standard energy canister, pack included, is four pounds (1.8 kg). A dual backpack is also available, with two energy canisters; when one is used up, the connector cable is removed and reattached to the second, full canister (takes one full melee round/15 seconds).

Black Market Cost: 40,000 credits and a hot commodity not commonly available.

CP-50 "Dragonfire" (New!)

Assault Pulse Laser & Grenade Launcher

The CP-50 "Dragonfire" is a second generation over and under heavy infantry weapon with high marks for durability and reliability in action. A pulse laser is the main, top mounted weapon with a pump action grenade launcher built-in under the laser barrel. Standard issue includes a passive nightvision scope and built-in laser targeting.

Weight: 10 lbs (4.5 kg)

Mega-Damage: 2D6 M.D. per single laser blast or 6D6 M.D. per rapid-fire pulse (three simultaneous blasts fired one micro-second after the other). The weapon can fire conventional M.D. rifle grenades doing 2D6 M.D. to a blast area of 12 feet (3.6 m), or new, micro-fusion grenades that inflict 6D6 M.D. to a 12 foot (3.6 m) diameter blast area/six foot (1.8 m) radius.

Rate of Fire: Laser: Equal to the number of combined hand to hand attacks of its user (usually 3-6).

Grenades: One aimed or four fired in rapid succession (burst if all at same target, wild if sprayed into an area).

Effective Range: Laser is 2000 feet (610 m).

 Grenade Launcher is 1200 feet (365 m)

Payload of Laser: 21 blasts (7 shots) per standard E-Clip, 30 blasts (10 shots) per long E-Clip. In the alternative, the CP-50 can be connected with an energy cable to a portable hip or backpack carried energy canister the same as the CP-40. The dual backpack is commonly issued with this weapon.

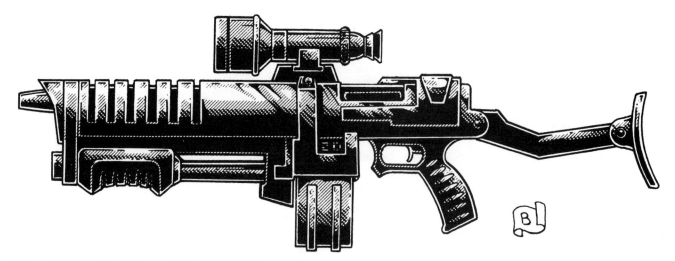

Payload Grenade Launcher: 12; an additional 24 to 48 grenades can be carried in a satchel or 12 on a bandoleer style belt.

Reloading the Launcher: One full melee round, 15 seconds, is required to manually reload the grenade launcher. As always, reloading an E-Clip takes about five seconds or equal to one melee action/attack

Black Market Cost: 50,000 credits and a hot commodity not commonly available. Standard grenades cost 550 credits apiece or 4500 a dozen. Micro-fusion grenades are extremely rare on the Black Market and cost 1500 to 3000 credits each!

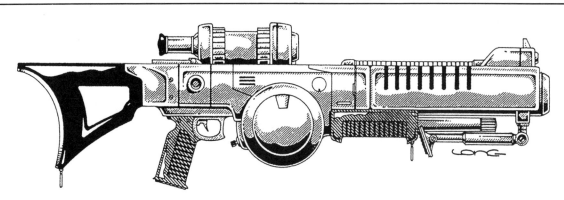

C-27 "Light" Plasma Cannon — Old Style

The C-27 plasma cannon has been reclassified from a heavy support infantry weapon to "light." It is dependable and inflicts good levels of damage. It is ideal against light to heavy body armor troops and light vehicles. Standard issue includes a telescopic and laser distancing scope.

Weight: 12 lbs (5.4 kg)

Mega-Damage: 6D6 M.D. per blast.

Rate of Fire: Equal to the number of attacks of the user; each blast counts as one melee action/attack.

Effective Range: 1600 feet (488 km).

Payload: 10 blasts per energy canister; hooked into the underside of the weapon.

Targeting Scope: Add a bonus of +1 to strike on an aimed shot.

Black Market Cost: 32,000 for the rifle; can only be used with an E-Clip Canister which costs 10,000 credits new and fully loaded. A recharge is 2000 credits.

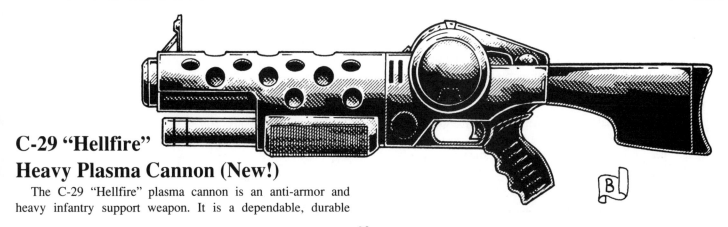

C-29 "Hellfire"
Heavy Plasma Cannon (New!)

The C-29 "Hellfire" plasma cannon is an anti-armor and heavy infantry support weapon. It is a dependable, durable weapon and inflicts incredible damage. If it has a shortcoming, it is limited firing range. Standard issue includes a telescopic and laser distancing scope.

Weight: 12 lbs (5.4 kg)
Mega-Damage: 1D6x10 M.D.
Rate of Fire: Equal to the number of attacks of the user; each blast counts as one melee action/attack.
Effective Range: 1400 feet (423 km).
Payload: 8 blasts per energy canister; mounted on the top-side of the weapon. In *addition*, the C-29 can be connected with an energy cable to a portable hip or backpack carried energy canister

the same as the CP-40. This gives the weapon a total initial payload of 16 blasts. The dual backpack is commonly issued with this weapon, with two to four additional energy canisters carried in a satchel; each canister weighs approximately four pounds (1.8 kg).

Targeting Scope: Add a bonus of +1 to strike on an aimed shot.
Black Market Cost: 32,000 for the rifle; can only be used with an E-Clip Canister which costs 10,000 credits new and fully loaded. A recharge is 2000 credits.

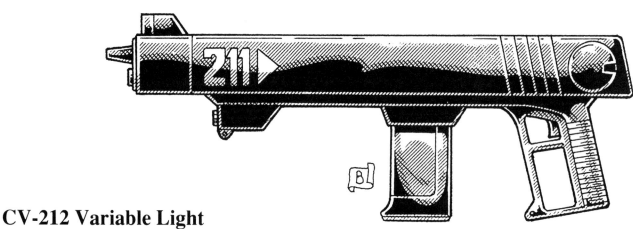

CV-212 Variable Light Frequency Laser Rifle

The CV-212 Variable Light Frequency Laser Rifle has become an official weapon of the Coalition Army. A microchip in the weapon's computer automatically analyzes an opponent's armor (if not already preprogrammed into its memory) and after one melee round (15 seconds) adjusts to the light frequency that will inflict full damage (the attacks for that first melee round do only half damage). It is a sturdy, reliable rifle that can survive a fair amount of combat abuse and activity without firing failure. However, M.D.C. damage (80%) is likely to disengage the computer analyzer (01-80%), making only manual frequency adjustments possible — it takes at least 1D4 melee rounds to find the optimum frequency and each adjustment attempt counts as one melee action/attack. The rifle can be set to fire in a single shot or a burst of three. It comes standard with a passive nightvision scope and laser targeting.

The CV-212 remains popular among Special Forces and is only issued to the infantry when they are expected to engage *Glitter Boys* or other enemy forces with laser resistant armor. Consequently, the CV-212 variable laser rifle is standard issue for approximately half the force committed to the Quebec Campaign. The CV-213 is fundamentally the same weapon, but designed specifically for use by Skelebots, particularly the original FASSAR-20 models, to overcome laser resistant armor.

Weight: 8 lbs (3.6 kg)
Mega-Damage: 2D6 M.D. per single shot or 6D6 M.D. per triple burst.
S.D.C. Damage: Special damage setting: 6D6 S.D.C. per single blast.
Rate of Fire: Equal to the combined number of hand to hand attacks of the user.
Effective Range: 2000 feet (610 m)
Payload: 21 blasts (7 pulse) per standard E-Clip, 30 blasts (10 pulse) per long E-Clip. In the alternative, the C-212 and C-213 can be connected with an energy cable to a portable hip or backpack carried energy canister (both are the same small size). The energy canister provides 60 single blasts or 20 triple blasts. The weight of the standard energy canister, pack included, is four pounds (1.8 kg). A dual backpack is also available, with two energy canisters; when one is used up, the connector cable is removed and reattached to the second, full canister (takes one full melee round/15 seconds). Skelebots are typically given the dual backpack. Note that six S.D.C. shots equals one, light, mega-damage blast.
Laser Targeting: Add +1 to strike on an aimed shot.
Black Market Cost: 50,000 credits for the rifle, 5000 credits for a new, fully charged, standard E-clip, 1500 for a recharge. An E-Clip canister costs 10,000 new and fully charged. A canister recharge costs 2000 credits.

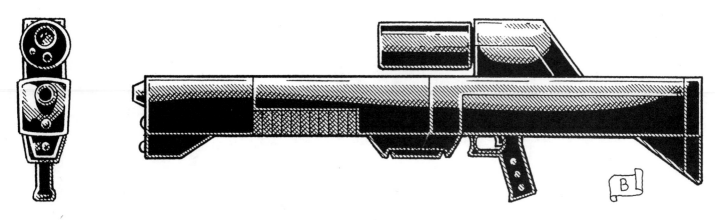

CTT-P40 Particle Beam Cannon

Power Armor Weapon

A giant-sized rifle with a dual weapon system. The main gun is a particle beam weapon with exceptional range (for a P-beam weapon). Mounted on the top of the rifle is a box laser targeting system and passive nightvision scope with telescopic capabilities (20x magnification; 3000 foot/910 m range). This weapon is standard issue for the Special Forces' Striker SAMAS and is frequently used by the Terror Trooper, full conversion 'Borgs, and the occasional CS Juicer.

Weight: 89 pounds (40 kg)
Primary Purpose: Anti-Personnel

Mega-Damage: Particle beam: 1D6×10 M.D. per single laser blast.
Maximum Effective Range: 2000 feet (610 m)
Rate of Fire: Equal to the number of hand to hand attacks per melee round.
Payload: 40 particle beam blasts — virtually the entire back half of the giant rifle/cannon is a rechargeable energy cell.

Notes: Using the weapon one-handed requires a P.S. of 24 or greater and even then one-handed shooting has a penalty of -2 to strike, unless a Terror Trooper or Super SAMAS.

CTT-M20 Missile Rifle

Power Armor Weapon

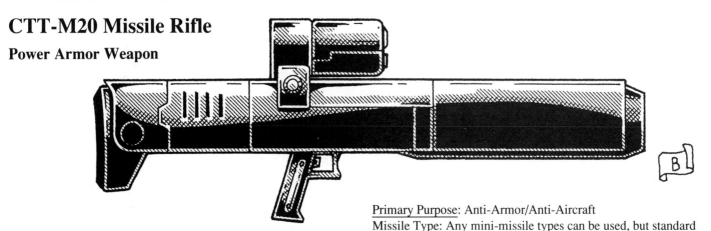

The CTT-M20 Missile Rifle is an over-sized heavy weapon that's about twice the size of the typical energy rifle. It was specifically designed for the *Terror Trooper Power Armor*, but has been adopted by SAMAS pilots, full conversion 'Borgs and the occasional CS Juicer (Crazies would love 'em too; need two hands and a P.S. of 24 or better to use the weapon effectively). The CTT-M20 is standard issue for the Terror Trooper, although the CTT-P40 or a rail gun can be substituted.

This weapons houses a row of mini-missiles down each of its long, twin barrels. Each pull of the trigger fires one mini-missile. Remember, mini-missiles are self-guided, so once launched they will find their target.

Mounted on the top of the rifle is a box that is both a laser targeting system and medium range laser.

Weight: 110 pounds (49.5 kg) fully loaded; roughly 30 pounds (13.6 kg) less unloaded.

Primary Purpose: Anti-Armor/Anti-Aircraft
Missile Type: Any mini-missile types can be used, but standard issue is armor piercing (1D4×10 M.D.) or plasma (1D6×10 M.D.).
Mega-Damage: Varies with missile type.
The laser does 2D6 M.D. per shot.
Maximum Effective Range: Mini-missiles: Usually about a mile (1.6 km). Laser: 2000 feet (610 m)
Rate of Fire: One at a time, or in volleys of two or four.
Payload: 20 total; 10 per launch tube. The laser mounted on the top of the CTT-M20 takes a standard E-clip (20 shots) or long E-clip (30 shots).

Notes: The lower port on the box laser is a targeting sight that provide a bonus of +1 to strike. Using the weapon one-handed requires a P.S. of 24 or greater and even then one-handed shooting has a penalty of -2 to strike, unless a the shooter is in Terror Trooper or Super SAMAS power armor or has a P.S. of 36 of higher.

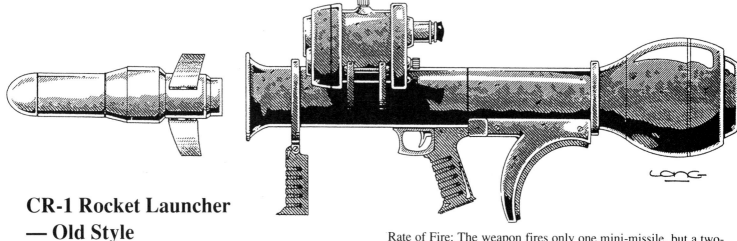

CR-1 Rocket Launcher
— Old Style

The CR-1 rocket launcher is a reusable mini-missiles launcher with a multi-optic scope. The capabilities of the scope include telescopic (x20 magnification, 2 mile/3.2 km range), infra-red (2000 foot/ 610 m range), passive night vision (2000 ft), and laser targeting.

Weight: The launcher weighs 14 lbs (6.3 kg), each missile weighs about one pound (0.45 kg).

Mega-Damage: Any mini-missile can be used, but usually armor piercing or plasma (1D4x10 or 1D6x10 M.D.C.)

Rate of Fire: The weapon fires only one mini-missile, but a two-man team can load and fire three missiles per melee/15 seconds. A single operator can only fire one per melee.

Effective Range: One mile.

Payload: A carrying side-pack can hold six mini-missiles (weighs about ten pounds/4.5 kg), a backpack can hold 12 missiles and a portable carrying case (10 M.D.C.) can hold 24 mini-missiles (weighs about 40 lbs/18 kg).

Black Market Cost: 18,000 for the launcher and 1000 credits for each light damage missile (5D6 M.D.) and 2200 for each plasma or armor piercing.

C-200 "Dead Man's" Rail Gun

This is a light, all-purpose weapon used by human troops wearing enhanced exoskeleton body armor or power armor, as well as cyborgs, skelebots, and characters with a strength of 24 or greater. The C-200 rail gun can use what is called a short clip with 200 rounds (10 bursts), light drum with 600 rounds (30 bursts), or a heavy belt feed drum containing 2000 round (100 bursts). The latter is typically reserved for robots and cyborgs and is carried as a backpack or carried by the partner in a two 'Borg team.

Primary Purpose: Assault

Secondary Purpose: Defense

Weight: Gun: 45 lbs (20.25 kg), short clip: 10 pounds (4.5 kg), light ammo-drum: 30 pounds (13 kg), or a heavy ammo-drum: 100 lbs (45 kg). Ammo-drums are hooked to the back of body armor or a housing on the back of borgs or bots. Skelebots are typically given the light or heavy drum.

Mega-Damage: A full damage burst fires 20 rounds and inflicts 4D6 M.D.; a single round does 1D4 M.D.

Rate of Fire: Equal to the character's hand to hand attacks per melee round (usually 3 to 6).

Maximum Effective Range: 4000 feet (1200 m)

Payload: The short clip holds 200 and is capable of firing ten full damage bursts (20 rounds).

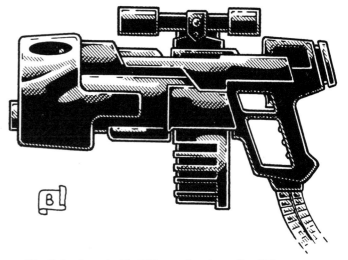

The light drum holds 600 round and can fire 30 bursts.

The 2000 round drum is capable of firing 100 full damage bursts (20 rounds each).

Reloading a drum will take about three minutes for those not trained, but a mere 30 seconds by a capable field mechanic. A strength of 24 or higher is required to handle the drum.

Special C-200 Features: A rail gun for human troops has its own laser targeting, telescopic and nightvision scope. Bot guns only have the laser targeting scope. Telescopic and laser targeting range is 6000 feet (1828 m). Targeting Bonus: +1 to strike.

Black Market Cost: 80,000 credits. Poor availability.

Short Range Missiles

Warhead	Mega-Damage	Speed	Maximum Range	Blast Radius	M.D.C.
High Explosive (light)	2D4×10	500mph (804kmph)	5 miles (8km)	10ft (3m)	5
High Explosive (medium)	2D6×10	500mph (804kmph)	5 miles (8km)	15ft (4.6m)	5
Fragmentation (light)	2D4×10	450mph (724kmph)	3 miles (4.8km)	20ft (6.1m)	5
Armor Piercing (medium)	2D6×10	650mph (1045kmph)	5 miles (8km)	5ft (1.5m)	5
Plasma/Napalm (medium)	2D6×10	500mph (804kmph)	3 miles (4.8km)	15ft (4.6m)	5
Tear Gas	None	200mph (321kmph)	1/2 mile (.8km)	10ft (3m)	5
Knock-Out Gas	None	200mph (321kmph)	1/2 mile (.8km)	10ft (3m)	5
Smoke (colors available)	None	300mph (482.7kmph)	1 mile (1.6km)	20ft (6.1m)	5
Fire Retardent	None	200mph (321kmph)	1/2 mile (.8km)	20ft (6.1m)	5

Medium Range Missiles

Warhead	Mega-Damage	Speed	Maximum Range	Blast Radius	M.D.C.
High Explosive (light)	2D4×10	1200mph (1929kmph)	50 miles (80.4km)	20ft (6.1m)	10
High Explosive (medium)	2D6×10	1200mph (1929kmph)	40 miles (64.3km)	20ft (6.1m)	10
High Explosive (heavy)	3D6×10	1200mph (1929kmph)	40 miles (64.3m)	30ft (9.1m)	10
Fragmentation (light)	2D6×10	1000mph (1608kmph)	40 miles (64.3km)	40ft (12.2m)	10
Armor Piercing (medium)	3D6×10	1600mph (2571kmph)	60 miles (96.5km)	20ft (6.1m)	10
Plasma/Napalm (medium)	4D6×10	1400mph (2251kmph)	40 miles (64.3km)	40ft (12.2m)	10
Multi-Warhead*	5D6×10	1200mph (1929kmph)	80 miles (128.7km)	20ft (6.1m)	10
Smoke (colors available)	None	1000mph (1608kmph)	40 miles (64.3km)	40ft (12.2m)	10

Long Range Missiles

Warhead	Mega-Damage	Speed	Maximum Range	Blast Radius	M.D.C.
High Explosive (medium)	3D6×10	2010mph (Mach 3)	500 miles (804km)	30ft (9.1m)	20
High Explosive (heavy)	4D6×10	2010mph (Mach 3)	500 miles (804m)	40ft (12.2m)	20
Fragmentation (light)	2D6×10	1400mph (2251kmph)	400 miles (643km)	80ft (24.4m)	20
Armor Piercing (medium)	3D6×10	2010mph (Mach 3)	800 miles (1286km)	30ft (9.1m)	20
Plasma/Heat (medium)	4D6×10	1400mph (2251kmph)	500 miles (804km)	40ft (12.2m)	20
Plasma/Heat (medium)*	5D6×10	1400mph (2251kmph)	500 miles (804km)	50ft (15.2m)	20
Proton Torpedo (heavy)*	6D6×10	2010mph (Mach 3)	1200 miles (1928km)	50ft (15.2m)	25
Nuclear (medium)*	1D4×100	2010mph (Mach3)	1000 miles (1608km)	40ft (12.2m)	20
Nuclear (heavy)*	1D6×100	2010mph (Mach 3)	1000 miles (1608km)	50ft (15.2m)	20
Nuclear Multi-warhead*	2D4×100	2010mph (Mach3)	1800 miles (2893km)	50ft (15.2m)	25

Mini Missiles
and Special Armaments

Warhead	Mega-Damage	Speed	Maximum Range	Blast Radius	M.D.C.
High Explosive	5D6	500mph (804kmph)	1 mile (1.6km)	5ft (1.5m)	1
Fragmentation	5D6	500mph (804kmph)	1/2 mile (0.8km)	20ft (6.1m)	1
Armor Piercing	1D4×10	1400mph (2251kmph)	1 mile (1.6km)	3ft (0.9m)	2
Plasma/Napalm (medium)	1D6×10	1200mph (1929kmph)	1 mile (1.6km)	15ft (1.5m)	1
Smoke (colors available)	None	500mph (804kmph)	1/2 mile (0.8km)	20ft (6.1m)	1

*Available as smart bombs, +5 to strike.

Enhanced Missiles

The Coalition Army has been able to significantly increase the damage of its missiles without having to increase missile size. Both the old, light damage types and the new, heavy damage missiles are available. The light damage missiles are generally being sent to military outposts, bases, and city defenders in low risk, low hostility posts, cities and territories. The new, heavy damage missiles are most commonly made available to frontline troops, infantry troops and military posts in hostile regions. See the new missile chart for the new missile damage.

CS Explosives

Fusion Blocks

A fusion block is a little square case about the size of a hand-held computer. On top of the block is a small key-pad for programming the time of detonation. An automatic 30 second delay is built into each fusion bomb as a safety feature to avoid instant detonation.

Mega-Damage: There are three types of fusion block bombs.
Light: 1D4x10 M.D.; cost: 1000 credits.
Medium: 2D6x10 M.D.; cost: 3000 credits.
Heavy: 4D6x10 M.D.C.; cost: 8000 credits.
Blast Radius: Each has a contained blast radius of 10 feet (3 m).
Range: The blocks are made for placement, not throwing or shooting, however, one can try throwing the explosive, typical range is 1D6x10 feet (3 to 18 m); fusion blocks are not aerodynamic.
Black Market Cost: listed with damage, above.

CS Hand Grenades

Smaller explosive canisters designed for throwing and exploding.
Fragmentation: 2D6 M.D. to a 20 foot (6 m) area.
Light High Explosive: 3D6 M.D. to a 6 foot (1.8 m) area.
Heavy High Explosive: 4D6 M.D. to a 6 foot (1.8 m) area.
Plasma: 5D6 M.D. to a 12 foot area (3.6 m) area.
Note: Micro-fusion grenades that inflict 6D6 M.D. to a 12 foot (3.6 m) diameter blast area are available only as rifle launched rounds.
Effective Range Throwing a Grenade: About 40 yards/meters.
Black Market Cost: 250 credits for fragmentation, 200 credits for light high explosive, 275 credits for heavy high explosive, and 350 credits for plasma.

Stun/Flash Grenade: This riot/anti-terrorist weapon is designed to disorient and confuse criminals who are holding hostages in confined places. The grenade makes a loud exploding boom and emits a bright flash followed by a shower of white-hot sparklets and some white smoke. The flash, burning sparks, and smoke should blind and startle any character without environmental armor or protective goggles. The victims of a stun/flash grenade are -8 to strike, parry and dodge, -1 on initiative and lose one melee attack/action for the next 1D4 melee rounds (15 to 60 seconds). Even those in armor should be momentarily distracted for 1D4 seconds and lose initiative. Cost: 100 credits.

Tear Gas Grenades: The gas will instantly affect all characters without protective masks or environmental body armor. The eyes burn, sting and water profusely, causing great discomfort and makes seeing clearly impossible. The gas also makes breathing difficult and irritates exposed skin. The effects last for 3D4 minutes. The 25 foot (7.6 m) cloud dissipates in about five minutes unless blown away by wind (dissipating more quickly in 1D4 minutes). The victims of tear gas are -10 to strike, parry and dodge, -3 on initiative and lose one melee attack/action for each of the next 1D6+1 melee rounds. Those in environmental armor are completely safe and not affected. Cost: 200 credits.

Smoke Grenades: This type of grenade releases a thick cloud of smoke that covers a 20 to 40 foot (6 to 12 m) radius. The smoke obscures vision in and through the cloud from those on the outside of it. Infrared cannot penetrate a smoke cloud or be used inside one. Those inside the cloud will be blinded and have trouble breathing. Those who are not protected by environmental suits or a gas mask and goggles will be -5 to strike, parry and dodge and -1 on initiative. Attackers firing into/through the cloud will be shooting wild. Note that passive nightscopes will work in a smoke cloud. Cost: 50 credits.

Hand-held Flare: This is the type of item truck drivers and road patrols use to signal for help or to warn others of an accident or danger. The flare burns for 20 minutes. Cost: One credit each.

Parachute Flares: This pyrotechnic device usually comes in a hand-held, throw-away launch tube. Three seconds after launching, it ignites into a bright, sparkling light that slowly drifts back down to earth. While in the air, the flare burns for 60 seconds and illuminates an area of roughly 150 feet (45.7 m) in diameter. Cost: 10 credits each. Note: This is NOT a weapon, but if shot into a person, the flare does 6D6 S.D.C. each melee round for one minute (four rounds). There is also a 50% chance of causing combustibles to catch fire.

Vibro-Blades & Other Hand Weapons

Vibro-blades were originally designed by the Weapons Research and Development Division at Chi-Town. Since their introduction, these weapons have become extremely popular not only among the CS military, but among armed forces, mercenaries and adventurers throughout the continent. "Knock-offs" of the CS vibro-blades are produced by virtually every weapon manufacturer in the Americas.

Vibro-knives, claws and sabers are typically available to Special Forces operatives and CS officers. They are also issued to ISS and NTSET officers and are the standard issue of Psi-Hounds. The blades are ideal for the Dog Pack squads assigned to urban duty (where a full 60% of all Dog Boys are assigned) because the weapons provide close combat mega-damage capabilities without the potential danger of long weapons which are incredibly hazardous to both human life and property. All Dog Pack city patrols are issued either two vibro-blades of choice, or a blade and a neural mace, along with their armor and spikes.

Vibro-Blades

All vibro-blades are blade weapons surrounded by an invisible, high-frequency energy field that gives them mega-damage capabilities.

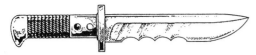

Vibro-Knife: 1D6 M.D. **Cost:** 7000 cr.

Vibro-Saber (short sword): 2D4 M.D. **Cost:** 9000 cr.

Vibro-Sword (larger, one handed sword): 2D6 M.D. **Cost** 11,000 cr.

Giant-Sized Sword: 3D6 M.D.; usually used by oversized power armor suits or by giant robot vehciles. **Cost:** 18,000 cr.

Vibro-ForearmClaws: 2D6 M.D.; usually three hooked blades attached to a forearm gauntlet or protective plate. Great for parrying and slashing. **Cost:** 11,000 cr.

Note: The ancient weapon proficiency skills and bonuses apply to the vibro-blades. Claws fall into the W.P. Knife category.

Neural Mace

Another hand-held weapon used by the Dog Packs is a neural mace. The mace is effectively a stun weapon that releases an energy charge that temporarily short-circuits the nervous system.

Damage: Nonlethal; the victim who is *stunned* is -8 to strike, parry, and dodge plus reduce the character's speed and number of attacks per melee round by half.

The accumulative effect on the nervous system of the body being repeatedly struck and stunned may knock the victim unconscious, even if he has previously saved. After being struck more than four times, the unprotected character may be stunned into unconsciousness for 2D4 melee rounds. When he recovers, he will suffer the stun penalties for 1D4 minutes. Roll to save, a failed roll means there is a 01-42% chance of being rendered unconscious. Note that in this case, even if the individual remains conscious, the charge will impair his movement as per the penalties previously described.

Physical damage from the mace is 2D4 S.D.C. plus P.S. attribute bonus. However, the mace is an M.D.C. structure and can be used to parry M.D. attacks from vibro-blades, 'Borgs, 'bots and power armor.

Duration of Stun Effects: 2D4 melee rounds. The duration of the impairment is increased 2D4 melee rounds for every hit by the mace in which the character does not save.

Save vs Neural Mace: 16 or higher; the same as saving against non-lethal poison. The character must save each time he or she is struck. A successful save means the character loses initiative and one melee attack/action that round but is otherwise okay.

Note: The mace is *ineffective* against environmental, M.D.C. body and power armor, but is effective against Dog Pack armor and half suits, or body armor without a helmet (not fully environmental without the helmet attached). **Cost:** 8000 cr.

Dog Pack Spikes

One of the Dog Pack's patented images is spikes. This is largely a stylistic gimmick to evoke the feeling of fear and power. Spiked collars, arm and wrist bands, knee pads and gloves are all available. **Damage** for all spikes is S.D.C. damage. The spiked gloves are weighted, sap gloves, and add 1D6+1 S.D.C. damage to punches. The knee pads have the weight and power of the leg behind it and add 1D6 S.D.C. to knee kicks. All others inflict 1D4 S.D.C. damage. The hand and arm spikes can also be used to parry normal S.D.C. attacks, +1 bonus when parrying with spiked arm bands or glove only. **Cost:** 100 cr.

New CS Body Armor

The new style of armor is designed to provide greater M.D.C. protection without adding significantly to the weight or decreasing mobility. The entire upper part of the helmet is a large, black tinted visor or face-plate made of one-way polyceramic glass that is as strong as mega-damage steel. The wearer can see out but his opponents cannot see the face behind the dark glass. This large transparent face-plate gives the soldier full use of his normal and peripheral vision. Targeting sights, coded messages, schematics, body armor system and damage reports, environmental data and other information provided by the built-in voice actuated computer and transmissions are projected on the visor via the Heads Up Display (HUD) system. Multi-optic enhancements can be either a cybernetic eye built right into the soldier's head or a patch worn over one eye. The overall design of the helmet also makes it more comfortable to wear.

The overlapping body plates are made of a new lightweight ceramic developed by Triax and shared with the CS. These plates add only slightly to the total weight of the armor while providing significantly more protection. The armor plating and decorative features have been designed to give the suit a frightening skeletal appearance with the idea that it will unnerve and intimidate the enemy.

Each suit of armor offers mega-damage protection and complete environmental systems, making it a self-contained unit, like a space suit. Air filters, circulation and cooling, and independent oxygen supply (engages when needed) means the wearer is protected from foul smells, toxic fumes, gas attacks, smoke and airborne particles. The suit is also radiation proof. The soldier becomes vulnerable only when the armored suit is breached, but this is a rare occurrence. **Note:** Typically, the armor's M.D.C. must be reduced to 15 points or less for a life threatening breach to appear and the environmental systems to fail. When the M.D.C. is reduced to zero, the armor is so battered and full of holes that it affords its wearer no mega-damage protection (equal to an A.R. 7, so even most S.D.C. attacks will penetrate and do damage directly to the body of the wearer).

All *new* "Dead Boy" body armor has the following features:

- M.D.C. protection of at least 80 points.
- Complete environmental battle armor suitable for use in all hostile environments including space.
- Computer controlled life support system that monitors and displays bio-data of the wearer as well as the capacity and failure of life support systems and damage to the armor. The wearer will know *approximately* how much M.D.C. is remaining and whether or not the armor has been breached.
- Computer controlled, independent oxygen supply and purge system that automatically engages in low oxygen or contaminated air environments. Five hour oxygen supply.
- Internal, voice actuated *support* computer and data base. This secondary computer provides mathematical computations and serves as a data base of basic military data, protocol, rules, laws and procedure. It also includes CS troop and vehicle recognition/identification based on verbal description or optical link (if it's not a friendly, it's probably an enemy). The computer can also "read" for the soldier (85% of all grunts are illiterate). This is done either by reading the letters composing the word (assuming the character knows the alphabet; 70% don't) or with an optic link via multi-optic eye patch or bionic eye linked to the computer. The new heavy armor has an automatic optic link built into the armor.
- Internal cooling and temperature control.
- Artificial air circulation systems, gas filtration, humidifier.
- Insulated, high-temperature resistant shielding for up to 300 degrees centigrade. Normal fires do no damage. Nuclear, plasma, magic fires and mega-damage fire and heat do full damage.
- Radiation shielded.
- Polarized and light-sensitive visor with a tint that automatically adjusts to the level of available light.
- Built-in loudspeaker; 80 decibels.
- Directional, short-range radio built into the helmet. Range is five miles (8 km).
- The helmet can be completely removed, but unlike the old armor, the face plate is not removable; it is one piece with a jointed back plate that is unlocked and opened to put on and remove the helmet quickly and easily.
- Ammo and supply waist belt, shoulder belts, and shoulder holsters are all standard issue. Pilots and officers have choice of shoulder or hip holster.
- Boot survival knife or vibro-blade for officers, military specialists and Special Forces.
- The light areas of the skeleton portions of armor are a light grey color. The material is light sensitive and darkens 20% in low light to prevent giving the enemy a nice, light target to aim for during night attacks.
- Prowl Penalty: -10% in CA-3 light armor, -20% in CA-4 standard armor and CA-5 Juicer armor, -30% in CA-6 heavy armor exoskeleton or cyborg armor.

Note: Standard issue of weapons to the infantry is a laser assault rifle, laser pistol, and a survival knife. Other weapons are available upon assignment.

CA-3 Light "Dead Boy" Armor (New!)

This Coalition armor is typically reserved for female troopers, scouts and special teams (Psi-officers, reconnaissance, Intelligence, Special Forces, etc.). The helmet is often given a plume or pony-tail of hair-like fibers to denote female officers and wilderness scouts; spikes are used for psionic officers.

Class: CA-3 light Coalition body armor.
Size: Human equivalent.
Weight: 12 pounds (5.4 kg).
Mobility: Very good to good; -5% to climb and -10% to prowl, swim, do acrobatics and similar physical skills/performance.
M.D.C. by Location:
    Head/Helmet — 70
    Arms — 55 each
    Legs — 70 each
    Main Body — 80
Special Weapon Systems or Features: None
Market Price: Not available; exclusive to the CS military.

CA-4 Standard "Dead Boy" Armor (New!)

The standard armor is what's worn by most Coalition soldiers, including commissioned and non-commissioned officers. The distinguishing feature on officers' is their symbol of rank and the adornment of spikes on the helmet or a plume of hair-like fibers. High ranking commissioned officers (Captain and up) can elect to wear light or heavy armor instead of the standard. Females who can handle the weight and bulk are also allowed to wear standard "Dead Boy" armor.

Note: Most pilots and soldiers in special divisions of the army typically wear CA-3 light armor or CA-4 standard armor. The only distinguishing difference is the design of their helmet.

Class: CA-4 standard Coalition infantry body armor.
Size: Human equivalent.
Weight: 20 pounds (9.1 kg).
Mobility: Good; -5% to climb and -20% to prowl, swim, perform acrobatics and similar physical skills/performance.
M.D.C. by Location:
    Head/Helmet — 70
    Arms — 60 each
    Legs — 80 each
    Main Body — 100
Special Weapon Systems or Features: None
Market Price: Not available; exclusive to the CS military.

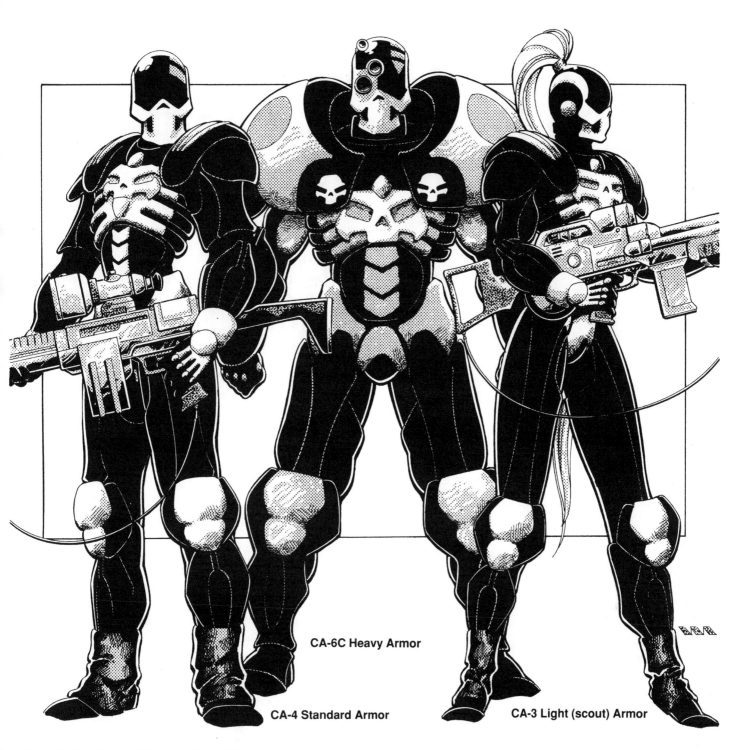

CA-6C Heavy Armor

CA-4 Standard Armor

CA-3 Light (scout) Armor

CA-5 Juicer "Dead Boy" Armor (New!)

Juicer armor is a slightly modified, heavier suit of standard armor with a heavier helmet and features to distinguish it from the standard troops. The heavier weight has no affect on Juicers. The right or left forearm also comes with a modular forearm weapon system that can also be used with CA-6 heavy armor.

Class: CA-5 Coalition Juicer body armor.
Size: Human equivalent.
Weight: 30 pounds (13.6 kg).
Mobility: Good (for Juicers, fair to poor for ordinary humans); -5% to climb and -20% to prowl, swim, perform acrobatics and similar physical skills/performance. Increase the penalty to climb to 15% and other physical skills to 30% if the armor

should fall into the hands of unauthorized personnel, and the character wearing the armor is not a Juicer, Crazy, full conversion 'borg or possesses supernatural strength.

M.D.C. by Location:
  Head/Helmet — 80
  Arms — 70 each
  Legs — 85 each
  Main Body — 125
Market Price: Not available; exclusive to the CS military.
Special Weapon Systems or Features: The CAJ-5 weapon arm is a detachable forearm weapon system. One is standard issue to all CS Juicers. This multi-weapon system is a menacing weapon in the hands of a Juicer. The weapon barrel is that of a plasma blaster. The small barrel is a light laser used primarily as a cutting tool. Three wicked vibro-blades protrude from

the forearm to extend beyond the fist to serve as a close combat weapon. The blades can be partially retracted so that the points of the blades end at the knuckles and can still be used in backhand strikes without extending them. When extended, the blades are used like a triple bladed sword to parry, slash and stab.

CAJ-5 Weapon Arm

Weight (overall): 15 pounds (6.7 kg)
Market Price: Not available; exclusive to the CS military.

Plasma Blaster:

Mega-Damage: 4D6 M.D.
Rate of Fire: Standard; same as an energy rifle.
Effective Range: 800 feet (243.8 m)
Payload: 10 shots per standard E-Clip or 50 when connected to a portable, energy hip or back pack (10 lbs/4.5 kg).

Light Laser Tool:

Mega-Damage: Three settings: 4D6 S.D.C., 1D4 M.D. and 1D6 M.D.
Rate of Fire: Standard; same as an energy rifle.
Effective Range: 800 feet (243.8 m)
Payload: 20 shots per standard E-Clip.

Vibro-Blades Tri-Claw:

Mega-Damage: 3D6 M.D.

Note: See **Rifts World Book 10: Juicer Uprising** for more special weapons for and details about Juicers.

CA-6C & CA-6EX
Heavy "Dead Boy" Armor (New!)

There are two types of heavy body armor, one designed for Coalition cyborgs and the other, an augmentation suit for humans.

CA-6C Cyborg Armor

The CA-6C is a large, heavily plated suit of Dead Boy armor designed for use by the Coalition's new *Cyborg Armored Division*. It is typically worn by full conversion cyborgs or partial 'borgs/headhunters with extensive reconstruction.

Class: CA-6C Heavy cyborg infantry armor.
Size: 6 feet, 6 inches (1.95 m) to 7 feet, 6 inches (2.25 m).
Weight: 60 pounds (27 kg).
Mobility for Full Conversion Cyborgs: Fair to Good; -15% to climb and -30% to prowl, swim, perform acrobatics and similar physical skills/performance.
M.D.C. by Location:

Head/Helmet — 100	Legs — 120 each
Arms — 100 each	Main Body — 200

Special Weapon Systems or Features: No special weapon systems per se, but the armor may be modified to allow the use of bionic systems.

The following optical and sensor capabilities are built into the CA-6C helmet and linked to the secondary computer and HUD system:

1. HUD Multi-Screen: A Heads Up Display (HUD) that can project data, charts or transmissions on the visor of the helmet for the wearer to see. As many as six different HUD viewing sections/images can be projected without impairing the vision of the wearer.

2. Computer & Video Link: The helmet can be patched into computers, televisions, cameras, monitors and sensory equipment. This means video transmissions and encoded audio or video signals can be displayed directly on the HUD. This requires "plugging in." Located in the ear section of the helmet is a universal headjack.

3. Optical Enhancements: Passive nightvision (2000 ft/610 m range), telescopic (10x magnification, 6000 ft/1830 m range), macro-lens (6x magnification), thermo-imager (1000 ft/305 m range) and light filters.

4. Laser distancer: Measures and indicates the exact distance of a target or item. Effective range: 1000 feet (305 m). Maximum range: 2000 feet (610 m) with a 20% margin for error.

5. Laser Targeting: Adds a +1 strike bonus. Effective range: 1000 feet (305 m). Maximum range: 2000 feet (610 m), no bonus to strike.

Market Price: Not available; exclusive to the CS military.

CA-6EX Armor

The "EX" in the classification stands for "exoskeleton." The CA-6EX is fundamentally the same heavily plated armor as the CA-6C except that it has an exoskeleton built into it. The exoskeleton enables ordinary humans to wear it, providing incredible armored protection and enhanced robotic strength and speed. This makes the EX a simple suit of power armor, an idea borrowed by the CS from the New German Republic (T-11 armor).

The enhanced body armor can be assigned to any of the Coalition Military O.C.C.s, but is typically reserved for Special Forces, platoon sergeants, commissioned officers, rail gunners and loyal soldiers who have an impressive natural strength or speed (21 or greater). It is also sometimes assigned to units using heavy weapons/equipment and construction forces.

Class: CA-6EX Heavy infantry armor and exoskeleton.
Size: 6 feet, 6 inches (1.95 m) to 7 feet, 6 inches (2.25 m).
Weight: 60 pounds (27 kg).
Bonuses: The exoskeleton adds the following bonuses to the attributes of the soldier who wears it: +8 to P.S., +14 to spd, +10 feet (3 m) to the length and height of leaps, and reduces the rate of fatigue by 50%.
Mobility Penalties: Good; -30% to prowl, but only -10% to swim, perform acrobatics and similar physical skills/performance, and no penalty to climb.
M.D.C. by Location:

Head/Helmet — 100
Arms — 100 each
Legs — 120 each
Main Body — 200

Special Weapon Systems or Features: As per the CA-6C, above.
Market Price: Not available; exclusive to the CS military.

Special Forces CA-7 Heavy "Dead Boy" Armor (New!)

Breaux

The Special Forces Division has its own suit of black body armor. The suit departs dramatically from the styling of the new armor and the old. The helmet, shoulder plates, elbows, and lower legs are studded in spikes. The face plate is a sinister skull. The armor has all the same features as the new "Dead Boy" armor and a few special ones as well; most notable are the retractable vibro-knives mounted on the top of each forearm at the wrist (1D6 M.D. each). A garrote wire can be pulled from a housing in the left wrist. A Special-Ops Mag-Five, silent jet pack can be attached to the mountings on the back to provide flight, or in the alternative, to secure a backpack ammo-drum or energy pack. An ammo-belt is typically slung across the chest along with a utility belt and holster at the waist. Additional ammo and equipment pouches can be magnetically attached to the armor at the waist or on the hips and lower leg. **Note:** Only the elite soldiers of the Special Forces are allowed to wear this armor.

Class: CA-7 Special Forces body armor.
Size: Human equivalent.
Weight: 20 pounds (9.1 kg).
Mobility: Good; -5% to climb and -20% to prowl, swim, perform acrobatics and similar physical skills/performance.

M.D.C. by Location:
Head/Helmet — 75
Arms — 60 each
Legs — 80 each
Main Body — 100

(rear view)

Elite Corps Helmets

Elite Corp Regular

Specialist (usually pilot's)

Officer

103

Special Weapon Systems or Features:

1. Retractable forearm vibro-blades (2): 1D6 M.D.

2. Garrote cord in left wrist (1): Used to strangle S.D.C. targets.

3. Special-Ops Mag-5 Jet Pack: This jet pack is equipped with a special silencing system that muffles the sound of the rocket jets. This reduces the speed of the system compared to other types and brands of jet packs, but provides the user with a reliable flight system ideal for espionage and reconnaissance. Maximum Speed: 60 mph (96.5 km); Maximum Altitude: 1200 feet (365 m); Power Supply: Four E-clips — the same types as used in CS weapons! Each E-clip provides 20 minutes of flight. The use of the E-clips is an alternative battery system that offers the special operative greater versatility; an E-clip in a weapon can be removed and used to power the jet pack and vice versa, E-clips are common and readily available throughout North America, they are small, lightweight, portable and can be recharged.

Market Price: Not available; exclusive to the CS military. Unauthorized possession of Special Forces armor is illegal, treasonous and a death sentence.

Old Style "Dead Boy" Armor

The original Death's head motif of the Coalition's armor and war machines had struck fear in the hearts of its opposition for nearly 40 years. The skull motif and ruthlessness of the soldiers earned them the nickname "Dead Boys."

The high recognition factor of the famous armor and its familiarity with the public has prompted the government to keep the armor in service, but making it exclusive to the *Internal Security Specialists* (ISS and its sub-divisions). This satisfies three areas of concern: First, it clearly differentiates the military from the internal security forces/police/psi-division. Second, it gives the citizens the welcomed appearance of the protectors they have come to know and trust; and third, it takes advantage of the huge inventory of old style armor which is perfectly suitable for civil defense and law enforcement. See the **Rifts® RPG** for complete stats. All allied Coalition States have adopted the old style for the ISS and the new armor for the army.

Class: CA-1 heavy and CA-2 light body armor.

Size: Human equivalent.

Weight: Heavy: 18 pounds (8.1 kg) or light: 9 pounds (4 kg).

Mobility: Heavy: Good; -10% to climb and -25% to prowl, swim, acrobatics and similar physical skills/performance. Light: Very good; -5% to climb and -10% to prowl, swim, acrobatics and similar physical skills/performance.

M.D.C. by Location:
Head/Helmet — 50
Arms — 35 each
Legs — 50 each
Main Body — 80 (heavy) or 50 (light)

Special Weapon Systems or Features: None

Market Price: Not available; exclusive to the CS military.

Dog Pack DPM Light Riot Armor

The Dog Pack force has proven to be an invaluable addition to the Coalition Armed Forces. They have also proven to be so loyal that their light armor has been upgraded slightly and Special Psi-Hound NTSET operatives are allowed to wear full suits of the old style Dead Boy armor. The head shapes of the different breeds of dogs prevents them from wearing the standard environmental helmet, so they are given a skull cap, goggles and air filter to protect the head.

The DPM armor offers none of the environmental systems of the full Dead Boy suits and serves mostly as protection against gunfire. Note that many Dog Packs (about 40%) assigned to wilderness and reconnaissance operations are given CA-2 light body armor.

- M.D.C.: 50
- Weight: 10 pounds (4.5 kg)
- Full mobility, no prowl penalty.

Note: Standard issue to city Dog Pack soldiers are fist and wrist spikes, a pair of vibro-blades or a blade and neural mace. A laser pistol may be issued in some situations. Infantry forces in the field are issued a vibro-blade of choice or neural mace and a C-12 laser rifle. Other arms may be issued as needed. Dog Boys in the field often add/purchase other non-official, non-Coalition weapons to their personal equipment.

Coalition Power Armor & Robot Vehicles

Power Armor
PA-100 Mauler
PA-200 Terror Trooper
PA-300 Glitter Boy Killer
PA-06A Old Style SAMAS
PA-07A Light Assault SAMAS
PA-08A Special Forces Strike SAMAS
PA-09A Super SAMAS

Robot Combat Vehicles
UAR-1 Enforcer (see *Rifts® RPG*)
IAR-2 Abolisher
IAR-3 Skull Smasher
IAR-4 Hellraiser
IAR-5 Hellfire
CR-003 Spider-Skull Walker (see *Rifts® RPG*)
CR-004 Scout Spider-Skull Walker
CR-005 Scorpion-Skull Walker

Skelebots
FASSAR-20 Old Style Skelebot
FASSAR-30 New Style Skelebot
FASSAR-40 New Hunter Skelebot
FASSAR-50 New Hellion Skelebot
FASSAR-60 Centaur Skelebot (experimental)

Power Armor

Power armor might be thought of as a sort of super-suit of body armor that protects its wearer completely, but is also an exoskeleton that enhances the abilities of the wearer and offers a array of weapons. It is a form of mechanical augmentation that does not require the user to submit to any physical alteration. The armor is basically a robot suit. The human pilot steps into it and activates the armor to becomes a self contained environmental combat system.

Traditionally, power armor was an augmented, environmental combat suit that was worn like the knights of old. However, with improvements in robotics and nano-technology, the line between power armor and manned robot has become blurred. So-called "suits" of power armor are frequently small, one-man robots in which the "wearer" is a pilot who sits inside the armor. The accepted standard is that any humanoid shaped robot construct that is manned by a single pilot, utilizes pedals and leg movement and is under 15 feet (4.6 m) tall, is a suit of power armor. Anything not humanoid in appearance, fully automated, seats more than one, and/or is larger than 15 feet (4.6 m) is considered to be a robot vehicle. All types of *SAMAS* and the *Mauler* are examples of the traditional power armor combat "suit." *The Terror Trooper* and *Glitter Boy Killer* (as well as the Glitter Boy) are examples of where the line between power armor and robot become unclear.

All Power Armor have the following features:

1. Nuclear Powered: Which means they effectively have an unlimited fuel capacity and power source with an average life of 15 to 20 years.

2. Radar (upgraded): Can identify 72 targets and track up to 48 simultaneously at a range of 10 miles (16 km).

3. Combat Computer: Calculates, stores, and transmits data onto the head up display (H.U.D.) of the pilot's helmet. It is linked to the targeting computer, weapon systems and radar.

4. Targeting Computer: Assists in tracking and identification of enemy targets. Ten mile range (16 km).

5. Laser Targeting System: Assists in the selection and focusing of specific targets and adds a bonus to strike when using long-range weapons. Does not apply to hand to hand combat.

6. Radio communication: Long-range, directional communication system with an effective range of about 500 miles (800 km).

As well as a directional, short-range radio with a range 5 miles (8 km).

7. Built-in loud speaker: 80 decibels.

8. Complete environmental battle armor: Suitable for use in all hostile environments including under water (from several hundred feet to one mile depending on the suit) and even outerspace. The following features are included.

- Computer controlled life support system.
- Internal cooling and temperature control.
- Artificial air circulation systems, gas filtration, humidifier.
- Computer controlled, independent oxygen supply and purge system that automatically engages in low oxygen or contaminated air environments. Eight hour oxygen supply, but with the air recycling, circulatory system the wearer/pilot can remain inside the suit for days with breathable air.
- Insulated, high temperature resistant shielding for up to 400 degrees centigrade. Normal fires do no damage. Nuclear, plasma, and magic fires do full damage.
- Radiation shielding.
- Polarized and light sensitive/adjusting tinted visor (when applicable).

9. Special Bonuses: +2 on initiative and +1 to strike from combat computer and targeting systems.

Mauler Power Armor

The PA-100 Mauler is the design from the Coalition State of Iron Heart for a ponderous, heavily armored, all-purpose suit of environmental power armor. The Mauler, also known as "No Neck" and the "No Neck Mauler," has performed best in field tests as an urban assault and riot control unit, construction, heavy infantry support (typically armed with a rail gun or missile rifle) and as an aquatic, deep sea power armor useful for underwater exploration, salvage and combat. Small maneuvering jets are located on the hips, forearms, shoulders and back to assist in jumps and to provide propulsion underwater. Above and behind the head are four lights. The two center ones are infrared and used for night operations and seeing in murky water; the two larger ones are conventional lights. A pair of small infrared lights are also built into the lower abdomen plates to illuminate the water beneath the armor's feet as it descends into the depths (also good for land operations at night). According to the designers, the armor can even withstand the conditions of space.

Mauler Power Armor
Model Type: PA-100
Class: Heavy All-Purpose Combat Power Armor
Crew: One
M.D.C. by Location:
* Hands (2) — 25 each
Arms (2) — 100 each
Legs (2) — 150 each
Plasma Shoulder Guns (2) — 65 each
Concealed Mini-Missile Launcher (1; back) — 50
Concealed Forearm Blasters (2) — 50 each
Retractable Vibro-Sabers (2) — 50 each
Rear Jet Thruster (1) — 50
Shoulder Thruster Units (2) — 30 each

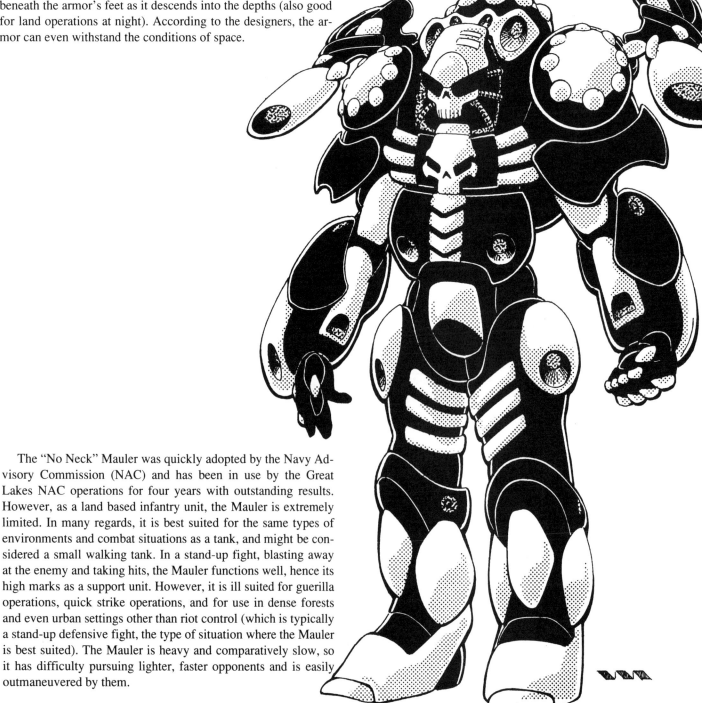

The "No Neck" Mauler was quickly adopted by the Navy Advisory Commission (NAC) and has been in use by the Great Lakes NAC operations for four years with outstanding results. However, as a land based infantry unit, the Mauler is extremely limited. In many regards, it is best suited for the same types of environments and combat situations as a tank, and might be considered a small walking tank. In a stand-up fight, blasting away at the enemy and taking hits, the Mauler functions well, hence its high marks as a support unit. However, it is ill suited for guerilla operations, quick strike operations, and for use in dense forests and even urban settings other than riot control (which is typically a stand-up defensive fight, the type of situation where the Mauler is best suited). The Mauler is heavy and comparatively slow, so it has difficulty pursuing lighter, faster opponents and is easily outmaneuvered by them.

* Maneuvering Jets (8) — 15 each
* Mini-Lights (6) — 1 each
** Head — 90
*** Main Body — 280

  * A single asterisk indicates a small and difficult target to strike, requiring the attacker to make a "called shot," but even then the attacker is -4 to strike.

  ** Destroying the head of the power armor will eliminate all forms of optical enhancement and sensory systems. The pilot must rely on his own human vision and senses. Any power armor bonuses to strike, parry and dodge are lost!

  The head is a small and difficult target to hit, tucked into the chest, between the two heavily plated shoulders. Thus, it can only be hit when an enemy makes a "called shot," but even then the attacker is -4 to strike.

  *** Depleting the M.D.C. of the main body will shut the armor down completely, rendering it useless.

Speed:

Running: 40 mph (64 km) maximum. Note that the act of running does tire its operator, but only at 10% of the usual fatigue rate.

Leaping: The robot legs and jet thrusters can propel the heavy and cumbersome power armor 15 feet (4.6 m) high or lengthwise with a short running start.

Underwater Capabilities: Swimming: The thruster system provides excellent mobility and control underwater but a sluggish speed of 15 mph (24 km/12.75 knots); roughly the same surface speed.

  Maximum Ocean Depth: One mile (1.6 km).

Statistical Data:
Height: 8 feet (2.4 m) from head to toe.
Width: 4.5 feet (1.4 m)
Length: 4 feet (1.2 m)
Weight: 1800 lbs (810 kg)
Physical Strength: Equal to a P.S. of 36.
Cargo: None
Power System: Nuclear, with an average energy life of 20 years.
CS Cost: 3.4 million credits.

Weapon Systems

1. Shoulder Plasma Ejectors (2): Mounted behind both shoulders is a short-range plasma ejector weapon. Both can rotate 180 degrees and have a 60 degree arc of fire.
Primary Purpose: Anti-Personnel
Secondary Purpose: Defense
Mega-Damage: 4D6 per laser blast.
Maximum Effective Range: 1200 feet (365.7 m).
Rate of Fire: Each can be fired twice per melee round.
Payload: Effectively unlimited, because the weapons are tied into the power supply of the suit.

2. Concealed, Back Mounted Mini-Missile Launcher (1): On the top of the jet thruster, built into the back of the power armor is what appears to be another set of small directional thrusters similar to the ones on the shoulders. However, this is a fake that conceals a mini-missile launcher.
Primary Purpose: Anti-Armor/Anti-Aircraft
Secondary Purpose: Defense
Missile Type: Any mini-missile types can be used, but standard issue is armor piercing (1D4×10 M.D.) or plasma (1D6×10 M.D.).

Mega-Damage: Varies with missile type.
Maximum Effective Range: Usually about a mile (1.6 km).
Rate of Fire: One at a time, or in volleys of two or three.
Payload: Eight. The launcher can be manually loaded by another power armor or soldier with a P.S. of 20; each missile takes about 10 seconds to reload.

3. Forearm Lasers (2): Concealed in the heavy forearm plates of each arm is a small laser. The pilot simply points and shoots.
Primary Purpose: Anti-Personnel
Secondary Purpose: Defense
Mega-Damage: 2D6 per laser blast.
Maximum Effective Range: 1200 feet (365.7 m).
Rate of Fire: Equal to the number of hand to hand attacks per melee round.
Payload: Effectively unlimited; tied to the armor's power supply.

4. Retractable Forearm Vibro-Sabers (2): Each arm can release a short vibro-sword from a housing in the underarm. The weapons can be used in close combat and to parry M.D. attacks, including energy blasts (-6 to parry), arrows and missiles (-4 to parry).
Mega-Damage: 2D4 M.D. each
Bonuses: +1 to strike and parry.

5. Energy Rifles, Rail Guns or other hand weapons can be used instead or in addition to the standard armaments.

6. Hand to Hand Combat: Rather than use a weapon, the pilot can engage in mega-damage hand to hand combat. The best the Mauler can perform is at the level of *Basic* training. See Basic Power Armor Combat Training in the **Rifts RPG**, page 45.

Terror Trooper Power Armor

The PA-200 Terror Trooper is another heavy armor, combat suit, but designed by the techs at Chi-Town with RPA pilots, Commandos and Special Forces in mind — the face plate is even reminiscent of the Special Forces skull design. Like most of the Coalition Army's war machines, the Terror Trooper power armor features the sinister Death's Head motif, is an ominous black color, lined with menacing spikes and offers a variety of built-in weapons. This power armor is similar to Triax's Ulti-Max in that the pilot sits in the chest area and manipulates robot arms, hands and legs with hand and foot controls. This offers superior protection and maximum firepower.

The Terror Trooper stands 11 feet (3.3 m) tall and is equipped with forearm housings that conceal medium-range, but high-powered lasers. The hands of the power armor are completely mechanical and contain extendable finger claws for close combat. The pair of tube-like protrusions from the back are cylindrical mini-missile launchers. The standard issue, hand-held weapon is the CTT-P40 particle beam cannon, although the CTT-M20 missile rifle or heavy rail guns can be used in the alternative. **Note:** The Terror Trooper illustration shows the CTT-M20 missile rifle while the Special-Ops Striker SAMAS shows the CTT-P40. Both weapons have a very similar shape although closer scrutiny will show that both are really fairly different

looking. These two weapons were specifically designed with power armor and cyborg troops in mind, but can also be used as over-sized two-handed weapons by CS Juicers.

The armor has good mobility and maneuverability and works well in all environments, from woodland and open fields to city streets. Its 11 foot height gives it a relatively low profile and makes it suitable for easy transport by truck, helicopter or APC. It is a favorite of commandos and RPA pilots assigned to infantry and Special missions that require ground operatives. The Terror Trooper, like most full environmental suits and bots, is suitable for use underwater, although it does not have any special propulsion system like the Mauler.

Terror Trooper Power Armor
Model Type: PA-200
Class: Heavy Assault Combat Power Armor
Crew: One
M.D.C. by Location:
   * Hands (2) — 45 each
   Arms (2) — 85 each
   Legs (2) — 160 each

Tube Mini-Missile Launchers (2; back) — 50 each

* Forearm Lasers (2) — 70 each

Rifle or Rail Gun (1) — 100

* Secondary Optics/Cameras (2; chest) — 5 each

** Head (Main sensors) — 100

*** Main Body — 400

* A single asterisk indicates a small and difficult target to strike, requiring the attacker to make a "called shot," but even then the attacker is -4 to strike. Two small camera lenses located in the chest of the power armor are video cameras with telescopic (×15 magnification) and passive night-sight capabilities which serve as a secondary or back-up optical system in case the head is destroyed.

** Destroying the head of the power armor will eliminate all radar, sensory systems and main optics. The pilot must rely on his own human vision and senses. Any power armor bonuses to strike, parry and dodge are lost!

The head is a small and difficult target to hit, tucked into the chest, between the two heavily plated shoulders. Thus, it can only be hit when an enemy makes a "called shot," but even then the attacker is -3 to strike.

*** Depleting the M.D.C. of the main body will shut the armor down completely, rendering it useless.

Speed:

Running: 60 mph (96.5 km) maximum. Note that the act of running does tire its operator, but only at 10% of the usual fatigue rate.

Leaping: The robot legs can propel the heavy power armor 15 feet (4.6 m) high or lengthwise with a short running start.

Underwater Capabilities: Swimming: The Terror Trooper has no thruster system so its mobility underwater is comparatively poor and slow. Basically, the pilot can *swim* using the same types of paddling leg and arm movements as a human. Maximum speed is roughly five mph (8 km/4.25 knots). It can also walk along the bottom of the sea at about 25% its normal walking/running speed.

Maximum Ocean Depth: One mile (1.6 km).

Statistical Data:

Height: 11 feet (3.3 m) from head to toe.

Width: 6 feet (1.8 m)

Length: 5 feet (1.5 m)

Weight: 1250 lbs (562.5 kg)

Physical Strength: Equal to a P.S. of 40.

Cargo: None

Power System: Nuclear, with an average energy life of 20 years.

CS Cost: 4.1 million credits.

Weapon Systems

1. **Forearm Laser Blasters (2):** Mounted on the forearm of each arm is a high-powered laser. The pilot simply points and shoots.

Primary Purpose: Anti-Personnel

Secondary Purpose: Defense

Mega-Damage: 3D6 per single laser blast. Both arms can be aimed and pointed at the same target and fired simultaneously doing 6D6 M.D. and counts as *one* melee attack, but is -2 to strike and nothing large like a rifle can be held in either hand (throws off balance).

Maximum Effective Range: 2000 feet (610 m)

Rate of Fire: Equal to the number of hand to hand attacks per melee round.

Payload: Effectively unlimited; tied to the armor's power supply.

2. **A pair of Mini-Missile Launcher Tubes (2):** Mounted in the back are two mini-missile tube launchers.

Primary Purpose: Anti-Armor/Anti-Aircraft

Secondary Purpose: Defense

Missile Type: Any mini-missile types can be used, but standard issue is armor piercing (1D4×10 M.D.) or plasma (1D6×10 M.D.).

Mega-Damage: Varies with missile type.

Maximum Effective Range: Usually about a mile (1.6 km).

Rate of Fire: One at a time, or in volleys of two or four.

Payload: 20 total; 10 per launch tube.

3. **CTT-M20 Missile Rifle (1):** A giant-sized rifle that is standard issue for the Terror Trooper (the CTT-P40 can be substituted). This weapon houses a row of mini-missiles down each of its long, twin barrels. Each pull of the trigger fires one mini-missile. Remember, mini-missiles are self-guided, so once launched, they will find their target.

Mounted on the top of the rifle is a box that is more than a laser targeting system. The lower port is a laser targeting sight (+1 to strike), but the larger one above it is a medium-ranged laser. The CTT-M20 is standard issue for the Terror Trooper, although the CTT-P40 or a rail gun can be substituted. It is also frequently used with other power armor suits, by SAMAS, full conversion 'Borgs and the occasional Juicer.

Primary Purpose: Anti-Armor/Anti-Aircraft

Secondary Purpose: Defense

Missile Type: Any mini-missile types can be used, but standard issue is armor piercing (1D4×10 M.D.) or plasma (1D6×10 M.D.).

Mega-Damage: Varies with missile type.

The laser does 2D6 M.D. per shot.

Maximum Effective Range: Mini-missiles: Usually about a mile (1.6 km). Laser: 2000 feet (610 m)

Rate of Fire: One at a time, or in volleys of two or four.

Payload: 20 total; 10 per launch tube. The laser mounted on the top of the CTT-M20 takes a standard E-clip (20 shots) or long E-clip (30 shots).

4. **CTT-P40 Particle Beam Cannon (1; Optional):** A giant-sized particle beam rifle with exceptional range (for a P-beam weapon). Mounted on the top of the rifle is a box laser targeting system and passive nightvision scope with telescopic capabilities (20x magnification; 3000 foot/910 m range). This weapon is standard issue with the Special Forces' Striker SAMAS and is frequently used by the Terror Trooper, full conversion 'Borgs and the occasional CS Juicer.

Primary Purpose: Anti-Personnel

Secondary Purpose: Defense

Mega-Damage: Particle beam: 1D6×10 M.D. per single laser blast.

Maximum Effective Range: 2000 feet (610 m)

Rate of Fire: Equal to the number of hand to hand attacks per melee round.

Payload: 40 particle beam blasts — virtually the entire back half of the giant rifle/cannon is a rechargeable energy cell.

5. **Energy Rifles, Rail Guns** or other heavy weapons can be used instead or in addition to the standard armaments.

6. Hand to Hand Combat: Rather than use a weapon, the pilot can engage in mega-damage hand to hand combat. See Basic and Elite Power Armor Combat Training in the **Rifts RPG**, page 45, for details. All abilities are the same except as follows:

Restrained Punch — 1D4 M.D.
Normal Punch or Kick — 2D4 M.D.
Normal Power Punch — 4D4 M.D. (costs two melee attacks)
Claw Strike (finger claws extended) — 2D6 M.D.
Claw Power Strike (finger claws extended) — 4D6 M.D.
Leap Kick — 2D6 M.D. (costs two melee attacks)
Body Flip/Throw — 1D6 M.D.
Body Block/Tackle — 1D6 M.D.

Glitter Boy Killer Power Armor

The PA-300 Glitter Boy Killer is a new experimental power armor that has performed well in training exercises but has had very little actual field battles against the Glitter Boy. This makes some military leaders nervous because it means the G.B. Killer will get a trial by fire when it faces the Glitter Boy Forces of Quebec. However, the power armor has functioned perfectly in all training exercises and has performed admirably in the field against other power armor and robots. The designers are so confident that their creation will be a powerful deterrent against the Glitter Boy that they have convinced the Coalition High Command to produce nearly 10,000 PA-300s, 90% of which are already on their way to the Quebec front-line.

In order to successfully fight toe to toe with a Glitter Boy, the PA-300 G.B. Killer has been designed to take advantage of the Glitter Boy's weaknesses, namely poor mobility, slow speed, and having to secure itself to the ground before it can fire the famous Boom Gun. To this end, the PA-300 has been given great speed, mobility and is armed with a diverse array of weaponry. The Glitter Boy Killer is especially effective in contained areas, urban settings and close quarters where it can blast and cut a Glitter Boy to ribbons. In the open, the G.B. Killer is vulnerable to the long range and devastating power of the Boom Gun.

To counter the long range of the Boom Gun, the G.B. Killer is armed with 10 plasma mini-missiles and a pair of small extra gun arms that are light rail guns. The main arms are well armored and equipped with a ranged weapon and a pair of wicked vibro-blades. The forearm weapons include an over and under plasma gun and ion blaster, while the right has four openings that fire M.D. rifle grenade rounds. Even the knee guards are lined with long spikes for kneeing blows to the enemy. The large, heavy feet help to balance the slightly top heavy power armor and allow for better traction when running. Only the triple barreled turret on the back, above the head, are lasers, and they are provided primarily as anti-missile and aircraft weapons.

The standard tactic of the Glitter Boy Killer is to target and destroy the Boom Gun, first with missiles, then with other weapons. If the Boom Gun can be destroyed, the Glitter Boy, even with its superior mega-damage armor becomes (comparatively) easy prey for the plasma gun, rail guns and grenade launcher, and even the giant slashing forearm blades. However, after the missiles, all the other weapons have a short range compared to the Boom Gun, forcing the PA-300 to close within dangerous striking distance (especially dangerous when in one on one confrontations). Theoretically, the Glitter Boy Killer's superior speed and agility gives it the edge in outmaneuvering his opponent. While it does give him an edge, particularly in environments where there is a great deal of ground cover, on open ground it is not enough to compensate. In fact, one on one field tests showed that when a G.B. Killer had to attack in open terrain from a distance of a half mile or more, the Glitter Boy won the confrontation three out of four times, although it usually suffered severe damage. Consequently, the Coalition Army *plans* to dispatch the G.B. Killers in pairs. Two to one confrontations showed the pair of PA-300s would devastate a single Glitter Boy better than three out of four times.

Like the Terror Trooper, the pilot of this armor sits in the chest and controls the robot arms and legs with a series of levers and foot pedals.

Glitter Boy Killer Power Armor

Model Type: PA-300
Class: Heavy Assault Combat Power Armor
Crew: One
M.D.C. by Location:

* Hands (2) — 25 each
Lower Arms (2) — 110 each
* Upper Arms (2; thin) — 55 each
* Forearm Plasma Gun (1; left) — 35
* Forearm Ion Gun (1; left) — 15
* Forearm Grenade Launcher (1; right) — 20
Small Forearm Vibro-Blades (2) — 50 each
Large Forearm Vibro-Blades (2) — 90 each
* Extra Gun Arms (2; shoulders) — 45 each
Triple Barrel Laser Turret (1; back) — 80
Legs (2) — 230 each
Feet (2) — 100 each
* Mini-Tube Mini-Missile Launchers (10; shoulders) — 10 each
Secondary Sensor Clusters (2; chest) — 45 each
** Head (Main sensors) — 90
*** Main Body — 440

* A single asterisk indicates a small and difficult target to strike, requiring the attacker to make a "called shot," but even then the attacker is -4 to strike.

** Destroying the head of the power armor will eliminate the main sensory system and optics, but does not impair the pilot. Two secondary sensor clusters located in the chest and shoulder area on either side of the head compensate for the loss of the head sensors. Only if all three are destroyed must the pilot rely on his own human vision and senses and loses any power armor bonuses to strike, parry and dodge.

The head is a small and difficult target to hit, tucked into the chest, between the two heavily plated shoulders. Thus, it can only be hit when an enemy makes a "called shot," but even then the attacker is -3 to strike.

*** Depleting the M.D.C. of the main body will shut the armor down completely, rendering it useless.

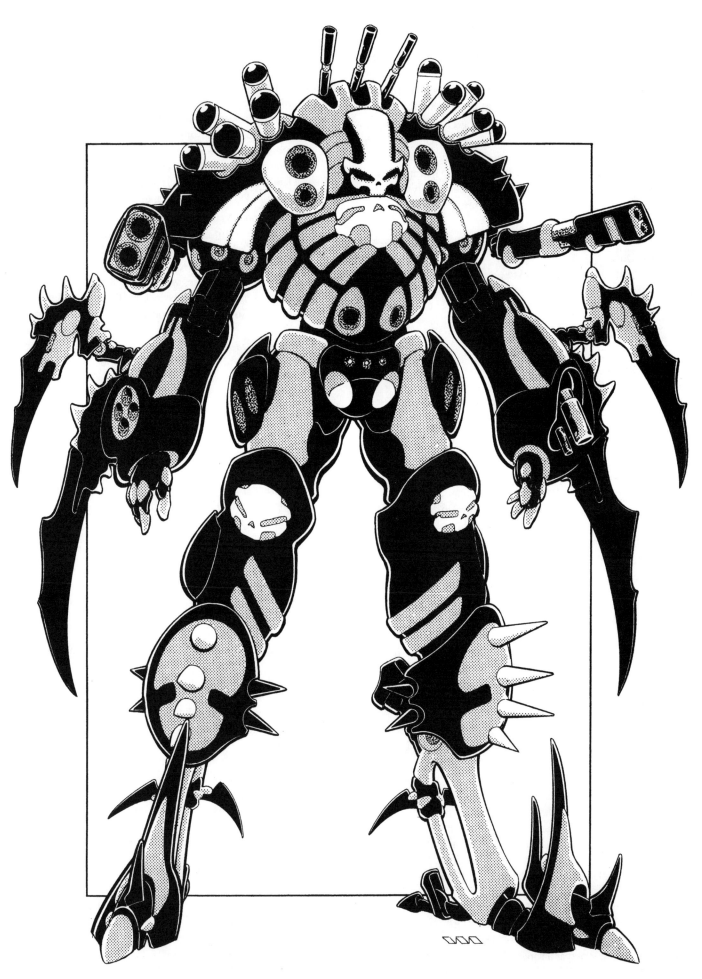

Speed:

Running: 100 mph (160 km) maximum; can go from zero to 60 mph (96.5 km) in 11 seconds. Note that the act of running does not tire its operator.

Leaping: The robot legs can propel the heavy power armor 20 feet (6 m) high or lengthwise with a short running start.

Underwater Capabilities: Swimming: The G.B. Killer has no thruster system so its mobility underwater is comparatively poor and slow. Basically, the pilot can *swim* using the same types of paddling leg and arm movements as a human. Maximum speed is roughly four mph (6.4 km/3.4 knots). It can also walk along the bottom of the sea at about 25% its normal walking/running speed.

Maximum Ocean Depth: 4000 feet (1200 m).

Statistical Data:

Height: 14 feet (4.3 m) from head to toe.

Width: 7 feet (2.1 m)

Length: 5 feet (1.5 m)

Weight: 2 tons

Physical Strength: Equal to a P.S. of 40.

Cargo: None

Power System: Nuclear, with an average energy life of 20 years.

CS Cost: 12.6 million credits.

Weapon Systems

1. **Forearm Plasma Gun (1):** Built into the left forearm is a plasma gun and an ion gun. The G.B. Killer points and shoots.

Primary Purpose: Anti-Glitter Boy/Anti-Armor

Secondary Purpose: Anti-Personnel and Defense.

Mega-Damage: 6D6 per single laser blast or 1D6×10 if both the plasma gun and ion gun are fired at the same target simultaneously. Counts as *one* melee attack.

Maximum Effective Range: 1600 feet (488 km)

Rate of Fire: Equal to the number of hand to hand attacks per melee round.

Payload: Effectively unlimited; tied to the armor's power supply.

2. **Forearm Ion Gun (1):** Built into the left forearm beneath the plasma gun is an ion gun. The G.B. Killer points and shoots.

Primary Purpose: Anti-Glitter Boy/Anti-Armor

Secondary Purpose: Anti-Personnel and Defense.

Mega-Damage: 3D6 per single laser blast or 1D6×10 if both the plasma gun and ion gun are fired at the same target simultaneously. Counts as *one* melee attack.

Maximum Effective Range: 1200 feet (366 km)

Rate of Fire: Equal to the number of hand to hand attacks per melee round.

Payload: Effectively unlimited; tied to the armor's power supply.

3. **Forearm Grenade Launcher (1):** In the right arm is a quad-grenade launch system that can fire rifle grenades.

Primary Purpose: Anti-Glitter Boy/Anti-Armor

Secondary Purpose: Anti-Personnel and Defense.

Mega-Damage: The weapon can fire conventional M.D. rifle grenades doing 2D6 M.D. to a blast area of 12 feet (3.6 m), or *new, micro-fusion grenades* that inflict 6D6 M.D. to a 12 foot (3.6 m) diameter blast area/six foot (1.8 m) radius.

Maximum Effective Range: 1200 feet (365 km)

Rate of Fire: Equal to the number of hand to hand attacks per melee round, either one at a time or in volleys of two (counts as one attack).

Payload: 40 total.

4. **Forearm Vibro-Blades (4):** Each of the arms has pair of large vibro-blades. The largest blades are mounted in a fixed forward position. The smaller pair (still the size of vibro-swords) are mounted on small moveable mounts that can be moved back or forward in a stabbing motion. One ploy is to impale an opponent with the large vibro-sword and have the smaller blade stab the pinned victim repeatedly. When fixed forward, the small blade is almost as long as the large blade and can be used to strike as a double blade.

Mega-Damage: 3D6 M.D. from the large blade, 2D6 from the small blade or 5D6 from a simultaneous double blade strike.

5. **Extra Weapon Arms (2):** Mounted under the shoulder plates and above the main arms are a pair of small gun arms. These are light rail guns. They can be operated independent of the main arms and each other, or synchronized to mimic the motion of the main arm; i.e. when the main left arm points, the left weapon arm also points in that direction. When the left arm fires, the small, left weapon arm also fires (if a target is in range).

Primary Purpose: Assault

Mega-Damage: A full damage burst is 20 rounds and inflicts 4D6 M.D. At the flip of a switch the weapon can fire 10 shot bursts which inflict 2D6 M.D.

Maximum Effective Range: 4000 feet (1220 m)

Rate of Fire: Equal to the combined hand to hand attacks of the pilot (usually 4-6).

Payload: 3200 round drum for 80 bursts per weapon arm (160 total)!

6. **Triple Barrel Laser Turret (1):** This is an anti-missile and anti-aircraft weapon. The three barrels are synchronized to all move at once and can rotate up and down in a 180 degree arc of fire; front and back.

Primary Purpose: Anti-Glitter Boy/Anti-Armor

Secondary Purpose: Anti-Personnel and Defense.

Mega-Damage: 2D6 per single laser blast or 6D6 if all three lasers are fired at the same target simultaneously. Counts as *one* melee attack.

Maximum Effective Range: 2000 feet (610 km)

Rate of Fire: Equal to the number of hand to hand attacks per melee round.

Payload: Effectively unlimited; tied to the armor's power supply.

7. **Energy Rifles** or other heavy weapons *cannot* be used because of the shape of the forearms and position of the hands. However, the hands can be used to pick up and carry a variety of items.

8. **Hand to Hand Combat:** Rather than use a weapon, the pilot can engage in mega-damage hand to hand combat. See Basic and Elite Power Armor Combat Training in the **Rifts RPG**, page 45, for details. All abilities are the same except as follows:

Normal Punch or Kick — 1D6 M.D.

Power Punch — 2D6 M.D., but counts as two melee attacks.

Vibro-Blade Strike (single blade) — 3D6 or 2D6 M.D.

Vibro-Blade Strike (double blade) — 5D6 M.D.

Vibro-Blade Power Strike (double blade) — 1D6×10 M.D., but counts as two melee attacks.

Leap Kick — 2D6 M.D., but counts as two melee attacks.

Body Flip/Throw — 1D4 M.D.

Body Block/Tackle — 1D6 M.D.

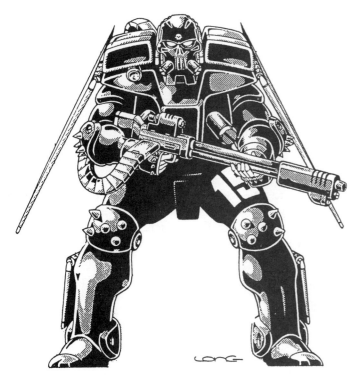

Old-Style "Death's Head" SAMAS

The original PA-06A SAMAS has been a workhorse for the Coalition States, proving to be fast, maneuverable and deadly in all environments, from open combat to city streets. The SAMAS' amazing versatility has made it equally useful in infantry assault, frontline combat, surgical strikes, troop support, seek and destroy, reconnaissance, rescue, espionage and defense. It can hover, fly, and make tight turns while traveling at maximum speed. Being roughly man-sized and having a relatively short wingspan, it maneuvers through narrow streets and corridors, yet does not sacrifice firepower or armor protection for size and maneuverability. Its folding wings enables the armor to make Vertical Take-Offs and Landings (VTOL) with the wings in a down position, as well as allowing the wings to be folded partially or entirely and still rocket down narrow hallways and through open doors. The Death's Head SAMAS quickly became "the" power armor of the CS and is famous and feared throughout North America.

The success of the SAMAS has prompted the Coalition Military to expand on its design, leading to the creation of the *Light Assault SAMAS, Super SAMAS* and *Special Forces Striker SAMAS*. The old-style PA-06A "Death's Head" SAMAS has been semi-retired from *military* service and has become part of the ISS, where it is widely used. Over 3.2 million PA-06A SAMAS are stockpiled; half are currently in use by the ISS and its subdivisions (the SAMAS is perfect for city operations, even in the walled, fortress super-cities). The old "Death's Head" SAMAS is also available to commandos, Special Forces and the elite RPA SAMAS pilots.

Note: Unknown to anybody outside the Coalition's Military High Command and the Emperor, the PA-06A SAMAS is a slightly modified version of a pre-Rifts power armor suit developed by the Air Force of the old American Empire. It was about to be put into production when the world was shattered by the Great Cataclysm that signaled the Coming of the Rifts. Only the Coalition State of Chi-Town (and unknown to them, the New Republic of Japan) possess these top secret plans.

"Death's Head" SAMAS Power Armor

Nickname: Old Sam
Model Type: PA-06A
Class: Strategic Armor Military Assault Suit
Crew: One
M.D.C. by Location:

* Shoulder Wings (2) — 50 each (improved M.D.C.)
 Main Rear Jets (2) — 60 each
 Lower Maneuvering Jets (2; small) — 25 each
* Ammo Drum (rear) — 35
* Rail Gun — 50
 Forearm Mini-Missile Launcher (1; left) — 50
* Hands (2) — 25 each
 Arms (2) — 50 each
 Legs (2) — 100 each
** Head — 70
*** Main Body — 250

    * A single asterisk indicates a small and difficult target to strike, requiring the attacker to make a "called shot," but even then the attacker is -4 to strike.

    ** Destroying the head of the power armor will eliminate all forms of optical enhancement and sensory systems. The pilot must them rely on his own human vision and senses. No power armor combat bonuses to strike, parry, and dodge!

    The head is a small and difficult target to hit, shielded by exhaust tubes and a weapon drum. Thus, it can only be hit when a character makes a "called shot" and even then the attacker is -3 to strike.

    *** Depleting the M.D.C. of the main body will shut the armor down completely, making it useless. **Note:** Destroying a wing will make flight impossible. However, even with no wing(s) the SAMAS can make jet powered leaps and hover stationary above the ground.

Speed

Running: 60 mph (96 km) maximum; can go from zero to 60 mph (96.5 km) in 12 seconds. Note that the act of running does tire out its operator, but at 10% of the usual fatigue rate, thanks to the robot exoskeleton.

Leaping: The powerful robot legs can leap up to 15 feet (4.6 m) high or across unassisted by the thrusters.

A jet thruster assisted leap can propel the unit up to 100 feet (30.5 m) high and 200 feet (61 m) across without actually attaining flight.

Flying: The rocket propulsion system enables the SAMAS to hover stationary up to 200 feet (61 m) or fly. Maximum flying speed is 300 mph (480 km), but cruising speed is considered to be 150 mph (240 km). Maximum altitude has been suggested to be limited to about 500 feet (152 m), but use in the field has proven that the PA-06A SAMAS can easily attain and maintain an altitude of 6000 feet (1829 m; a little over one mile/1.6 km)). Higher than this, high winds and rough weather make flight both erratic and dangerous. The SAMAS is just too small and light, it was designed to be a low altitude power armor suit that could hug the ground and slip under enemy radar, which it does admirably. *Optimum altitude range* is ground level to about 1000 feet (305 m).

Flying Range: The nuclear power supply gives the SAMAS decades of life but the jet rockets get hot and need to cool after a maximum of 10 hours of continuous flight at speeds above cruising, 24 hours at cruising speed. It can fly and indefinitely with rest stops every few hours.

Underwater Capabilities: Swimming: The SAMAS can *swim* using the same types of paddling leg and arm movements as a human at a maximum speed of roughly four mph (6.4 km/3.4 knots). It can also walk along the bottom of the sea at about 25% its normal running speed. Using the jet thrusters, the SAMAS can travel on the surface of water at 50 mph (80 km/42.5 knots), underwater at 40 mph (64 km/34 knots) or fly above the water's surface at normal speeds.

Maximum Ocean Depth: 1000 feet (305 m).

Statistical Data

Height: 8 feet (2.4 m)
Width: Wings down, 3.5 feet (1.06 m)
  Wings extended, 10 feet (3 m)
Length: 4 feet, 6 inches (1.4 m)
Weight: 340 lbs (153 kg) without rail gun.
Physical Strength: Equal to a P.S. 30
Cargo: None
Power System: Nuclear, average SAMAS energy life is 20 years.
Black Market Cost: 1.6 million credits for a new, undamaged, fully powered suit complete with rail gun and one full ammo-drum. Rarely available.

Weapon Systems

1. **C-40R SAMAS Rail Gun (1):** This is standard equipment for the "Death's Head" SAMAS and is considered to be the most powerful, accurate, and lightweight rail gun in the world. It requires no separate power pack, because it is hooked directly to the armor's nuclear power supply. Other heavier rail guns can be substituted. Likewise, the new CTT-M20 missile rifle or CTT-P40 rifle can be used as an oversized two-handed weapon.

Primary Purpose: Assault
Secondary Purpose: Defense
Weight: Gun: 92 lbs (41.4 kg), One SAMAS Ammo-Drum: 190 lbs (85.5 kg).
Mega-Damage: A burst is 40 rounds and inflicts 1D4×10 M.D., one round does 1D4 M.D.
Rate of Fire: Equal to number of combined hand to hand attacks (usually 4-6).
Maximum Effective Range: 4000 feet (1200 m)
Payload: 2000 round drum, that's 50 bursts. A second drum can be hooked to the undercarriage of the rocket jets, but first the used drum must be manually removed by another SAMAS or character with a strength of 26 or higher and the new ammo drum put in its place. Reloading a drum will take about 5 minutes for those not trained, but a mere one minute by somebody trained in the use of SAMAS power armor.

2. **CM-2 Rocket Launcher:** The forearm not used to operate the rail gun, usually the left, is armed with a simple, two rocket, mini-missile launcher.

Primary Purpose: Anti-Aircraft
Secondary Purpose: Defense
Missile Type: Any mini-missile can be used, but standard issue is armor piercing (1D4×10 M.D.) or plasma (1D6×10). Fragmentation will be used for anti-personnel operations.

Mega-Damage: Varies with missile type.
Range: Usually about a mile.
Rate of Fire: One or two.
Payload: Two

3. **Energy Rifles:** The "Death's Head" SAMAS is small enough that it can use any of the standard infantry weapons from pistols and vibro-blades to rifles. Any of these items can be substituted for the rail gun or kept as a back-up weapon; usually slung at the waist on an extra large utility belt or holstered on the upper leg. Space limitations and the bulk of the armor usually limits additional man-sized weapons to one handgun and/or one rifle. Grenades can also be carried in a satchel (typically 6-12) and dropped like bombs. Grenades cannot be carried hooked to a belt or bandolier for fear of being pulled off when travelling at great speed. The CTT-M20 missile rifle or CTT-P40 rifle can also be used as an over-sized two-handed weapon.

4. **Hand to Hand Combat:** Rather than use a weapon, the pilot can engage in mega-damage hand to hand combat. See *Basic and Elite* Power Armor Combat Training on page 45 of the **Rifts® RPG** for combat bonuses.

5. **Sensor System Note:** The SAMAS has full optical systems, including laser targeting, telescopic, passive nightvision (light amplification), thermo-imaging, infrared, ultraviolet, and polarization. Plus all other features common to all power armor.

Sensor Bonuses: The SAMAS gets a bonus of +1 to strike and +1 to dodge in addition to the power armor target bonus and Basic or Elite Power Armor Combat Training bonuses.

New "Smiling Jack" Light Assault SAMAS

The PA-07A Light Assault SAMAS is patterned after the original PA-06A as a low altitude, all environment power armor fighter. Like the PA-06A, the Smiling Jack is fast, tough, reliable and capable of infantry assaults, frontline combat, surgical strikes, troop support, seek and destroy, reconnaissance, rescue, espionage and defense. It can fly, hover, make tight turns and is small enough to maneuver through narrow streets and corridors without sacrificing firepower or armor protection.

The armor styling of the Smiling Jack is similar to the new Coalition body armor but is still recognizable as a SAMAS. The helmet has a large one way glass (tough as M.D. steel) that gives the pilot optimum peripheral vision. The lower jaw portion appears to be locked in a smiling position, showing a set of broad flat teeth, hence its nickname, "Smiling Jack." The PA-07A has all the same basic features, weapons and capabilities of the old, Death's Head SAMAS. The only difference is its appearance, one large air intake jet above the head, less bulky but equally strong armor, mini-missile launchers built into the wings, and five lower, secondary jet thrusters to give the suit better control and mobility at altitudes above 1000 feet (305 m).

"Smiling Jack" SAMAS Power Armor

Model Type: PA-07A
Class: Strategic Armor Military Assault Suit
Crew: One

M.D.C. by Location:
 * Shoulder Wings (2) — 85 each
 * Wing Mini-Missile Launchers (6 total) — 8 each
 Main Rear Jets (2) — 60 each
 Lower Maneuvering Jets (5) — 25 each
 Intake Jet (1; top) — 40
 * Ammo Drum (rear) — 35
 * Rail Gun — 50   Legs (2) — 100 each
 * Hands (2) — 25 each   ** Head — 70
 Arms (2) — 50 each   *** Main Body — 250

       * A single asterisk indicates a small and difficult target to strike, requiring the attacker to make a "called shot," but even then the attacker is -4 to strike.

** Destroying the head of the power armor will eliminate all forms of optical enhancement and sensory systems. The pilot must then rely on his own human vision and senses. No power armor combat bonuses to strike, parry, and dodge!

The head is a small and difficult target to hit, shielded by exhaust tubes and weapon drum. Thus, it can only be hit when a character makes a "called shot" and even then the attacker is -3 to strike.

*** Depleting the M.D.C. of the main body will shut the armor down completely, making it useless. **Note:** Destroying a wing will make flight impossible. However, even with no wing(s), the SAMAS can make jet powered leaps and hover stationary above the ground.

Speed

Running: 60 mph (96 km) maximum. Note that the act of running does tire out its operator, but at 10% of the usual fatigue rate.

Leaping: The powerful robot legs can leap up to 15 feet (4.6 m) high or across unassisted by the thrusters.

A jet thruster assisted leap can propel the unit up to 100 feet (30.5 m) high and 200 feet (61 m) across without actually attaining flight.

Flying: The rocket propulsion system enables the SAMAS to hover stationary up to 1000 feet (305 m) or fly. Maximum flying speed is 300 mph (480 km), but cruising speed is considered to be 150 mph (240 km). Maximum altitude is 6000 feet (1829 m; a little over one mile/1.6 km). Higher than this, high winds and rough weather make flight both erratic and dangerous. The Smiling Jack SAMAS is still too small and light even with the additional thrusters, to safely fly at greater heights. *Optimum altitude range* is ground level to about 4000 feet (1200 m). Like its predecessor, the Smiling Jack is designed to be a low altitude power armor suit that can hug the ground and slip under enemy radar.

Flying Range: The nuclear power supply gives the SAMAS decades of life but the jet rockets get hot and need to cool after a maximum of 10 hours of continuous flight at speeds above cruising, 24 hours at cruising speed. It can fly indefinitely with rest stops every few hours.

Underwater Capabilities: Swimming: The SAMAS can *swim* using the same types of paddling leg and arm movements as a human at a maximum speed of roughly four mph (6.4 km/3.4 knots). It can also walk along the bottom of the sea at about 25% its normal running speed. Using the jet thrusters, the SAMAS can travel on the surface of water at 50 mph (80 km/42.5 knots), underwater at 40 mph (64 km/34 knots) or fly above the water's surface at normal speeds.

Maximum Ocean Depth: 1000 feet (305 m).

Statistical Data

Height: 8 feet (2.4 m) from head to toe. The top mounted air foil adds another two feet (0.6 m) for an overall height of 10 feet (3 m).
Width: Wings down, 3.5 feet (1.06 m)
  Wings extended, 12 feet (3.6 m)
Length: 4 feet 6 inches (1.4 m)
Weight: 500 lbs (225 kg) without the rail gun and ammo drum.
Physical Strength: Equal to a P.S. 30
Cargo: None

Power System: Nuclear, average SAMAS energy life is 20 years.

CS Cost: 1.8 million credits for a new, undamaged, full powered suit complete with rail gun and one full ammo-drum. None have yet fallen into the hands of the Black Market.

Weapon Systems

1. C-40R SAMAS Rail Gun (1): This is standard equipment for the "Smiling Jack" SAMAS. Other heavier rail guns can be substituted. Likewise, the new CTT-M20 missile rifle or CTT-P40 rifle can be used as an over-sized two-handed weapon.
Primary Purpose: Assault
Secondary Purpose: Defense
Weight: Gun: 92 lbs (41.4 kg), One SAMAS Ammo-Drum: 190 lbs (85.5 kg).
Mega-Damage: A Burst is 40 rounds and inflicts 1D4×10 M.D., one round does 1D4 M.D.
Rate of Fire: Equal to number of combined hand to hand attacks (usually 4-6).
Maximum Effective Range: 4000 feet (1200 m)
Payload: 3000 round drum, that's 75 bursts. A second drum can be hooked to the undercarriage of the rocket jets, but first the used drum must be manually removed by another SAMAS or character with a strength of 26 or higher before it can be replaced with the new one. Reloading a drum will take about 5 minutes for those not trained, but a mere one minute by somebody trained in the use of SAMAS power armor.

2. SJ-6 Mini-Missile Launchers: Each of the wings have three small, tube mini-missile launchers.
Primary Purpose: Anti-Aircraft
Secondary Purpose: Defense
Missile Type: Any mini-missile can be used, but standard issue is armor piercing (1D4×10 M.D.) or plasma (1D6×10). Fragmentation will be used for anti-personnel operations.
Mega-Damage: Varies with missile type.
Range: Usually about a mile.
Rate of Fire: One at a time or in volleys of two, four or six.
Payload: Six total; three per wing.

3. Energy Rifles: Same as the "Death's Head" SAMAS. The "Smiling Jack" SAMAS is small enough that it can use any of the standard infantry weapons from pistols and vibro-blades to rifles. Or the CTT-M20 missile rifle or CTT-P40 rifle can also be used as an over-sized two-handed weapon.

4. Hand to Hand Combat: Rather than use a weapon, the pilot can engage in mega-damage hand to hand combat. See *Basic and Elite* Power Armor Combat Training on page 45 of the **Rifts® RPG** for combat bonuses.

5. Sensor System Note: The SAMAS has full optical systems, including laser targeting, telescopic, passive nightvision (light amplification), thermo-imaging, infrared, ultraviolet, and polarization. Plus all other features common to all power armor.

Sensor Bonuses: The SAMAS gets a bonus of +1 to strike and +1 to dodge in addition to the power armor target bonus and Basic or Elite Power Armor Combat Training bonuses.

New Super SAMAS

The PA-09A Super SAMAS is patterned after the original PA-06A and resembles its Light Assault brother, right down to the toothy grin. Nicknamed the "Grinning Demon;" it is a fast, tough, and reliable power armor suitable for all types of combat missions. However, it is also a heavy, high and low altitude, all environment power armor fighter designed specifically as a front-line combat and support unit.

The quad-thruster jets and heavy armor enable it to reach an altitude of three miles (4.8 km) and engage skycycles and light aircraft. In addition to a hand-held weapon (usually a rail gun or other heavy weapon), a pair of high-powered plasma ejectors

and light lasers are mounted above the shoulders and mini-fusion grenades can be fired from the forearms. The forearms are also lined with three vibro-blades that are used to rake opponents or clip propellers of combat helicopters as the SAMAS flies bys. Small thrusters in the back and in the feet help to give the power armor pilot better control and maneuverability.

The speed and firepower of the Super SAMAS makes it ideal for engaging slow to medium speed aircraft, hover vehicles, enemy power armor, and flight capable creatures such as dragons, demons and troops magically empowered with the ability to fly. In dogfights against such enemies, they are virtually unmatched, especially when dispatched in squads of 4-10 members. The only aircraft the Super SAMAS is not well equipped to handle are those that travel faster than sound (Mach One or greater). The heavily armored, fast moving power armor is also an effective weapon against Glitter Boys and tanks — again, especially when a Super SAMAS squad outnumbers the tank or G.B. two to one, or better.

If the Super SAMAS has any combat weakness, it is that, except for the rail gun, its weapon systems are limited to medium-range, requiring close-combat dogfighting to be truly effective. Of course, the elite RPA SAMAS pilots (see **Rifts® RPG**) and RPA "Fly Boys" who pilot them, seem to relish such death-defying combat.

Super SAMAS Power Armor

Nicknames: Include the "Grinning Demon" and "Super-Sam," but it is most frequently called simply, the "Super SAMAS."

Model Type: PA-09A

Class: Strategic Armor Military Assault Suit

Crew: One

M.D.C. by Location:

* Shoulder Wings (2) — 95 each
  Main Rear Jets (4) — 100 each
* Lower Maneuvering Jets (3; rear) — 30 each
  Twin Air-Intake Jets (2; top) — 100 each
* Ammo Drum (1; hip mounted) — 35
* Rail Gun (1) — 50
  CTT-M20 or CTT-P40 rifle (1; instead of rail gun) — 100
  Dual Plasma/Laser Guns (2; shoulders) — 40 each
* Forearm Vibro-Blades (6) — 50 each
* Forearm Grenade Launchers (2) — 50 each
* Hands (2) — 45 each
  Arms (2) — 120 each
  Legs (2) — 200 each
** Head — 90
*** Main Body — 425

* A single asterisk indicates a small and difficult target to strike, requiring the attacker to make a "called shot," but even then the attacker is -4 to strike.

** Destroying the head of the power armor will eliminate all forms of optical enhancement and sensory systems. The pilot must then rely on his own human vision and senses. No power armor combat bonuses to initiative, strike, parry, and dodge!

The head is a small and difficult target to hit, shielded by the two large air intake jets and rear jet thrusters. Thus, it can only be hit when an attacker makes a "called shot" and even then he is -5 to strike.

*** Depleting the M.D.C. of the main body will shut the armor down completely, making it useless. **Note:** Destroying a wing will make flight impossible. However, even with no wing(s), the SAMAS can make jet powered leaps and hover stationary above the ground. Destroying one jet thruster reduces speed by 25%.

Speed

Running: 40 mph (64 km) maximum with the flight pack attached, 60 mph (96.5 km) without it. Note that the act of running does tire out its operator, but at 10% of the usual fatigue rate.

Leaping: The fully equipped Super SAMAS is so top heavy that leaps are only possible when assisted by jet thrusters. However, the Super SAMAS can unlock and remove the huge flight pack to which the wings, jet thrusters and plasma/laser guns are attached. This lightens the power armor by 50%! The ammo-drum for the rail gun can then be moved up to a modular mount

on the back. This detachable flight system was designed so that "downed" flyers weren't stuck with a ton of worthless metal holding them down. It takes two melee rounds (30 seconds) to remove the huge flight pack, but requires 2D4 minutes and the help of two other power armored troops or a crane to reattach it.

Without the flight pack, the powerful legs can leap up to 20 feet (6 m) high or across unassisted by the thrusters. Using the feet thrusters, the SAMAS can leap 40 feet (12.2 m).

A jet thruster assisted leap with the flight pack attached can propel the unit up to 200 feet (61 m) high and 300 feet (91.5 m) across without actually attaining flight.

Flying: The rocket propulsion system enables the Super SAMAS to hover stationary in mid-air at any altitude and fly at superior speeds. The armor clad, human missile can attain a maximum flying speed of 500 mph (804.5 km), but cruising speed is considered to be 150-200 mph (240-321.8 km).

Maximum altitude is 16,000 feet (4876.8 m) or roughly three miles (4.8 km). Higher than this, high winds and rough weather make flight both erratic and dangerous. Unlike its predecessor, the Super SAMAS is designed for both high and low altitude operations.

Flying Range: The nuclear power supply gives the SAMAS 20 years of life but the jet rockets get hot and need to cool after a maximum of eight hours of continuous flight at speeds above cruising, 16 hours at cruising speed. It can fly and indefinitely with rest stops every few hours.

Underwater Capabilities: Swimming: The Super SAMAS can *swim* by using the same types of paddling leg and arm movements as a human at a maximum speed of roughly four mph (6.4 km/3.4 knots). It can also walk along the bottom of the sea at about 25% its normal running speed. Using the jet thrusters, the SAMAS can travel on the surface of water at 100 mph (160 km/85 knots), underwater at 70 mph (112.6 km/59.5 knots) or fly above the water's surface at normal speeds.

Maximum Ocean Depth: 3000 feet (910 m).

Statistical Data

Height: 10 feet (3 m) from head to toe. The top mounted air intake jets add another three feet (0.9 m) for an overall height of 13 feet (3.96 m).

Width: Wings down, 5 feet (1.5 m)
 Wings extended, 16 feet (4.87 m)

Length: 6 feet (1.8 m)

Weight: 2.4 tons without the rail gun or other heavy, hand-held weapon. The flight pack weighs 1.2 tons by itself.

Physical Strength: Equal to a P.S. 38.

Cargo: None

Power System: Nuclear, average SAMAS energy life is 20 years.

CS Cost: 5.8 million credits for a new, undamaged, fully powered suit complete with rail gun and one full ammo-drum. None have yet fallen into the hands of the Black Market.

Weapon Systems

1. **SS-09 Dual Plasma & Laser Weapon System:** Mounted above and behind the shoulders on the flight pack, is a dual weapon system used for aerial combat and strafing. Each weapon can be operated independently or in synchronization with each other. Both can rotate side to side 180 degrees and can move up and down to provide a 90 degree arc of fire. **Note:** If each gun is turned on two *different* targets, each blast

from each weapon counts as one of the pilot's melee attacks and *NO* initiative or strike bonuses apply to the attack on either one. Furthermore, the plasma gun and laser cannot be fired simultaneously; one or the other must be selected for use.

Primary Purpose: Anti-Aircraft & Anti-Power Armor.

Secondary Purpose: Anti-Armor & Anti-Personnel.

Mega-Damage: Plasma: 1D6×10 M.D. per single blast or 2D6×10 M.D. per dual synchronized blasts from both plasma weapons!

Laser: The small barrel underneath the large gun is a light laser that inflicts 3D6 damage from a single blast or 6D6 M.D. per dual synchronized blast from both laser weapons.

Rate of Fire: Equal to the combined number of attacks of the pilot. Each single or simultaneous double blast at the same target counts as one melee attack.

Effective Range: Plasma: 1600 feet (488 km).

  Laser: 2000 feet (610 m).

Payload: Effectively unlimited. The plasma and laser weapons of the dual system are powered by the energy supply of the armor.

2. **Forearm Grenade Launchers (2):** The top part of the bulbous forearm housing contains a rapid-fire grenade launcher that fires rifle grenades.

Primary Purpose: Anti-Glitter Boy/Anti-Armor

Secondary Purpose: Anti-Personnel and Defense.

Mega-Damage: The weapon can fire conventional M.D. rifle grenades doing 2D6 M.D. to a blast area of 12 feet (3.6 m), but is typically loaded with the *new, micro-fusion grenades* that inflict 6D6 M.D. to a 12 foot (3.6 m) diameter blast area/six foot (1.8 m) radius.

Maximum Effective Range: 1000 feet (305 km)

Rate of Fire: Equal to the number of hand to hand attacks per melee round either one at a time or in volleys of two, four, six or eight! One volley, regardless of the number of rounds in that volley, counts as one melee attack.

Payload: 80 total; 40 per each arm.

3. **Forearm Vibro-Blades (6):** Each of the arms has a set of three large, fin-like vibro-blades. These weapons are used to slash and stab (with a backhand motion) enemy power armor, robots and aircraft. They can also be used to clip the propellers of helicopters or airplanes. This tactic has a 01-45% chance of breaking the propeller and causing the aircraft to make an emergency landing or crash (the latter if damage is sufficient to destroy the blade). However, a failed roll (46-00) means that the Super SAMAS gets caught by the blade, one of the vibro-blades is torn out of the armor, the SAMAS suffers 2D4×10 M.D. and is slung 2D4×100 feet away from the aircraft, in any direction.

Mega-Damage: 2D6 M.D. from a single blade, 6D6 M.D. from an attack in which all three blades strike.

4. **Energy Rifles or Rail Guns:** The Super SAMAS does not have a standard issue hand weapon. Typically, a rail gun or the CTT-M20 missile rifle or CTT-P40 rifle is used as an over-sized two-handed weapon; actually the Super SAMAS can fire the weapon one-handed without penalty. Furthermore, the hands of the SAMAS are small enough that it can use any of the standard infantry rifles or a vibro-blade. However, the Super SAMAS often enters into combat without any additional hand-held weapons.

5. **Hand to Hand Combat:** Rather than use a weapon, the pilot can engage in mega-damage hand to hand combat. See *Basic and Elite* Power Armor Combat Training on page 45 of the **Rifts® RPG** for combat bonuses. The basic bonuses and abilities of "elite" Power Armor Training are the same with the following extra bonuses and increased damage capabilities:

+3 to pull punch.

+2 on initiative

Restrained Punch — 1D4 M.D.

Full Strength Punch — 2D4 M.D.

 Power Punch — 3D6 M.D. but counts as two melee attacks.

Tear or Pry with hands: 1D4 M.D.

Kick Attack: 2D6 M.D

Running Leap Kick: 6D6 M.D.! This attack must be used at the beginning of a melee round and uses up all but one melee attack, but inflicts excellent damage.

Body Block/Tackle: 1D6 M.D.

Full Speed Running or flying Ram: 5D6 M.D. This attack uses up three attacks and inflicts 1D4 to the Super SAMAS.

6. **Sensor System Note:** Same as the other SAMAS.

Special Forces "Striker" SAMAS

The PA-08A "Striker" SAMAS is a cross between the old style Death's Head SAMAS, which it more closely resembles, and the Super SAMAS with its heavier armor and weapon systems. The Striker was specifically designed for the exclusive use of the Special Forces and is only rarely made available to the Elite RPA SAMAS pilot on special missions, usually with Special Forces. Like its light predecessors, it is a low altitude, all environment power armor fighter, but used primarily for espionage and special missions. Such covert operations include penetrating the enemy line in order to sabotage the enemy, hit special targets, guerilla warfare, assassination, intercept, anti-armor, anti-supernatural missions, special reconnaissance in hostile territory, surgical strikes, seek and destroy, rescue, espionage and defense. It can fly, hover, make tight turns and is small enough to maneuver through narrow streets and corridors without sacrificing firepower or armor protection.

The armor styling of the "Striker" is the familiar black color with the same Death's Head face plate as the Special Forces body armor. A pair of extra sensor clusters are located in the chest with a pair of spotlights, one conventional the other infrared, in the center of the chest. Mini-missile launchers are built into the shoulder plating, wings, and forearms. The CTT-P40 particle beam rifle is standard issue.

Special Forces "Striker" SAMAS Power Armor

Model Type: PA-08A

Class: Strategic Armor Military Assault Suit

Crew: One

M.D.C. by Location:

   * Shoulder Wings (2) — 80 each

   * Wing Mini-Missile Launchers (6 total) — 8 each

   * Chest Mini-Missile Launchers (6 total) — 8 each

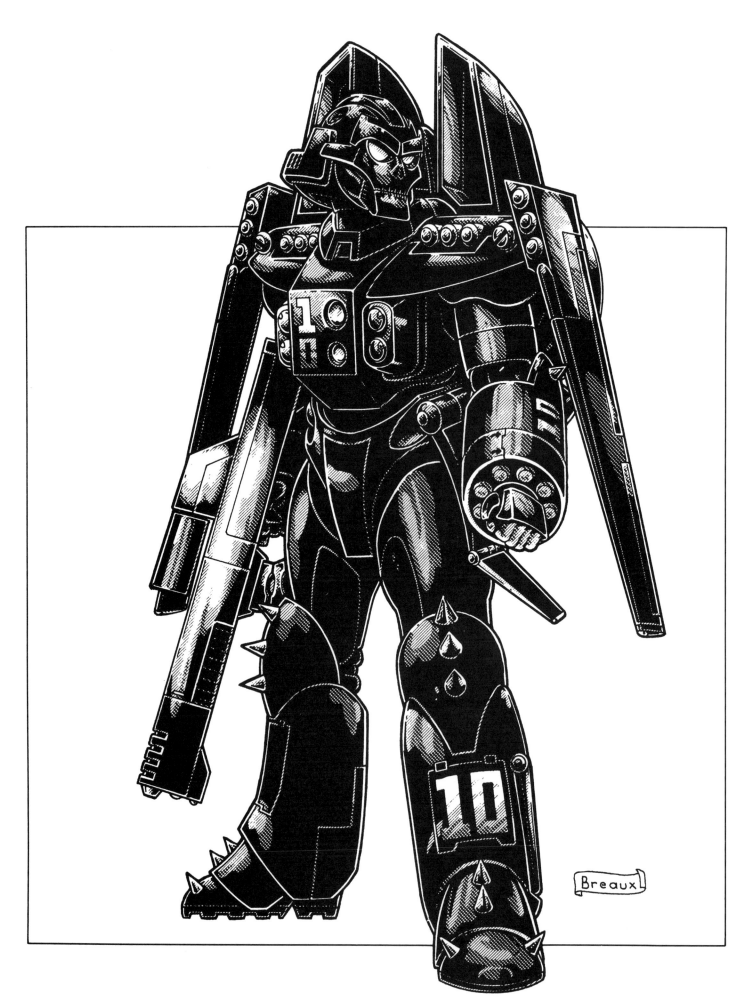

* Forearms with Missile Launchers (2) — 80 each
Upper Arms (2) — 70 each
* Hands (2) — 25 each
Legs (2) — 130 each
Main Rear Jets (2) — 60 each
Lower Maneuvering Jets (3) — 30 each
Intake Jets (2; top) — 50 each
* Ammo Drum (rear) — 35
* Rail Gun — 50
CTT-M20 or CTT-P40 rifle (1; instead of rail gun) — 100
** Head — 90
*** Main Body — 325

* A single asterisk indicates a small and difficult target to strike, requiring the attacker to make a "called shot," but even then the attacker is -4 to strike.

** Destroying the head of the power armor will eliminate all forms of optical enhancement and sensory systems. The pilot must then rely on his own human vision and senses. No power armor combat bonuses to strike, parry, and dodge!

The head is a small and difficult target to hit, shielded by the air intake tubes and weapon drum. Thus, it can only be hit when a character makes a "called shot" and even then the attacker is -3 to strike.

*** Depleting the M.D.C. of the main body will shut the armor down completely, making it useless. **Note:** Destroying a wing will make flight impossible. However, even with no wing(s), the SAMAS can make jet powered leaps and hover stationary above the ground.

Speed

Running: 70 mph (112.6 km) maximum. Note that the act of running does tire out its operator, but at 10% of the usual fatigue rate.

Leaping: The powerful robot legs can leap up to 20 feet (6 m) high or across unassisted by the thrusters.

A jet thruster assisted leap can propel the unit up to 100 feet (30.5 m) high and 200 feet (61 m) across without actually attaining flight.

Flying: The rocket propulsion system enables the SAMAS to hover stationary in mid-air or fly. Maximum flying speed is 330 mph (528 km), but cruising speed is considered to be 150 mph (240 km). Maximum altitude is 6000 feet (1829 m; a little over one mile/1.6 km). Higher than this, high winds and rough weather make flight both erratic and dangerous. *Optimum altitude range* is ground level to about 4000 feet (1200 m). Like its predecessor, the "Striker" is designed to be a low altitude power armor suit that can hug the ground and slip under enemy radar.

Flying Range: The nuclear power supply gives the SAMAS decades of life but the jet rockets get hot and need to cool after a maximum of 10 hours of continuous flight at speeds above cruising, 24 hours at cruising speed. It can fly indefinitely with rest stops every few hours.

Underwater Capabilities: Swimming: The SAMAS can *swim* by using the same types of paddling leg and arm movements as a human at a maximum speed of roughly four mph (6.4 km/3.4 knots). It can also walk along the bottom of the sea at about 25% its normal running speed. Using the jet thrusters, the SAMAS can travel on the surface of water at 50 mph (80 km/42.5 knots), underwater at 40 mph (64 km/34 knots) or fly above the water's surface at normal speeds.

Maximum Ocean Depth: 2000 feet (610 m).

Statistical Data

Height: 8 feet, 6 inches (2.4 m) from head to toe. The top mounted air intake jets adds another two feet (0.6 m) for an overall height of 10.6 feet (3.25 m).
Width: Wings down, 3.5 feet (1.06 m)
  Wings extended, 12 feet (3.6 m)
Length: 4 feet 6 inches (1.4 m)
Weight: 600 lbs (270 kg) without the rail gun and ammo drum.
Physical Strength: Equal to a P.S. 36
Cargo: None
Power System: Nuclear, average SAMAS energy life is 20 years.
CS Cost: 2.6 million credits for a new, undamaged, fully-powered suit complete with rail gun and one full ammo-drum. None have yet fallen into the hands of the Black Market.

Weapon Systems

1. C-40R SAMAS Rail Gun (1): This is standard equipment for the "Smiling Jack" SAMAS. Other heavier rail guns can be substituted. Likewise, the new CTT-M20 missile rifle or CTT-P40 rifle can be used as an over-sized two-handed weapon.

Primary Purpose: Assault
Secondary Purpose: Defense
Weight: Gun: 92 lbs (41.4 kg), One SAMAS Ammo-Drum: 190 lbs (85.5 kg).
Mega-Damage: A burst is 40 rounds and inflicts 1D4×10 M.D., one round does 1D4 M.D.
Rate of Fire: Equal to number of combined hand to hand attacks (usually 4-6).

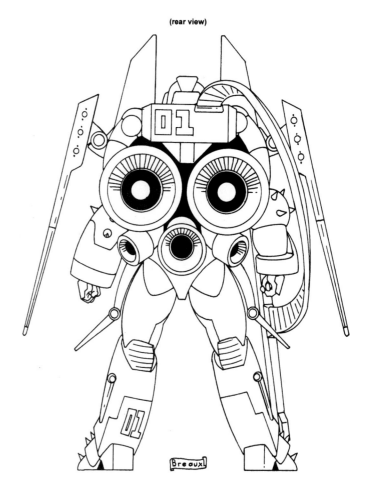

(rear view)

121

Maximum Effective Range: 4000 feet (1200 m)

Payload: 3000 round drum, that's 75 bursts. A second drum can be hooked to the undercarriage of the rocket jets, but first the used drum must be manually removed by another SAMAS or character with a strength of 26 or higher before it can be replaced with the new one. Reloading a drum will take about five minutes for those not trained, but a mere one minute by somebody trained in the use of SAMAS power armor.

2. Striker-6 Mini-Missile Wing Launchers: Each of the wings have three small, tube mini-missile launchers.

Primary Purpose: Anti-Aircraft and Anti-Missile.

Secondary Purpose: Defense

Missile Type: Any mini-missile can be used, but standard issue is armor piercing (1D4×10 M.D.) or plasma (1D6×10). Fragmentation will be used for anti-personnel operations.

Mega-Damage: Varies with missile type.

Range: Usually about a mile.

Rate of Fire: One at a time or in volleys of two, four or six.

Payload: Six total; three per wing.

3. Striker-6 Mini-Missile Chest Launchers: Located in each of what would be the collar bone of a human, are three small, tube mini-missile launchers (six total).

Primary Purpose: Anti-Aircraft

Secondary Purpose: Defense

Missile Type: Any mini-missile can be used, but standard issue is armor piercing (1D4×10 M.D.) or plasma (1D6×10). Fragmentation will be used for anti-personnel operations.

Mega-Damage: Varies with missile type.

Range: Usually about a mile.

Rate of Fire: One at a time or in volleys of two, three or six.

Payload: Six total.

4. Striker-8 Forearm Mini-Missile System: Each of the forearms is encased in an oversized plate armor that has an eight mini-missile launch system.

Primary Purpose: Anti-Aircraft

Secondary Purpose: Defense

Missile Type: Any mini-missile can be used, but standard issue is armor piercing (1D4×10 M.D.) or plasma (1D6×10). Fragmentation will be used for anti-personnel operations.

Mega-Damage: Varies with missile type.

Range: Usually about a mile.

Rate of Fire: One at a time or in volleys of two, four or six.

Payload: 16 total; eight per arm.

5. Energy Rifles: The "Striker" SAMAS typically uses the CTT-P40 particle beam rifle as its standard issue, but the CTT-M20 missile rifle or any rail gun can be substituted. Note that firing the two oversized guns with one hand is possible, but the character is -2 to strike. The "Striker" is also small enough that it can use any of the standard infantry weapons from pistols and vibro-blades to rifles, same as the "Death's Head" SAMAS.

6. Hand to Hand Combat: Rather than use a weapon, the pilot can engage in mega-damage hand to hand combat. See *Basic and Elite* Power Armor Combat Training on page 45 of the **Rifts® RPG** for combat bonuses.

7. Sensor System Note: The SAMAS has full optical systems, including laser targeting, telescopic, passive nightvision (light amplification), thermo-imaging, infrared, ultraviolet, and polarization. Plus all other features common to all power armor.

Sensor Bonuses: The SAMAS gets a bonus of +1 on initiative, +1 to strike and +1 to dodge in addition to the power armor targeting computer bonus and Basic or Elite Power Armor Combat Training bonuses.

Skelebots

Reprinted with updated material from the Rifts® Sourcebook One

The introduction of the Coalition Skelebots is one of the Coalition's greatest military achievements, giving them unparalleled military power and strength of numbers. The bots are completely automated, meaning they require no human pilot or controller. Each unit is identical except for the identifying number emblazoned on its chest and weapon, and the serial number etched into its internal I.D. plate.

In keeping with the ominous Death's Head symbolism, Skelebots are designed to resemble animated skeletons. Indeed, to stand against a company of Skelebots (let alone an entire division), their black-hued skin reflecting in the cascade of light from the battlefield, eyes glowing red, and making with no sound as they rush forward with weapons blazing, is like fighting a tide of dead risen from the very pits of hell!

Since their introduction into military service approximately seven years ago, Skelebots have been used primarily for border patrols and base defenders in hostile territories too dangerous for human troops. This has included reconnaissance and seek and destroy missions in the ruins of Old Chicago, the Magic Zone, Xiticix Territory, and the western and northern wildernesses of North America. Skelebots are typically given the simple mission to seek out and destroy nonhuman life-forms or specific enemy troops. They are also programmed to respond to aggression with aggression, so if attacked by hostile forces the bots will respond in kind. Now, for the first time, Skelebots will be used as frontline combat troops to soften up the enemy in campaigns against Tolkeen and Quebec. Six Skelebot divisions (34,560 bots) are on their way to Quebec, while eight divisions (46,080) are already in place for the siege on Tolkeen. Another two divisions (11,520 robots) patrol the borders of the Coalition States or are on limited missions in hostile territories.

Skelebots are programmed with rudimentary combat responses and to function as members of large and small combat formations. They communicate silently between each other through scrambled radio transmissions and computer codes. Each bot is programmed for standard strategic and tactical field maneuvers that are executed with expert efficiency (standard squad/reconnaissance, assault and defensive actions). The combat computer automatically selects the best action, working as a team, to contain or subdue the enemy, and so on. The combat computer is also programmed to recognize over 2000 enemy targets, from vehicles and robots to D-bees and insignias.

Chi-Town developers are quick to point out the many safety measures they have implemented to prevent the robots from running amok. First, the robots are designed to recognize all Coali-

123

tion troops, vehicles and personnel (via uniforms) and are not to attack such troops unless attacked first, and then, only if all reasonable means of identification have failed. Secondly, should a unit go berserk and act contrary to its programming, it can be tracked via an internal homing device and destroyed by detonation of the anti-tampering unit built inside the bot. Third, the self same anti-tampering unit is designed to detonate if there is any attempt to invade the bot's internal workings, which is necessary to subvert its programming or to effect physical repairs. A secret code and procedure is required to gain access to the Skelebot's programming and internals without causing detonation. As part of that safety feature, the explosion is contained by the Skelebot's exterior armor, preventing injury to those around it, but completely destroying its internal workings, turning it into a useless piece of scrap metal.

The Skelebot program forces robots to obey any recognize Coalition officers above the rank of Sergeant Major, otherwise it will avoid interaction with human troops. Also, to avoid perceptual problems, the programming and objectives have been kept predominately simple. The machines are primarily designed for assault and operate away from densely populated areas within the territories of the allied States. Consequently, the chance of CS troops or civilians getting hurt by a Skelebot is unlikely. Furthermore, Skelebots are programmed *not* to attack humans if there is the slightest amount of confusion as to whether the human(s) is friend or foe — such targets are to be ignored.

Those uncomfortable with the robots argue that the Skelebot is a merciless killing machine that can be programmed to destroy every nonhuman, alien and monstrous life forms it encounters without discretion. Even if this were desirable (and a majority of people believe it *is*), such action without human analysis of the situation could result in unnecessary conflicts with hostile forces that may not have been hostile to begin with.

Chi-Town's generals have two answers. One, Skelebots are usually programmed to seek out and destroy as few as one to about a dozen specific enemy targets or species. For example: Skelebots sent into Minnesota may be programmed only to terminate Xiticix life forms and will ignore all others. However, in all practicality, the Skelebots' range of possible targets is seldom that narrow and is likely to include scores of monsters and D-bees. Second, one or two human operatives typically (85% of the time) accompanies each Skelebot squad or platoon; usually a SAMAS, Terror Trooper, Hellfire or Spider Scout (any trooper, power armor or robot vehicle can be substituted). The presence of one or more humans as squad leader eliminates, in theory, any inappropriate combat action by the robots and adds the element of human response, choice and discretion to any given situation (as well as human hatred, anger and vengeance).

The addition of Skelebots to the Coalition Army was wildly supported by Chi-Town, Lone Star, and Fort El Dorado (Arkansas). The wide use of Skelebots had been the subject of at least some controversy, especially from the Coalition State of Free Quebec. Most opponents to the robots fear that the robots could be captured, sabotaged, and turned against their creators, or even possessed and controlled by supernatural forces. **G.M. Note (subplot):** A.R.C.H.I.E. Three (see *Rifts® Sourcebooks One & Two*) has captured, analyzed, copied and seized control of over a half dozen CS Skelebots. Archie-3 has already toyed with the idea of infiltrating the CS with its own army of fake Skelebots,

but hasn't yet figured out what the advantage of such an action would be. For the moment, Archie-3 is satisfied watching the CS from a safe distance.

Despite all assurances, the Coalition State of Free Quebec had expressed great concern over the use of artificial intelligence in war machines without a human pilot to control or countermand its actions, and were suspicious of the robots' applications in war. Noting that the unmanned units, armed with variable frequency laser rifles, seemed to have been designed to combat the negligible forces that utilize laser resistant armor. Armor used almost exclusively in the construction of *Glitter Boys*. The government leaders at Free Quebec feared (and rightly so) that the "Skelebots" were designed specifically to combat their substantial force of Glitter Boys, should that day come.

Skelebot Tactical Deployment

Skelebots are comparatively inexpensive to mass produce, and although they have a high mortality/destruction rate considering their intended deployment, they are seen as the perfect substitute for human, front-line troops. Since the Emperor and the Coalition High Command are genuinely concerned with the saving human lives, they have embraced the Skelebots as a way to save their combat troops.

A typical Skelebot squad is comprised of 4-10 robots; one armed with a C-27 plasma cannon or CR-1 rocket launcher while all others are armed with the standard CV-213 variable laser rifle or C-200 "Dead Man's" Rail Gun. In most cases, the squad is led/supervised by a human officer in power armor. However, at least 25% of all Skelebot squads are unsupervised. Unsupervised Skelebot squads are commonly found in the most dangerous or remote regions where as many as 40% may be unsupervised by a human agent. The squad can be dispatched on a specific mission and told to return to base when the mission is accomplished, or sent on long-term or multiple missions that can last months or even years.

Skelebot platoons may contain 20 to 40 robots supervised by one or two humans in power armor or robot combat vehicles. Even among these larger squads, 20% have no human supervision.

Skelebot companies have only recently been deployed. This large number of troops (140 bots) are used in major assaults against the enemy as well as a first strike infantry unit. A company is usually composed of three or four platoons — 120-140 bots.

Skelebot battalions have not yet been deployed. This large number of troops will be deployed in major assaults against the enemy and used primarily as a first strike infantry unit. A battalion is usually composed of three or four companies.

A division is typically composed of 5760 Skelebots, plus human supervisors.

Skelebots as Player Characters?

Skelebots should *not* be used as player characters. These particular robots are extremely limited and comparatively dumb. The level of skill and abilities are rudimentary and the standard program is narrow and restrictive. The Skelebot is a killing machine without human ethics, reasoning or emotions.

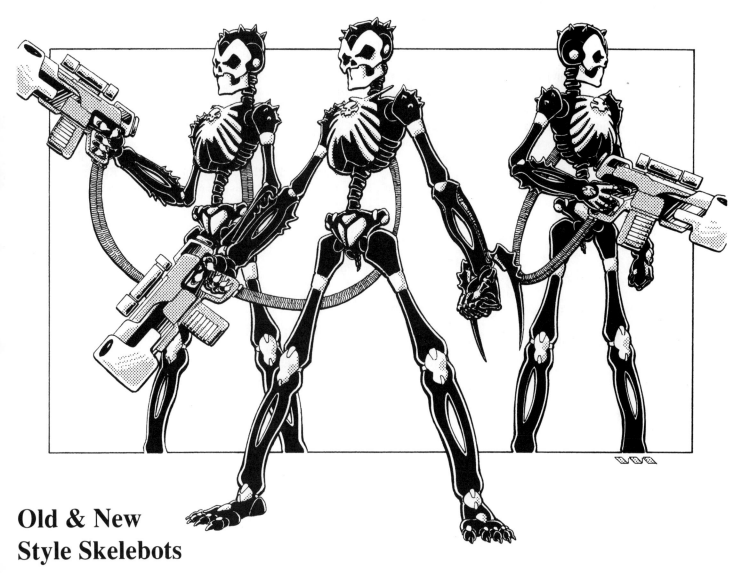

Old & New Style Skelebots

Both old and new style Skelebots are in service. The FAS-SAR-20 and FASSAR-30 are both fundamentally the same. The main differences are the new bots utilize a retractable, "wing" style pair of vibro-blades on each arm, get the C-200 "Dead Man's" rail gun as their standard weapon, and the body styling of the FASSAR-30 more closely resembles the new, Coalition "Dead Boy" armor with an even more skeletal appearance. **Note:** Both have been beefed up in regard to mega-damage capacity.

The following data applies to both the old style FASSAR-20 and new style FASSAR-30. The different weapons of the FAS-SAR-30 are listed at the end of the description.

Coalition Skelebot:
Robot/artificial intelligence

Model Type: FASSAR-20 (old style) and FASSAR-30 (new style)

Class: Fully Automated Self-Sufficient Assault Robot

Crew: None; artificial intelligence

M.D.C. by Location:

Hands (2) — 22 each
Arms (2) — 45 each
Vibro-Blades (2) — 25 each
CV-213 Laser Rifle (1) — 30
Legs (2) — 70 each
* Head — 60
** Main Body — 150

* Destroying the head of the robot will eliminate all optics and sensory systems. In most cases the robot shuts down as a safety feature. However, in some cases, about one in ten, the robot continues to fight, blasting away blindly until its ammunition is expended, and even then it will continue to grope around, lashing out and hitting anything it touches. Under these conditions the robot enjoys no combat bonuses to strike, parry, or dodge!

The head is a small and difficult target to hit, especially on a moving target. Thus, it can only be hit when a character makes a "called shot," and even then the attacker is -2 to strike.

** Depleting the M.D.C. of the main body will effectively destroy the bot, shutting it down completely. **Note:** Additional body armor or power armor cannot be worn by Skelebots.

Speed

Running: 90 mph (144 km) maximum. Note that the act of running does NOT tire the robot and maximum speed can be maintained indefinitely.

Leaping: The robot legs, although strong, are not designed for leaping, thus leaps are limited to approximately 6 feet (1.8 m) high or across.

Flying: None, without the addition of the conventional CS jet pack or vehicle.

Range: The nuclear power pack gives the Skelebot approximately two years of life even under the most strenuous and constant amount of use, nearly three years under less active conditions. The robot is intentionally given a much shorter energy "life" as yet another fail-safe and because of their high rate of mortality.

Underwater Capabilities: Skelebots are not particularly well suited for underwater operations. The best it can do walk along the bottom of the sea at about 25% its normal running speed.

Maximum Ocean Depth: 1000 feet (305 m).

Statistical Data

Height: 7 feet (2.1 m)
Width: 3 feet (0.9 m)
Length: 2 feet, 9 inches (0.9 m)
Weight: 390 lbs (175 kg)
Physical Strength: Equal to a P.S. 30
Cargo: None
Power System: Nuclear, average Skelebot energy life is two (2) years.
Black Market Cost: Three million credits for a new, undamaged, fully powered unit complete with an assault rifle. Rarely available; exclusive to the CS military (nobody has dared to make a knock-off).

Weapon Systems

1. **FASSAR-20: CV-213 Robot Variable Laser Rifle (1):** The CV-213 is the robot-modified version of the Coalition's human C-212 variable light frequency laser rifle. It is designed to overcome laser resistant armor like that used by the Glitter Boy. In the case of the CV-213, the robot's combat computer will automatically analyze an opponent's armor (if not already preprogrammed into its memory) after one melee round to instantly adjust to the light frequency that will inflict maximum damage.

   The CV-213 has an additional robot feature that makes it the obvious choice for the Skelebots. A special connection in the handle allows the robot to link with the weapon. The link ties the weapon directly to the robot, its combat computer, and nuclear power pack. The link to the power pack gives the weapon an indefinite and constant energy supply. If the link is damaged, the CV-213 has an energy clip reserve with a 20 shot payload. See the weapon section for more details.

Primary Purpose: Assault
Weight: 7 lbs (3.2 kg)
Mega-Damage: 2D6 M.D. or 4D6 M.D.; two settings
Rate of Fire: Equal to the number of hand to hand attacks.
Effective Range: 2000 feet (610 m)
Payload: E-clip is 20 or power pack hand link is effectively unlimited. Note that the new FASSAR-30 does *not* have the hand link, so any use of the CV-213 means having to use conventional E-clips or E-canisters.

2. **FASSAR-20: 18 inch (0.45 m) Vibro-Blades (2):** Hidden between the slot of each skeletal forearm is a retractable vibro-saber that swings out and down, locking into close combat position. The only limitation is that no other weapon or item can be held/used in the hand from which the vibro-saber is extended. The blades can be used simultaneously or independently; in the latter case, the Skelebot can still fire a weapon from one hand and use one of the vibro-blades in the other (see illustration).

Primary Purpose: Assault
Secondary Purpose: Defense
Weight: 2 lbs (0.9 kg)
Mega-Damage: Vibro-Saber: 2D6 M.D.
Range: Hand to hand with about a 5.6 foot (1.7 m) reach.
Rate of Attack: Five per melee; hand to hand combat skill.
Payload: Not applicable

3. **FASSAR-20 & 30: Energy Rifles** and other normal weapons can be substituted in an emergency or as a back up weapon.

4. **FASSAR-20 Hand to Hand Combat:** Rather than use a weapon, the Skelebot can engage in mega-damage hand to hand combat using its fists or vibro-blades. **Five (5) attacks per melee!** Equal to Hand to Hand Expert.

Damage:
Restrained Punch — 2D6+15 S.D.C.
Full Strength Punch, Elbow, or Knee — 1D6
Power Punch — 2D6 but counts as two melee attacks.
Kick — 2D4 M.D.
Body Block: 1D6 M.D.
Head Butt: 1D6 M.D.
Vibro-Sabers (2) — 2D6 M.D. each

Bonuses: Includes all bonuses from programming, robotics and sensors: +2 to strike with an automatic rifle, energy pistol, or energy rifle (see W.P. skills), +5 to strike on an aimed shot, +4 to strike with vibro-blades or hand to hand attack (punch, kick, etc.), +5 to parry with fists/arms, +7 to parry with vibro-blade or knife/sword, +6 to dodge, +4 to parry and dodge attacks from behind (motion detectors), +2 to roll with impact or fall (no pull punch), critical strike on natural roll of 19 or 20. Impervious to poison, gas, and biological agents, as well as psionic and magic mind control, charms, bio-manipulation, and S.D.C. attacks. See sensors for optical capabilities.

5. **FASSAR 20 & 30: Sensor Systems of Note:**

   Optics: The Skelebots have full optical systems, including the visible light spectrum, infrared, ultraviolet, and polarization, passive nightvision (light amplification), thermo-imaging, laser targeting, and telescopic. **Telescopic optics** function like built-in binoculars with a range of about two miles (3.2 km). All the other optic systems have a range of about 3000 feet (914 m).

   Radar: Can identify and track up to 12 targets simultaneously at a range of two miles (3.2 km). Applicable to flying targets at 500 feet above the ground or higher only. Radar can not track ground movement.

   Motion Detector: 100 foot radius (30.5 m), adds to ability to parry and dodge (see bonuses).

   Radio Communication: Medium-range directional radio for coded messages between Skelebots. Range: 10 miles (16 km). Can also scan and communicate via code on conventional radio channels/frequencies; same range. Can also eavesdrop on enemy transmissions and track transmissions (60% success level) to its source. Range 10 miles (16 km). **Note:** Understands English, Spanish, and Techno-can languages; can identify all others but can not understand or communicate in them.

   Speech: The Skelebots can not speak, although they do understand the spoken word of the common languages. Communicates via radio transmission rather than out loud. However, the Skelebots can say the following commands or statements:
"Affirmative."
"Negative."

"Does not compute."
"Error."
"Identify."
"Be silent!"
"Halt! Do not move."
"Remain calm."
"Come with me."
"Move along."

"Surrender or be destroyed!"
"Warning! Enemy! Warning!"
"Attack!"
"All is clear."
"Evacuate the area!"

6. FASSAR 20 & 30: Skill Programs of Note: Combat skills: W.P. sword, W.P. blunt, W.P. automatic rifle, W.P. energy pistol, W.P. energy rifle, W.P. paired weapons: means it can use two hand held weapons or vibro-blades in one simultaneous attack (double damage, counts as one attack/melee action) or attack with one and parry with the other. Hand to Hand Expert equal to 8th level skill (See number 4 for bonuses).

Other skills: Pilot automobile 96%, pilot hover cycle 96%, pilot jet pack 80%, radio: basic 96%, intelligence 76%, land navigation 86%, and climb 96%/86% (4× faster than the average humanoid). Languages include: English, Spanish, Euro, Dragonese, Gobblely, and Techno-can, each at 96%; basic math 96%.

Programming and memory enables the Skelebot to identify all Coalition State military ranks, uniforms, insignia, soldiers, dog pack, robots, power armor, vehicles, weapons, equipment, generals and the Emperor and his son. CS data also includes the location of current Coalition territory and major military bases.

Memory also includes the identification of 2000 different enemy targets, including specific races, non-human features and powers, insignia, uniforms, enemy robot and vehicle designs, acts of aggression, and notorious enemies of the State.

Combat programming directs the actions and reactions to encounters and attacks.

FASSAR-30 Exclusive Systems:

FASSAR-30: C-200 "Dead Man's" Rail Gun: This light, all-purpose weapon is standard use for the FASSAR-30 Skelebot. It is fundamentally the same as the weapon used by human troops wearing enhanced exoskeleton body armor or power ar-

mor with a strength of 24 or greater. The C-200 rail gun can use what is called a short clip with 200 rounds (10 bursts), light drum with 600 rounds (30 bursts), or a heavy belt-feed drum containing 2000 rounds (100 bursts). The latter is typically reserved for robots and cyborgs and is carried as a backpack or carried by the partner in a two 'Borg team.

Primary Purpose: Assault
Secondary Purpose: Defense
Weight: Gun: 45 lbs (20.25 kg), short clip: 10 pounds (4.5 kg), light ammo-drum: 30 pounds (13 kg), or a heavy ammo-drum: 100 lbs (45 kg). Ammo-drums are hooked to the back of body armor or housing on the backs of the 'Borgs or bots. Skelebots are typically given the light or heavy drum.
Mega-Damage: A full damage burst fires 20 rounds and inflicts 4D6 M.D.; a single round does 1D4 M.D.
Rate of Fire: Equal to the bot's hand to hand attacks per melee round (five).
Maximum Effective Range: 4000 feet (1200 m)
Payload: The short clip holds 200 and is capable of firing ten full damage bursts (20 rounds).

The light drum holds 600 rounds and can fire 30 bursts.

The 2000 round drum is capable of firing 100 full damage bursts (20 rounds each).

Reloading a drum will take about three minutes for those not trained, but a mere 30 seconds by a capable field mechanic. A strength of 24 or higher is required to handle the drum.

Special C-200 Features: As a rail guns for human troops it has its own laser targeting, telescopic and nightvision scope. Bot guns only have the laser targeting scope. Telescopic and laser targeting range is 6000 feet (1828 m). Targeting Bonus: +1 to strike.

Black Market Cost: 80,000 credits. Poor availability.

2. FASSAR-30 Hand to Hand Combat: Rather than use a weapon, the Skelebot can engage in mega-damage hand to hand combat using its fists or vibro-blades. Equal to hand to hand expert with five attacks per melee!

Damage:

Restrained Punch — 3D6+15 S.D.C.
Full Strength Punch, Elbow, or Knee — 1D6
Power Punch — 2D6 but counts as two melee attacks.
Kick — 2D4 M.D.
Body Block: 1D6 M.D.
Head Butt: 1D6 M.D.
Vibro-Wing Blade (2) — 2D6 M.D.
Bonuses: Same as the FASSAR-20.

Experimental Skelebots

Skelebot Hunter

FASSAR-40 Experimental Heavy Assault Robot

The FASSAR-40 Hunter is an experimental bot that is larger and more heavily armored than the FASSAR-20 or 30. The body styling is also different, with extra plating and a two chamber secret compartment in its chest (the wing or rib design flips open). Unlike its basic infantry predecessors, the Hunter is programmed with the skill to prowl, track and snipe, although without the faculties of a human-like brain, these skills are comparatively low. All the other basic combat skills and programming of the FASSAR-20 and 30 are also included.

The FASSAR-40 is quickly becoming something of a messenger bot used to deliver audio and/or video recorded messages which can be placed on one and three inch disks and as many as 50 can be stored in each of the two chest compartments. In the alternative, computer disks, small articles and specimens, nothing bigger than a handgun, a few books and/or a half dozen grenades per compartment, can be stored inside this Skelebot. A mini-computer accessible via finger jack or key pad inside the chest cavity, is used to program into the Skelebot information as to whom the information/disks should be delivered to. Once programmed, the Hunter's prime directive is to deliver the information or materials, come hell or high water. It will fight to its complete destruction to keep the information out of the wrong hands. Furthermore, it will automatically self-destruct at the moment of its demise (M.D.C. of main body is reduced to zero) to insure any sensitive materials were destroyed along with it.

The FASSAR-40 is known as the Hunter, rather than messenger, because it is primarily used as an automated exterminator that ferrets out D-bees, monsters and enemy targets and engages in a methodical hunt and eradication of them. Similarly, the bot is relentless in hunting down the proper authorities for deliveries.

Unlike the other Skelebots, the Hunter is typically dispatched as a lone unit or in pairs, although one or two may be included in Skelebot and human reconnaissance patrols. The Hunter Skelebot has no standard issue weapon. Just about any rail gun or rifle can be used.

Coalition Hunter Skelebot

Model Type: Experimental model FASSAR-40
Class: Fully Automated Self-Sufficient Assault Robot
Crew: None; artificial intelligence
M.D.C. by Location:

> Hands (2) — 32 each
> Arms (2) — 65 each
> Vibro-Blades (2) — 50 each
> C-200 Rail Gun (1) — 50
> Legs (2) — 100 each
> Chest Compartment Plates/Hatch (2) — 40 each
> * Head — 90
> ** Main Body — 210

* Destroying the head of the robot will eliminate all optics and sensory systems. In most cases the robot shuts down as a safety feature. However, in some cases, about one in ten, the robot continues to fight, blasting away blindly until its ammunition is expended, and even then it will continue to grope around, lashing out and hitting anything it touches. Under these conditions the robot enjoys no combat bonuses to strike, parry, or dodge!

The head is a small and difficult target to hit, especially on a moving target. Thus, it can only be hit when a character makes a "called shot," and even then the attacker is -2 to strike.

** Depleting the M.D.C. of the main body will effectively destroy the bot, shutting it down completely. **Note:** Additional body armor or power armor cannot be worn by Skelebots.

Speed:

Running: 90 mph (144 km) maximum. Note that the act of running does NOT tire the robot and maximum speed can be maintained indefinitely.

Leaping: The robot legs, although strong, are not designed for leaping, thus leaps are limited to approximately 6 feet (1.8 m) high or across.

Flying: None, without the addition of the conventional CS jet pack or vehicle.

Range: The nuclear power pack gives the Skelebot approximately two years of life even under the most strenuous and constant amount of use, nearly three years under less active conditions. The robot is intentionally given a much shorter energy "life" as yet another fail-safe and because of their high mortality rate.

Underwater Capabilities: The Skelebot is not particularly well suited for underwater operations. The best it can do is walk along the bottom of the sea at about 25% of its normal running speed.

Maximum Ocean Depth: 1000 feet (305 m).

Statistical Data
Height: 8 feet (2.4 m)
Width: 3 feet, 6 inches (1 m)
Length: 3 feet (0.9 m)
Weight: 600 lbs (270 kg)
Physical Strength: Equal to a P.S. 40.
Cargo: None
Power System: Nuclear, average Skelebot energy life is three years.
CS Cost: 3.8 million credits; not available on the Black Market.

Weapon Systems: All fundamentally the same as the FASSAR-20 and 30. Any weapon system from rail guns to infantryman rifles can be assigned as its hand weapon. A vibro-saber is concealed in the forearm housing of each arm. The only difference is that they do not interfere with the use of the bot's hands.

Programming: Fundamentally the same as the FASSAR-20 and 30, with the addition of useful "hunting" abilities: detect ambush 60%, prowl 60%, track humanoids 50%, and sniper (+2 to strike on *aimed* shots).

FASSAR-40 Hand to Hand Combat: Rather than use a weapon, the Hunter Skelebot can engage in mega-damage hand to hand combat using its fists or vibro-blades. Equal to hand to hand expert with five attacks per melee!

Damage:

Restrained Punch — 3D6+30 S.D.C.

Full Strength Punch, Elbow, or Knee — 2D6

Power Punch — 4D6 but counts as two melee attacks.

Kick — 2D6 M.D.

Body Block: 1D6 M.D.

Head Butt: 1D6 M.D.

Vibro-Saber (2) — 2D6 M.D.

Bonuses: Same as the FASSAR-20, plus +1 on initiative.

Hellion Skelebot

FASSAR-50 Experimental Assault Robot

The FASSAR-50 Hellion is an experimental bot that is demonic in appearance, has four arms (two large, two a bit smaller) and a prehensile tail that is used as a whip and for balance. The horns are more for show than anything else, but they can be used to head butt and ram. In addition to the extra attacks per melee round from the four arms and tail (seven total) it can leap and dodge. In fact, the Hellion typically sways on its thin, multijointed legs even when standing still, and can dodge by bobbing and weaving its upper body rather than leaping or stepping out of the way (automatic dodge same as the Commando O.C.C.).

Only a few hundred of these Skelebots have been released for field testing in the Quebec campaign and patrols into the west and southwest.

Coalition Hellion Skelebot

Model Type: Experimental model FASSAR-50

Class: Fully Automated Self-Sufficient Assault Robot

Crew: None; artificial intelligence

M.D.C. by Location:

- Hands (2) — 32 each
- Arms (2) — 65 each
- Vibro-blade (2) — 50 each
- C-200 Rail Gun (1) — 50
- Legs (2) — 100 each
- * Head — 90
- ** Main Body — 200

* Destroying the head of the robot will eliminate all optics and sensory systems. In most cases the robot shuts down as a safety feature. However, in some cases, about one in ten, the robot continues to fight, blasting away blindly until its ammunition is expended, and even then it will continue to grope around, lashing out and hitting anything it touches. Under these conditions the robot enjoys no combat bonuses to strike, parry, or dodge!

The head is a small and difficult target to hit, especially on a moving target. Thus, it can only be hit when a character makes a "called shot," and even then the attacker is -2 to strike.

** Depleting the M.D.C. of the main body will effectively destroy the bot, shutting it down completely. **Note:** Additional body armor or power armor cannot be worn by Skelebots.

Speed:

Running: 70 mph (112.6 km) maximum. Note that the act of running does NOT tire the robot and maximum speed can be maintained indefinitely.

Leaping: The legs of the Hellion are made for quick movement, dodging and leaping. Thus, it can leap up to 20 feet (6 m) high and 30 feet (9 m) lengthwise with only a few lunging strides or 50 feet (15.2 m) lengthwise from the momentum of a short run.

Flying: None, without the addition of the conventional CS jet pack or a vehicle.

Range: The nuclear power pack gives the Skelebot approximately two years of life even under the most strenuous and constant amount of use, nearly three years under less active conditions. The robot is intentionally given a much shorter energy "life" as yet another fail-safe and because of their high mortality rate.

Underwater Capabilities: The Skelebot is not particularly well suited for underwater operations. The best it can do is walk along the bottom of the sea at about 25% its normal running speed.

Maximum Ocean Depth: 1000 feet (305 m).

Statistical Data

Height: 12 feet (3.6 m) standing erect, although it can crouch and weave to look half that height.

Width: 4 feet (1.2 m)

Length: 3 feet (0.9 m)

Weight: 800 lbs (360 kg)

Physical Strength: Equal to a P.S. 30.

Cargo: None

Power System: Nuclear, average Skelebot energy life is three years.

CS Cost: 4.6 million credits; not available on the Black Market.

Weapon Systems: The Hellion currently has no built-in weapons, not even vibro-blades, so any weapon at its disposal must be hand-held. The fingers on the hands are spiked and do slashing damage and the two large arms have protruding spines that are particularly good for parrying mega-damage swords and similar attacks. The prehensile tail can slash and strike as a whip as well as strangle.

Any weapon system from rail guns to infantryman rifles can be assigned as its hand weapon. The four arms and hands mean as many as four different weapons can be used, or one two-handed heavy weapon like the CTT-P40A cannon and two smaller, lighter guns or vibro-blades.

Programming: Fundamentally the same as the FASSAR-20 and 30.

FASSAR-50 Hand to Hand Combat: Rather than use a weapon, the Hellion Skelebot can engage in mega-damage hand to hand combat using its fists and tail. Equal to hand to hand expert, plus the advantage of extra arms and a tail give it *seven* attacks per melee round!

Damage:

Restrained Punch — 2D6+15 S.D.C.

Full Strength Punch, Elbow, or Knee — 1D6 M.D.

Full Strength Claw Strike — 2D4 M.D.

Power Punch — 2D6 but counts as two melee attacks.

Tail Strike — 1D6 M.D.

Kick — 2D6 M.D.

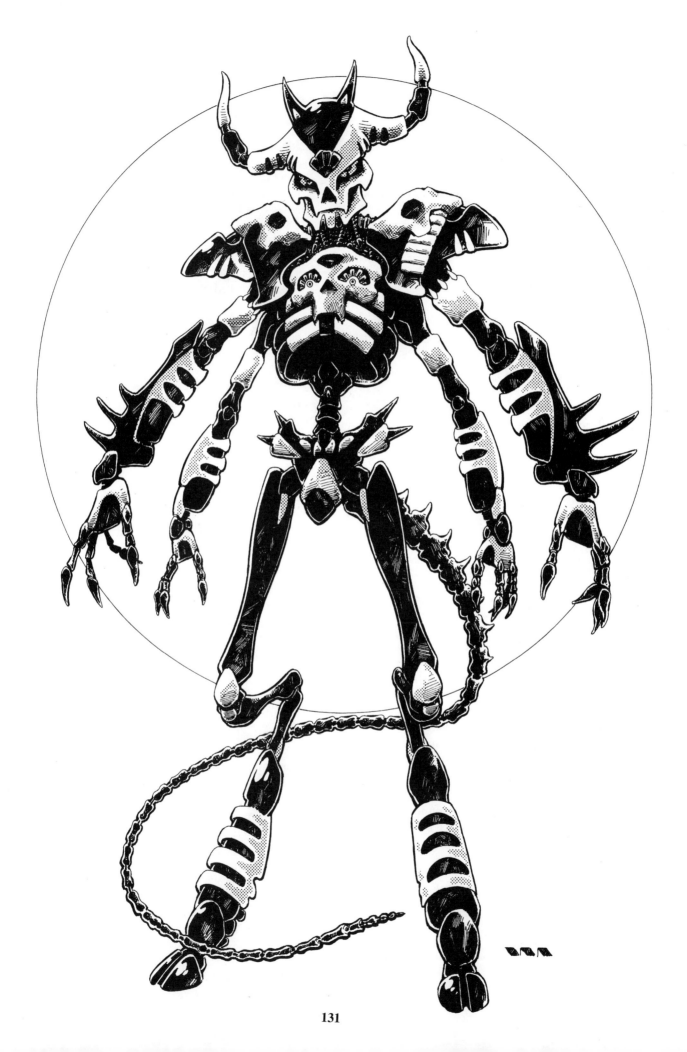

Body Block: 1D6 M.D.

Head Butt: 2D4 M.D.

Running Leap Kick: 4D6 M.D. This attack must be used at the beginning of a melee round and uses up all but one melee attack. In addition, there's a 01-35% chance of knocking giant-sized opponents to the ground and 01-70% likelihood if human-sized. The victim loses two melee actions and initiative as well as suffers damage.

Body Block/Ram: 1D6 M.D.

Full Speed Running Ram: 4D6 M.D. This attack uses up three attacks, but inflicts excellent damage.

Bonuses: Same as the FASSAR-20, plus the following in addition to standard bonuses:

+2 to roll with impact, punch or fall.

+2 on initiative

+1 to strike

+2 to parry

+4 to automatic dodge (see Commando O.C.C. for description)

Centaur Skelebot

FASSAR-60 Experimental Assault Robot

The FASSAR-60 is a centaur design that is completely experimental and not likely to ever see mass production. The FASSAR-60 has the upper torso of a humanoid skeleton and the lower body of a horse-like creature. Mounted on the back is a pair of mini-missile launchers. The forearms have a cluster of three, short-range energy weapons and pair of sensor rods on the hips of the back legs.

Despite its apparent speed and weapon systems, the Centaur Skelebot has been a design failure. The running speed is not dramatically greater than other bots and vehicles, nor is its leaping ability especially impressive. The missiles on its back tend to be unbalancing and the design of the fingers and hands prevents the bot from using normal guns for additional firepower (vibro-blades and oversized weapons are usable). Furthermore, Emperor Prosek is opposed to having a Skelebot that looks so "inhuman;" he has similar reservations about the Hellion. The other Skelebots may look like the dead brought to life as walking skeletons, but they are reminiscent of the human skeleton and not something alien. The Emperor, his Executive Counsel and officers of the Military High Command don't want anything *alien* to become acceptable the human culture of the Coalition States. This design is just too alien.

Only a dozen or so have been manufactured for preliminary field testing. The Centaur Skelebot will not be approved for phase two field tests.

Coalition Centaur Skelebot

Model Type: Experimental model FASSAR-60

Class: Fully Automated Self-Sufficient Assault Robot

Crew: None; artificial intelligence

M.D.C. by Location:

    Hands (2) — 30 each

    Arms (2) — 45 each

    Forearm Weapons (2) — 25 each

    Mini-Missile Cluster Launchers (2; back) — 50 each

    Legs (4) — 75 each

    Sensor Rods (2) — 10 each

    * Head — 90

    ** Main Body — 180

* Destroying the head of the robot will eliminate all optics and sensory systems. In most cases the robot shuts down as a safety feature. However, in some cases, about one in ten, the robot continues to fight, blasting away blindly until its ammunition is expended, and even then it will continue to grope around, lashing out and hitting anything it touches. Under these conditions the robot enjoys no combat bonuses to strike, parry, or dodge!

The head is a small and difficult target to hit, especially on a moving target. Thus, it can only be hit when a character makes a "called shot," and even then the attacker is -2 to strike.

** Depleting the M.D.C. of the main body will effectively destroy the bot, shutting it down completely. **Note:** Additional body armor or power armor cannot be worn by Skelebots.

Speed:

Running: 120 mph (192 km) maximum. Note that the act of running does NOT tire the robot and maximum speed can be maintained indefinitely.

Leaping: The Centaur can leap up to 20 feet (6 m) high and 30 feet (9 m) lengthwise with only a few lunging strides or 60 feet (18.3 m) lengthwise with a running start.

Flying: None.

Underwater Capabilities: None.

Statistical Data

Height: 10 feet (3 m)

Width: 4 feet (1.2 m)

Length: 10 feet (3 m)

Weight: 800 lbs (360 kg)

Physical Strength: Equal to a P.S. 30.

Cargo: None

Power System: Nuclear, average Skelebot energy life is three years.

CS Cost: 4.8 million credits; not available on the Black Market.

Weapon Systems:

1. Mini-Missile Cluster Launchers (2): Two launchers are mounted on the back of the upper torso.

Primary Purpose: Anti-Missile and Anti-Aircraft.

Secondary Purpose: Anti-Personnel

Missile Type: Any type of mini-missile can be used, but standard issue is fragmentation (anti-personnel, 5D6 M.D.) and plasma (1D6×10).

Mega-Damage: Varies with missile type.

Range: About one mile.

Rate of Fire: One at a time or in volleys of two, three, or four.

Payload: 20 total; ten per each launcher.

2. Double-Barrel, Forearm Laser (1): On the right forearm is a short-range laser. Point and shoot.

Primary Purpose: Defense

Secondary Purpose: Assault

Mega-Damage: 2D6 M.D. per single blast or 4D6 M.D. per simultaneous double blast (a double blast counts as one melee ac-

tion). Both forearm weapons cannot fire simultaneously at the same target.

Range: 2000 feet (610 m)

Rate of Attack: Each single or multiple blast counts as one melee attack.

Payload: Effectively unlimited.

3. Triple-Barreled Ion Forearm Blaster (1): On the left forearm of the Centaur bot is a short-range ion blaster.

Primary Purpose: Anti-Personnel

Secondary Purpose: Defense

Mega-Damage: 2D6 M.D. per single blast, 4D6 M.D. per simultaneous double blast or 6D6 M.D. per triple blast. Both forearm weapons cannot fire simultaneously at the same target.

Rate of Fire: Each single or multiple blast counts as one melee attack.

Effective Range: 1200 feet (336 m)

Payload: Effectively unlimited.

Programming: Fundamentally the same as the FASSAR-20 and 30. Five attacks per melee round.

FASSAR-60 Hand to Hand Combat: Fundamentally the same as the FASSAR-20, plus Kick at 2D6 M.D.

Robot Vehicles

All Robot Vehicles have the following features.

1. Nuclear Powered: Which means they have an effectively unlimited fuel capacity and power source. Average life is 15 to 20 years.

2. Radar: Can identify 72 and track up to 32 targets simultaneously at a range of 30 miles (48 km).

3. Combat Computer: Calculates, stores and transmits data onto the Heads Up Display (H.U.D.) of the pilot's helmet, as well as monitors on the control panel. It is linked to the targeting computer, weapon systems and radar.

4. Targeting Computer: Assists in tracking and identification of enemy targets. 30 mile range (48 km).

5. Laser Targeting System: Assists in the selection and focusing of specific targets and adds a bonus of +1 on initiative and +1 to strike when using long-range weapons. Does not apply to hand to hand combat or SAMAS.

6. Radio communication: Long-range, directional communication system with an effective range of about 500 miles (800 km). The typical giant robot also has a directional, short-range radio with a five miles (8 km) range, plus a built in loud speaker; 80 decibels.

7. External Audio Pick-up: A sound amplification listening system that can pick up a whisper 300 feet (91.5 m) away.

8. Spotlights: Most will have at least one or two spotlights. Typical range is 600 feet (182 m).

9. Ejector seat: In case of an emergency, the pilot and crew can be instantly ejected (about 1000 feet) and parachute to safety.

10 Self-Destruct: A last resort measure to prevent one's robot from being captured by the enemy. The explosive damage is fairly self-contained, destroying most of the internal systems with 3D6×10 M.D. Those within a ten foot (3 m) radius of the bot will suffer 6D6 M.D. from concussion and/or flying debris. It is very likely, 01-89% chance, that the nuclear power system will rupture and spew forth deadly levels of radiation!

11. Voice Actuated Locking System: The robot's access hatch is sealed by an automatic locking system. A six digit spoken code programmed to a specific voice(s) pattern (six voice memory) is standard operating procedure. A manual key pad is provided in case of system failure/over-ride.

12. Complete reinforced, environmental pilot and crew compartment: The compartment can usually seat 2-6 people and is reinforced to protect the occupants from mega-damage. It is airtight, pressurized and suitable for use in all hostile environments including underwater (typically a one-half to one mile depth) as well as outer space. The following features are included:

- Computer controlled life support system.
- Internal cooling and temperature control.
- Air purification and circulation systems, gas filtration, humidifier/dehumidifier automatically engages when needed. Can recirculate breathable air for up to four weeks before getting too stale to breathe.
- Computer controlled, independent oxygen supply and purge system that automatically engages in low oxygen or contaminated air environments. Twelve hour oxygen supply.
- Insulated, high temperature resistant shielding for up to 450 degrees centigrade. Normal fires do no damage. Nuclear, plasma, and magic fires do full damage.
- Radiation shielded.
- Polarized and light sensitive/adjusting tinted windshields when applicable.

Coalition IAR-2 Abolisher Robot

The Abolisher series of Infantry Assault Robot (IAR-2) is another giant vehicle that is part of the Coalition States' military forces. Unlike the UAR-1 Enforcer (see **Rifts® RPG**), which is designed specifically to combat ground troops in an urban/city environment, the Abolisher is a front-line infantry unit with long-range capabilities and heavy firepower. It is used to obliterate enemy troops, bots, and armored vehicles with a focus on anti-robot and anti-tank mission, hence the six heavy cannons bristling around what appears to be the head. The rim of cannons has given the 30 foot (9 m) robot the nickname "Thorn Head."

In reality, the Abolisher has no head. The heavily armored bot is a massive, humanoid shaped, all-terrain assault vehicle designed to withstand heavy bombardment. A head would make the robot too vulnerable. However, in keeping with the frightening Death's Head motif, the Abolisher is designed to look like a massive skull with arms and legs. The two eyes are infrared and conventional light searchlights for night assaults. The upper skull body can rotate 360 degrees and is operated by a five man crew. Three gunners operating two cannons each, the pilot and the co-pilot/communications engineer (either the pilot or co-pilot can fire the small forward facing, dual laser turret) and the top hatch gunner, usually a SAMAS.

The big guns are devastating weapons that can blast an enemy from all angles simultaneously. The robot's arms and hands are powerful and lethal in hand to hand confrontations (can rotate 180 degrees at the shoulders). On top of the behemoth is a Gunner's Hatch which allows a SAMAS or soldier to perch himself on the head and fire at the enemy from the top of the robot. An inner hatch (50 M.D.C.) locks automatically, preventing the enemy from gaining easy access should the top gunner be killed; the inner hatch can only be opened by one of the pilots.

The only real disadvantage to the 30 foot (9 m) giant is that its incredible weight and large size reduces its speed and maneuvering capabilities. Although great in the field as an outer perimeter defense or as an infantry assault unit (e.g. a tank with arms and legs), its slowness and size make it an easy target (hence the heavy armor). Unless one wishes to destroy a city, the

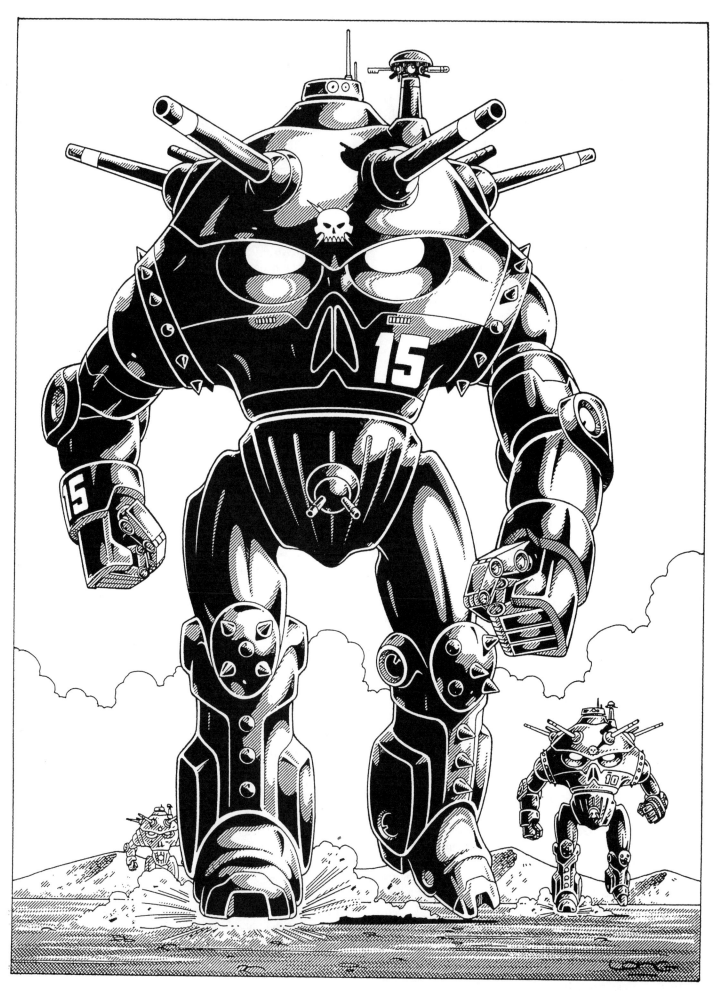

bot is not well suited for city conflicts; its weapons are too powerful for use in the city and its size and bulk makes maneuvering through narrow streets difficult. Still, it is excellent for city defense, troop support and infantry assaults.

Note: Improvements in mega-damage armor technology have increased the Abolisher's M.D.C. armor protection from those listed in **Rifts® Sourcebook One.** Some other minor improvements have also been incorporated such as having three gunners instead of two and a somewhat larger payload for the cannons. Both models are still in use, although 70% are the improved versions.

IAR-2 Abolisher Assault Robot

Model Type: IAR-2

Class: Infantry Assault Robot

Crew: Six: one pilot, co-pilot, communications officer and three gunners (each operates a pair of cannons). The top hatch gunner, usually a SAMAS or armored soldier with a heavy weapon can be added as well. Plus, it can seat two additional passengers.

M.D.C. by Location (increased armor):

   Hands (2) — 100 each
   Arms (2) — 190 each
   Legs (2) — 240 each
   Main Auto-Cannons (6) — 100 each
   Belly Gun (1, turret) — 25
   Chest Spotlight Eyes (2) — 10 each
   * Sensor Turret (left shoulder) — 80
   ** Gunner's Hatch (1; top) — 100
   Inner Hatch (1; top) — 50
   *** Main Body — 590
   Reinforced Pilot's Compartment — 250

   * Destroying the top mounted sensor turret will destroy the main radar and targeting system (no bonuses to strike, parry or dodge). The pilot must rely on his own human vision and less accurate computer and sensory systems. **Note:** The sensor turret is a small and difficult item to hit, especially on a moving target. Thus, it can only be hit when a character makes a **called shot** and even then the attacker is -3 to strike.

   ** Depleting the M.D.C. of the gunner's hatch makes the robot vulnerable to entry by the enemy from the top. The inner hatch has only 50 M.D.C.

   *** Depleting the M.D.C. of the main body will effectively destroy the bot, shutting it down completely, rendering it useless. **Note:** The chest spotlights are destroyed when the main body has suffered 300 points of damage.

Speed

   Running: 70 mph (112 km) maximum. Note that the act of running does not tire the robot and speed can be maintained indefinitely. Leaping: Not recommended because of the weight and disproportionately heavy head/upper body. Leaps are possible only from a running start and limited to approximately 20 feet (6 m) lengthwise and a height of only five or six feet (1.8 m). The chance of falling is high, roll percentile for every jump/leap. 1-70% likelihood of falling over. Fall causes the IAR-2 to lose all its attacks for one melee round (15 seconds) while the crew struggles to get the bot to stand back up.

   Underwater Capabilities: The IAR-2 is not particularly well suited for underwater operations. The best it can do is walk along the bottom of the sea at about 25% its normal running speed.

Maximum Ocean Depth: 4000 feet (1200 m).

Statistical Data

Height: 30 feet (9.1 m)

Width: 14 feet (4.3 m)

Length: 14 feet (4.3 m)

Weight: 60 tons fully loaded.

Physical Strength: Equal to a P.S. 60

Cargo: Minimal storage space; about four feet (1.2 m).

Power System: Nuclear; average energy life is 20 years.

Black Market Cost: 80 million credits for a new, undamaged, fully powered unit complete with fully functioning weapon systems. Rarely available.

Weapon Systems

1. C-144 Auto-Cannons (6): The IAR-2's main weapon is its six, automatic, self-loading cannons. Two cannons are operated by each of the three gunners. In case of an emergency, the pilot and/or co-pilot can fire the cannons but the number of attacks per melee are reduced by half. Each cannon is capable of 90 degree rotation from side to side and up and down. This gives the weapons an excellent arc of fire and can be used against ground and air targets. However, it also means there is a 20 foot (6 m) blind spot at its feet and directly above its head.

Primary Purpose: Anti-Tank, Anti-Armor, and Anti-Dragon.

Secondary Purpose: Defense

Weight: 2 tons each

Mega-Damage: 2D4×10 M.D. per single blast or 4D4×10 M.D. per double blast (two cannons firing simultaneously at the same target).

Rate of Fire: 2, 4, 6, or 12 times. Each cannon can fire twice per melee round for a total of 12 single shots or six double shots. However, to rapid-fire all 12 times at the same target will mean having to rotate the entire upper body, repositioning each cannon every time, making the last six or three double blasts -3 to strike. This also means the top hatch gunner and the lower laser turret can *not* attack for the entire melee round. Also, the next melee round, the IAR-2 can only fire a total of six single shots or three double; however, the following melee it can again fire 12 times.

   To fire at one target without rotating the body means two cannons can fire for a total of two double blasts or four single shots per melee round. Of course, it can train its other four cannons on two to four different targets simultaneously from the rear and/or sides. One of the advantages of the IAR-2 is that it can engage the enemy from all sides simultaneously!

Effective Range: 6000 feet (1828 m) — maximum range is 10,000 feet (3048 m) but the bot is -2 to strike targets over 6000 feet (1828 m) to about 7000 feet (2286 m) and -4 to hit targets beyond that point.

Payload: 240 total; each cannon has a payload of 40 shells. If one cannon is destroyed, its payload is automatically diverted to the other available weapons. The gunners can also divert payloads from one gun to another (i.e. the forward guns' ammunition is nearly exhausted while the side cannons' payloads are full, they can have the loading system move the side cannon's payload to the front).

2. CR-3T Dual Laser Turret (1, Belly gun): A single double-barreled laser turret is located on the lower teeth area of the Abolisher. Its primary use is to disperse enemy ground troops in the blind spot of the main cannons. The turret can rotate 180 degrees.

Primary Purpose: Defense
Secondary Purpose: Assault
Mega-Damage: 4D6 M.D.
Range: 2000 feet (610 m)
Rate of Attack: Two (2) per melee.
Payload: Effectively unlimited.

3. **Top Gunner's Hatch (1):** Designed to allow a SAMAS or other gunman to perch himself on the crown of the robot and fire down. The outer hatch has 100 M.D.C., the inner hatch locks automatically and has 50 M.D.C.

4. **Hand to Hand Combat:** Rather than use a weapon, the robot can engage in mega-damage hand to hand combat using its fists. Combat abilities are identical to the UAR-1 Enforcer with the following exceptions.

+4 to parry
Restrained Punch: 1D6 M.D.
Full Strength Punch: 3D6 M.D.
Power Punch: 5D6 M.D.
Body Block: 2D6 M.D.
Stomp: 2D4 M.D.
Kick: 1D6 M.D.
Leap Kick is NOT possible.

5. **Special Sensory Systems of Note:**

1. Enhanced Radar: Can identify and simultaneously track up to 96 different targets. Range: 50 miles (80 km). Ground targets are more difficult to track, as usual, unless on open ground and giant-size or flying 100 feet above treetop level.

2. Thermo-Imager: A special optical heat sensor that allows the infrared radiation of warm objects to be converted into a visible image. Enables the pilot to see in the dark, in shadows, and through smoke. Range: 2000 feet (610 m).

3. Infrared and Ultraviolet Optics: This optical system projects a beam of infrared light that is invisible to the normal eye. The infrared beam enables the pilot to see in the dark and to see other infrared beams. The ultraviolet system enables the pilot to see into the ultraviolet spectrum of light and is mostly used to detect the light beams of ultraviolet detection systems. **Note:** The infrared light beam *can* be seen by anybody who also has an infrared optics system and can follow the beam back to its source. Smoke impairs the infrared beam, making it impossible to see.

4. Nightvision and Video Camera System: The sensor array on the left shoulder has a standard multi-optic system with passive nightvision, telescopic sight and video camera (images transmitted to video screens inside the pilot's compartment).

5. Infrared Searchlights: Built into the face of the Abolisher are a pair of red eyes. These are actually a pair of infrared searchlights. The lights can be used to scan an area at night, using the invisible light to avoid detection. Only somebody who can also see infrared light will see the beams. Range: 500 feet (152 m).

6. Sensor Bonuses: +1 strike bonus to the long-range cannons in addition to other bonuses that may be available. See Robot Combat Training in the Robot Combat section of the **Rifts® RPG**.

IAR-3 Skull Smasher

The IAR-3 Skull Smasher joins the ranks of the other Coalition combat robots as another lethal frontline assault unit and heavy support unit. This walking tank is designed for speed and versatility of combat. Weapon systems include a long-range heavy laser over the right shoulder, a medium-range missile launchers behind the right and left shoulders, mini-missile launcher in the center above the skull face, double-barreled ball laser turrets on the forearms, and a double-barrel, heavy particle beam cannon in the mouth of the Death's Head. In addition, the Skull Smasher can run at speeds that belie its massive bulk and size. Consequently, a favorite tactic is to run, full tilt, and slam into another robot, tank or the wall of a building. Likewise, its heavy fists and powerful arms can pound into other bots, armored vehicles and fortifications with the shattering power of mini-missiles, hence its name. The knees and elbows are spiked to look more menacing than to inflict rather more damage. The eyes are sensor clusters with a pair of high-intensity spotlights to the sides and below them, on either side of the mouth.

Watching this bot in action when driven by daring and experienced RPA pilots is like watching a giant frenetic, black whirling dervish, slamming into opponents, performing leap kicks (an amazing sight) and blasting away with its weapons. One legendary combat report recounts how an IAR-3 single-handedly took on an adult Great Horned dragon. In the end, the dragon stood triumphant over the battered robot — literally torn limb from limb — but the great beast looked as if it had gone through hell, and respected the valiant men inside enough to spare their lives. The IAR-3 is the most heavily armored, and perhaps most powerful, robot war machine in the Coalition's armored division. Six hundred are already in service with another six hundred in production and expected to be on-line within six months.

IAR-3 Skull Smasher

Model Type: IAR-3
Class: Infantry Assault Robot
Crew: Five: one pilot, co-pilot, one communications officer, and two gunners; one operates the long-range laser cannon and missiles, the other operates the particle beam gun and the monitors weapon systems. The pilot operates the forearm guns. Two additional passengers can fit comfortably in the pilot's/crew compartment.

M.D.C. by Location:
Hands (2) — 110 each
Arms (2) — 250 each
Legs (2) — 350 each
Heavy Laser Cannon (1; top right) — 140
Medium-Range Missile Launchers (2; top left & right) — 130
* Mini-Missile Launchers (3; center) — 40 each
* P-Beam Mouth Cannon (1) — 75 each
* Forearm Turrets (2) — 120 each
* Chest Spotlights (4) — 15 each
* Sensor Cluster Eyes (2) — 80
*** Main Body — 990
Reinforced Pilot's Compartment — 250

* A single asterisk indicates a small and difficult target to strike, requiring the attacker to make a "called shot," but even then the attacker is -4 to strike.

** Depleting the M.D.C. of the gunner's hatch makes the robot vulnerable to entry by the enemy from the top. The inner hatch has only 50 M.D.C.

*** Depleting the M.D.C. of the main body will effectively destroy the bot, shutting it down completely, rendering it useless. **Note:** The chest spotlights are destroyed when the main body has suffered 300 points of damage.

Speed

Running: 90 mph (144.8 km) maximum. Note that the act of running does not tire the robot and speed can be maintained indefinitely. Leaping: The IAR-3 is an exceptional leaper, able to jump 30 feet (9 m) lengthwise or high with a short running start. A favorite tactic is to perform a running leap or jump kick inflicting incredible amounts of damage and having a 01-75% likelihood of knocking its opponent to the ground (victim loses two melee actions and initiative as well as suffers damage).

Underwater Capabilities: The IAR-3 is not particularly well suited for underwater operations. The best it can do is walk along the bottom of the sea at about 25% its normal running speed.

Maximum Ocean Depth: One mile (1.6 km).

Statistical Data

Height: 28 feet (9.1 m)
Width: 14 feet (4.3 m)
Length: 14 feet (4.3 m)
Weight: 80 tons fully loaded.
Physical Strength: Equal to a P.S. 60
Cargo: Minimal storage space; about four feet (1.2 m).
Power System: Nuclear, average energy life is 20 years.
CS Cost: 74 million credits for a new, fully loaded IAR-3. These bots are not available on the Black Market — exclusive to the CS.

Weapon Systems

1. Heavy Laser Cannon (1): Mounted above the head of the IAR-3 is a high-powered, heavy laser cannon. The arm the weapon is mounted on can move up and down in a 45 degree arc of fire. Other than its missiles, the laser cannon is its only other long-range weapon.

Primary Purpose: Anti-Aircraft and Anti-Armor.
Secondary Purpose: Defense
Mega-Damage: 1D6×10 M.D. per single blast.
Rate of Fire: Equal to the number of attacks per melee round of its gunner (typically 3-5).
Effective Range: 6000 feet (1828 m)
Payload: Effectively unlimited.

2. Medium-Range Missile Launchers (2): The missiles are used against heavy armor, fortifications and targets miles away.

Primary Purpose: Anti-Aircraft
Secondary Purpose: Anti-Armor (tanks, robots, dragons).
Missile Type: Any medium-range missile can be used, but standard issue is high explosive (heavy), plasma, or multi-warhead smart bomb (+5 to strike).
Mega-Damage: Varies with missile type.
Range: About 40 to 80 miles.
Rate of Fire: One at a time or in volleys of two, three, or four.
Payload: Six total; three per launch system.

3. Mini-Missile Launchers (3): The three small circular caps in the center of the robot above the head are rapid-fire mini-missile launchers.

Primary Purpose: Anti-Missile and Anti-Aircraft.
Secondary Purpose: Anti-Personnel
Missile Type: Any type of mini-missile can be used, but standard issue is fragmentation (anti-personnel, 5D6 M.D.) and plasma (1D6×10).
Mega-Damage: Varies with missile type.
Range: About one mile.
Rate of Fire: One at a time or in volleys of two, three, or four.
Payload: 21 total; seven per launch tube.

4. Double-Barreled Particle Beam Cannon (1): Inside the mouth of the Screaming Death's Head is a double-barreled particle beam cannon. This weapon has devastating power but is only effective against close-range targets. It is primarily used against heavy armored vehicles, fortifications and supernatural monsters.

Primary Purpose: Anti-Aircraft and Anti-Armor.
Secondary Purpose: Defense
Mega-Damage: 1D4×10 M.D. per single blast or 2D4×10 per simultaneous double blast (a double blast counts as one melee action).
Rate of Fire: Equal to the number of attacks per melee round of its gunner (typically 3-5).
Effective Range: 1400 feet (426.7 m)
Payload: Effectively unlimited.

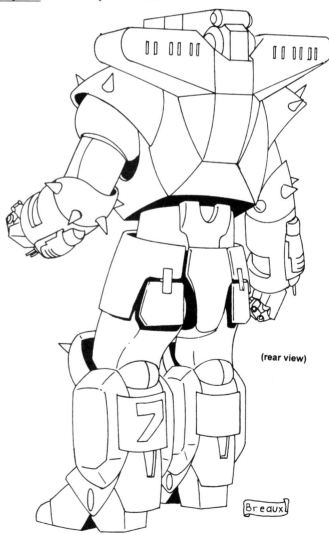

(rear view)

Breaux

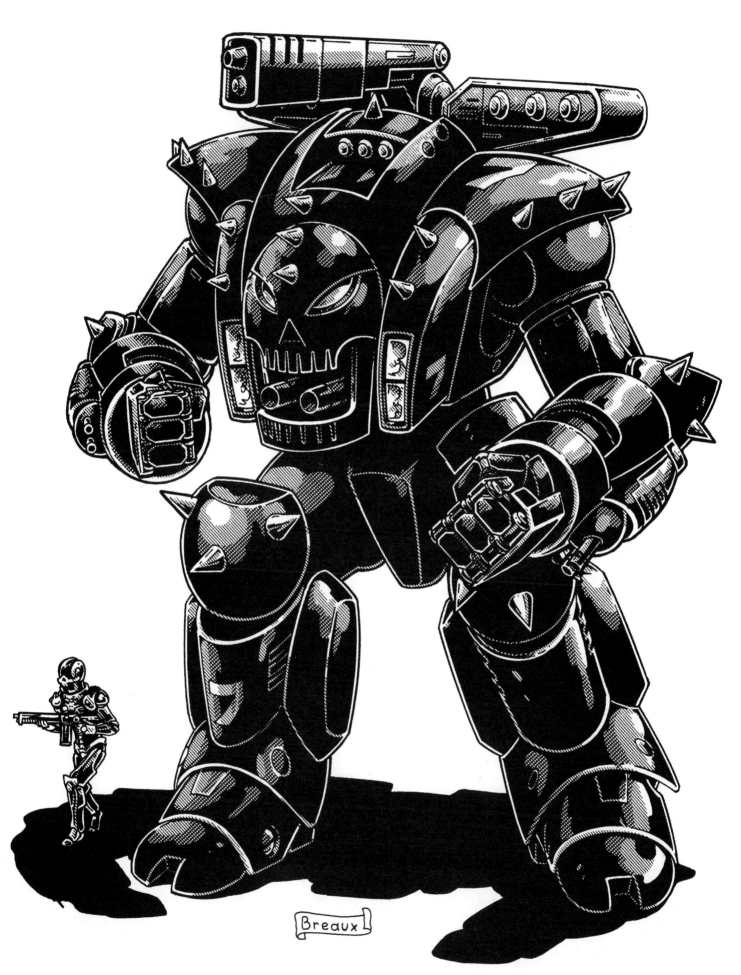

5. Double-Barreled, Forearm, Ball Laser Turrets (2): Each of the forearms has a laser turret that can rotate 180 degrees side to side and 90 degrees up and down. They are primarily used against light armored vehicles, power armor and ground troops.

Primary Purpose: Defense

Secondary Purpose: Assault

Mega-Damage: 4D6 M.D. per single blast or 1D4×10+8 per simultaneous double blast (a double blast counts as one melee action). Both forearm weapons cannot fire simultaneously at the same target.

Range: 4000 feet (1200 m)

Rate of Attack: Equal to the hand to hand attacks of the pilot or gunner operating them.

Payload: Effectively unlimited.

6. Hand to Hand Combat: The IAR-3 Skull Smasher exhibits astonishing speed, mobility, agility and hitting power. It is such an amazing machine that it gets its own "Elite" Combat Training table. Those not skilled in "elite" combat training with the IAR-3 use the *Robot Basic Combat Training* stats. Rather than use a weapon, the robot can engage in mega-damage hand to hand combat using its fists.

Two hand to hand attacks per melee round, plus those of the pilot at level one. Add one at levels three, six, ten, and fourteen. Remember, all bonuses are in addition to the pilot's own hand to hand combat training and attribute bonuses. They do *not* apply to the pilot's physical abilities outside the robot.

Critical strike is the same as the pilot's.

+2 to roll with impact, punch or fall.

+2 on initiative

+2 to strike in hand to hand combat.

+4 to parry

+2 to dodge

+3 to pull punch.

Restrained Punch: 1D6 M.D.

Full Strength Punch, Elbow or Knee attack: 5D6 M.D.

Power Punch: 1D6×10 M.D., but counts as two melee attacks.

Tear or Pry with hands: 3D6 M.D.

Kick Attack: 5D6 M.D

Running Leap Kick: 2D4×10 M.D.! This attack must be used at the beginning of a melee round and uses up all but one melee attack, but inflicts incredible damage. In addition, there's a 01-75% likelihood of knocking its opponent to the ground. Victims of knock-down looses two melee actions and initiative as well as suffers damage.

Body Block/Ram: 4D6 M.D.

Full Speed Running Ram: 2D4×10 M.D. This attack uses up three attacks, but inflicts incredible damage. In addition, there's a 01-80% likelihood of knocking its opponent to the ground. Victims of knock-down looses two melee actions and initiative as well as suffers damage.

Stomp: 3D6 M.D.; effective only against objects smaller than 12 feet (3.6 m) tall.

7. Special Sensory Systems of Note: Same as the IAR-2.

IAR-4 Hellraiser

The IAR-4 Hellraiser is another new addition to the Coalition's family of deadly, infantry robot vehicles. This one is comparatively small, standing only 18 feet (5.5 m) tall. It can engage enemy ground troops, power armor and light armored vehicles, but is specifically designed to combat other robots and tanks. This "Robot Killer" is fast, maneuverable and deadly, and armed with a battery of weapons and unique combat capabilities. It is a favorite of commandos, military specialists and RPA ground robot pilots.

Above the right shoulder is an extendable and retractable stun-gun that fires an electronic discharge that temporarily stuns unarmored opponents and can "fry" unshielded computers and electronics (01-55%). Unfortunately, the electric shock has a serious chance of killing rather than stunning (01-33%); not that the CS usually cares. The squarish protrusion next to it, above the right shoulder, is a short-range, heavy plasma ejector. Over the left shoulder is a short-range missile launcher. Mounted on the back of the left shoulder is a small laser turret that can slide forward to fire upon surprised troops. The head is actually a sensor cluster with video capabilities. The Quatro-Gun is a multi-system weapon and tool combined. The pronged, mega-damage claw in place of a left hand is more deadly than it appears. The claw can be used as a vibro-blade to slash and stab, but it can also spin around in a clockwise motion to function as a giant (and deadly) mega-damage drill! It can punch through mega-damage armor, cut holes into fortifications, and sabotage support beams.

Many of the robot's designers and RPA pilots have argued that the *Hellraiser* is a better "Glitter Boy Killer" than the PA-300 power armor assigned with the task. Of course, one of the controversies is whether or not the PA-300 Glitter Boy Killer should be considered a power armor suit or a small, one-man robot. Considering its somewhat smaller size and single pilot, the G.B. Killer is a formidable adversary, but the larger, nearly as quick, powerful and versatile Hellraiser is undeniably one of the best all-around, "robot (and power armor) killers" to walk North America!

Note: The Hellraiser is the giant robot depicted on the front cover of this book, as well as in the illustration accompanying this description; both by artist John Zeleznik.

Shown in the cover painting is the Hellraiser's *gunner*, wearing the Coalition version of the *Urban Warrior* padded environmental body armor: 50 M.D.C., weight: 11 lbs/5 kg, good mobility: -10% to prowl, -5% on other physical skills. The main difference between it and the civilian version is the "skull-face" helmet.

IAR-4 Hellraiser

Model Type: IAR-4

Class: Infantry Assault Robot

Crew: Two: one pilot and one gunner. The gunner typically operates the shoulder plasma cannon, laser turret and missiles. The pilot usually operates the Quatro-Gun and vibro-claw. Either one can operate the electro-stunner. A communications officer or one passenger can fit comfortably in the pilot's/crew compartment.

M.D.C. by Location:

Hand (1; right) — 90
Vibro-Claw (1; left) — 90
Arms (2) — 210 each
Legs (2) — 250 each
Electro-Stunner (1; top right) — 40
Plasma Ejector (1; top right) — 140
Short-Range Missile Launcher (1; top left) — 120
Small Laser Turret (1; left cover) — 35
Quatro-Gun (1; hand-held) — 100
** Head/Sensor Cluster — 90
*** Main Body — 690
Reinforced Pilot's Compartment — 200

* A single asterisk indicates a small and difficult target to strike, requiring the attacker to make a "called shot," but even then the attacker is -4 to strike.

** Destroying the head of the robot will eliminate all forms of optical enhancement and sensory systems. The pilot must rely on his own human vision and senses. Any robot combat bonuses are lost!

The head is a small and difficult target to hit, which is tucked into the chest, between the two heavily plated shoulders. Thus, it can only be hit when an enemy makes a "called shot," but even then the attacker is -3 to strike.

*** Depleting the M.D.C. of the main body will shut the robot down completely, rendering it useless.

Speed

Running: 90 mph (144.8 km) maximum; it can go from zero to 60 mph (96.5 km) in 10 seconds. Note that the act of running does not tire its operator and maximum speed can be maintained indefinitely.

Leaping: The IAR-4 can leap 20 feet (6 m) lengthwise or heightwise with a short running start. It can also perform running leaps or jump kicks inflicting serious amounts of damage and has a 01-45% chance of knocking giant-sized opponents to the ground (victim loses two melee actions and initiative as well as suffers damage).

Underwater Capabilities: The IAR-4 is not particularly well suited for underwater operations. The best it can do is walk along the bottom of the sea at about 25% its normal running speed.

Maximum Ocean Depth: One mile (1.6 km).

Statistical Data

Height: 18 feet (9.1 m) standing fully erect; the Hellraiser tends to stand and run in a crouched position.
Width: 10 feet (3.6 m)
Length: 6 feet (1.8 m)
Weight: 35 tons fully loaded.
Physical Strength: Equal to a P.S. 50
Cargo: Minimal storage space; about four feet (1.2 m).
Power System: Nuclear; average energy life is 20 years.
CS Cost: 47 million credits for a new, fully loaded IAR-4. These bots are not available on the Black Market — exclusive to the CS.

Weapon Systems

1. **H-02 Electro-Stunner (1):** Mounted above and behind the right shoulder is the Electro-Stunner. To fire, it must be raised out of its back mounted housing. The weapon fires an electronic discharge intended to temporarily stun unarmored opponents or "fry" unshielded computers and electronics (01-55% chance of shorting them out). The problem with the Electro-Stunner is that it frequently electrocutes (01-33%) its victim instead of stunning him! This is particularly a problem when used against D-bees and supernatural beings because they may be more vulnerable to and suffer more damage from electricity than humans.

Primary Purpose: Anti-Personnel; used to incapacitate and capture enemy personnel.
Secondary Purpose: Anti-Electronic systems.
Mega-Damage: Three settings: 1D6×10 S.D.C., 2D6 M.D. or 4D6 M.D. per single blast. If the damage exceeds the victim's damage capacity, he is electrocuted rather than stunned.
Rate of Fire: Limited to twice per melee round.
Effective Range: 200 feet (61 m)
Payload: Effectively unlimited.

2. **H-40 Plasma Ejector (1):** Mounted above and behind the right shoulder is a plasma ejector. This is a comparatively short-range weapon used to combat power armor, bots and armored vehicles.
Primary Purpose: Anti-Armor.
Secondary Purpose: Defense
Mega-Damage: 1D4×10 M.D. per blast.
Rate of Fire: Equal to the number of attacks per melee round of its gunner (typically 3-5).
Effective Range: 2000 feet (610 m)
Payload: Effectively unlimited.

3. **Short-Range Missile Launcher (1):** The missiles are used against heavy armor, fortifications and targets a few miles away.

Primary Purpose: Anti-Armor
Secondary Purpose: Anti-Aircraft and Missiles.
Missile Type: Any short-range missile can be used.
Mega-Damage: Varies with missile type.
Range: Two to five miles.
Rate of Fire: One at a time or in a volley of two or three.
Payload: Three total.

4. **H-L24 Double-Barreled Laser Turret (1):** Mounted on the back of the left shoulder is a small laser turret that slides up and forward to fire. This concealed weapon frequently surprises the enemy. The laser turret can rotate 180 degrees side to side and has a 45 degree, up and down, arc of fire. It is primarily used against vehicles, power armor, missiles and troops.
Primary Purpose: Anti-Missile
Secondary Purpose: Anti-Personnel
Mega-Damage: 4D6 M.D. per simultaneous double blast (counts as one melee action); the weapon always fires in tandem.
Range: 2000 feet (610 m)
Rate of Attack: Equal to the hand to hand attacks of the pilot or gunner operating it.
Payload: Effectively unlimited.

5. **H-4 Quatro-Gun (1):** The Quatro-Gun is a multi-system weapon and tool designed for penetrating armor. The small, top barrel is a short-range laser tool used for cutting and soldering. The large, second barrel is a high-powered, long-range laser. The large, third barrel fires particle beams, while the small, bottom one is a torch used for cutting and welding, as well as a flame thrower. **Note:** Only one of the energy weapons can be fired at a time. For example, the long-range laser and P-beam *cannot* be fired simultaneously. The H-4 Quatro is an experimental weapon and although it has passed its field tests, it still has some "quirks" (the design team refuses to call them "bugs" or glitches). One is when using the particle beam setting exclusively and continually in combat for more than five minutes at a time. This will often (01-50%) cause the weapon to overheat and jam — none of the settings will fire for 1D4+1 melee rounds (30+ seconds). Another is that after four consecutive flame thrower blasts from the torch, any subsequent blasts will be at half range for five minutes, then resume to normal.
Primary Purpose: Multiple weapon and tool.
Mega-Damage: Short-Range Laser: 2D6 M.D. per blast.
Long-Range Laser: 4D6 M.D. per blast.
Particle Beam: 1D4×10 M.D. per blast.
Torch/Flame thrower: 1D6 M.D. per short blast; 2D6 M.D. when used as cutting or welding tool.
Range: Short-Range Laser: 1000 feet (305 m)
Long-Range Laser: 3000 feet (914 m)
Particle Beam: 1400 feet (426.7 m)
Torch/Flame thrower: 100 feet (30.5 m)
Rate of Attack: Equal to the hand to hand attacks of the pilot or gunner operating it. Each blast, regardless of the weapon setting, counts as a melee attack.
Payload: Effectively unlimited. The H-4 is connected to the Hellraiser's power supply with a power cable (25 M.D.C. and can only be hit by a called shot with a penalty of -7 to strike). If the cable is severed the flow of energy automatically stops, leaving the weapon powerless. An operator or field armorer may be able to patch the cable together (roll under engineering or field armorer skill), but it will take 1D6×10 minutes.

142

6. **HV-60 Vibro-Claw (1):** The Hellraiser has a double-bladed vibro-claw in place of a left hand. The blade can be used to slash and stab as usual, but it can also spin around in a clockwise motion to function as a giant, mega-damage drill! The drill can be used to punch through mega-damage armor, cut holes into fortifications, drill through mega-damage materials and sabotage support beams. It is primarily used against heavily armored vehicles, robots, fortifications and supernatural monsters.

Primary Purpose: Anti-Armor

Secondary Purpose: Drilling tool

Mega-Damage: 5D6 M.D. as a giant vibro-claw. 1D4×10+10 as a drill.

Rate of Fire: Hand to hand equal to the combined number of attacks of the pilot (typically 3-6).

Effective Range: Arm's reach is roughly 14 feet (4.2 m).

7. **Hand to Hand Combat:** The IAR-4 Hellraiser has its own "Elite" Combat Training skill. Those not skilled in "elite" combat training with the IAR-4 use the *Robot Basic Combat Training* stats. Two hand to hand attacks per melee round, plus those of the pilot at level one. Add one at levels three, seven, and eleven. Remember, all bonuses are in addition to the pilot's own hand to hand combat training and attribute bonuses. They do *not* apply to the pilot's physical abilities outside the robot.

Critical strike is the same as the pilot's.

+3 to roll with impact, punch or fall.

+2 on initiative

+2 to strike in hand to hand combat.

+2 to parry

+2 to dodge

+4 to pull punch

Restrained Punch: 1D6 M.D.

Full Strength Punch, Elbow or Knee attack: 2D6 M.D.

Power Punch: 4D6 M.D., but counts as two melee attacks.

Vibro-Claw — see #6 above.

Tear or Pry with hand: 1D6 M.D.

Kick Attack: 2D6 M.D

Running Leap Kick: 1D4×10 M.D.! This attack must be used at the beginning of a melee round and uses up all but one melee attack. In addition, there's a 01-45% chance of knocking giant-sized opponents to the ground. The victim loses two melee actions and initiative as well as suffers damage.

Body Block/Ram: 3D6 M.D.

Full Speed Running Ram: 1D4×10 M.D. This attack uses up three attacks, but inflicts excellent damage.

Stomp: 1D6 M.D.; effective only against objects smaller than 10 feet (3 m) tall.

8. **Special Sensory Systems of Note:** Same as the IAR-2.

IAR-5 Hellfire

Robot Scout & Light Assault Unit

A pair of IAR-5 Hellfires are frequently dispatched as the partners of a Hellraiser, Skull Smasher or 1D4 Terror Troopers; a standard combination for patrols in Old Chicago, border patrols, and seek and destroy missions against robots and tanks. They can also be dispatched as advance scouts for Spider Skull-Walkers, tank patrols, armored reconnaissance teams, and in squads of 4-8 for search and destroy missions.

The Hellfire is another experimental design for the Coalition States. It is a small, two-man robot vehicle made for scouting and quick, hit and run style assaults. It is equipped with a pair of rail guns, mini-missiles, double-barreled plasma ejector and light lasers. The entire upper body where the weapons are housed can rotate 360 degrees, so the Hellfire can spin to face an enemy behind it in a heartbeat, without having to move its legs. The legs and sleek, low profile body are made for speed, leaping and maneuvering through all terrains. The access hatch is located between the legs and incorporates a double entry system with a heavy outer hatch (90 M.D.C.) and light inner hatch (50 M.D.C.). In an emergency or to eject, the top flips open. The ostrich-like robot has no arms, so its hand to hand fighting capabilities are limited to kicks, stomps, and body blocks.

IAR-5 Hellfire

Model Type: IAR-5

Class: Light Infantry Assault Robot

Crew: Two: one pilot and a gunner. The gunner typically operates the rail guns and mini-missile launchers. The pilot usually operates the plasma weapon and light lasers. One passenger can be squeezed in behind the seats, but it's a tight fit and uncomfortable for long periods of time.

M.D.C. by Location:

Legs (2) — 250 each

Rail Guns (2; sides) — 90 each

* Plasma Ejector (1; double barrel, center) — 50

Mini-Missile Launchers (2; sides) — 120 each

* Small Laser Turrets (2; undercarriage) — 25 each

* Small Rear Trusters (2; undercarriage) — 30 each

*** Main Body — 480

Reinforced Pilot's Compartment — 180

* A single asterisk indicates a small and difficult target to strike, requiring the attacker to make a "called shot," but even then the attacker is -4 to strike.

*** Depleting the M.D.C. of the main body will shut the robot down completely, rendering it useless.

Note: The IAR-5 doesn't have a head. The domed upper section is the main body. Inflicting more than 380 M.D.C. will knock out the concealed sensor system, eliminating all optics, radar and sensors, and the combat bonuses they provide.

Speed

Running: 120 mph (192 km) maximum; it can go from zero to 60 mph (96.5 km) in 8 seconds. Note that the act of running does not tire its operator and maximum speed can be maintained indefinitely.

Leaping: The IAR-5 can leap 30 feet (9 m) high or lengthwise with a short running start. A pair of small jet thrusters are located in the rear above the leg joints which are used for jet assisted leaps and propulsion in the water. A jet assisted leap is 60 feet (18.3 m), either high or lengthwise.

The IAR-5 can also perform running leaps or jump kicks inflicting serious amounts of damage and a 01-35% chance of knocking giant-sized opponents to the ground (victim loses two melee actions and initiative as well as suffers damage).

Underwater Capabilities: The IAR-5 is adequately suited for underwater operations. It can walk along the bottom of the sea at about 25% its normal running speed or engage its thrusters to travel at a sluggish speed of 10 mph (16 km/8.5 knots); roughly the same surface speed.

Maximum Ocean Depth: 4000 feet (1200 m).

Statistical Data

Height: 14 feet (4.2 m)
Width: 10 feet (3.6 m)
Length: 7 feet (2.1 m)
Weight: 25 tons, fully loaded.
Physical Strength: Equal to a P.S. 45
Cargo: Minimal storage space; about three feet (0.9 m).
Power System: Nuclear; average energy life is 20 years.
CS Cost: 25 million credits for a new, full loaded IAR-5. These bots are not available on the Black Market — exclusive to the CS.

Weapon Systems

1. HF-36 Hellfire Rail Guns (2): Mounted on both sides of the IAR-5 are a pair of gatling-gun styled rail guns. They are fixed forward so the Hellfire pilot must bend its knees, pivot or rotate the upper body to shoot at a particular opponent — they are ideal against tanks and giant robots. Remember, the upper torso of the Hellfire robot can rotate 360 degrees in a heartbeat.

Primary Purpose: Assault
Secondary Purpose: Defense
Weight: Rail Gun: 300 lbs (135 kg) each.
Mega-Damage: A burst is 40 rounds and inflicts 1D4×10 M.D. from one gun or 2D4×10 M.D. from both simultaneously. However, the target must be large and wider than 11 feet (3.3 m) for both weapons to hit it simultaneously.
Rate of Fire: Equal to number of combined hand to hand attacks (usually 4-6).
Maximum Effective Range: 4000 feet (1200 m)
Payload: 10,000 rounds per drum, that's 250 bursts each or 500 total. Reloading an IAR-5's rail gun requires special equipment or another giant-sized robot. It will take about 10 minutes for those not trained, but a mere five minutes by somebody trained in robot mechanics (or who is an Operator O.C.C.).

2. HF-36 Double-Barrelled Plasma Ejector (1): Located in the center of the Hellfire is a double-barrelled plasma ejector. It can pivot up and down in a 45 degree arc of fire.

Primary Purpose: Anti-Armor
Secondary Purpose: Anti-Personnel
Mega-Damage: 5D6 per single blast (one barrel) or 1D6×10 M.D. per simultaneous double barrel blast.
Rate of Fire: Equal to the number of attacks per melee round of its gunner (typically 3-6).
Effective Range: 1600 feet (488 m)
Payload: Effectively unlimited.

3. Mini-Missile Launchers (2): Located in the area that might be considered the robot's shoulders, are a pair of mini-missile launchers.

Primary Purpose: Anti-Armor, Power Armor and Anti-Robots.
Secondary Purpose: Anti-Personnel
Missile Type: Any mini-missile can be used.
Mega-Damage: Varies with missile type.
Range: One mile (1.6 m).
Rate of Fire: One at a time or in a volley of two, four or eight.
Payload: 32 total; 16 in each of the launchers.

4. HF-12 Single-Barrelled Laser Turrets (2): Mounted on the undercarriage of each of the missile launchers is a small laser turret. The turret can rotate 360 degrees and has a 45 degree, up and down, arc of fire.

Primary Purpose: Anti-Personnel
Secondary Purpose: Defense
Mega-Damage: 3D6 M.D. per single shot. The two turrets cannot be used in tandem to fire at the same target.
Range: 2000 feet (610 m)
Rate of Attack: Equal to the hand to hand attacks of the pilot or gunner operating them.
Payload: Effectively unlimited.

5. Hand to Hand Combat: The IAR-5 Hellfire has its own "Elite" Combat Training skill. Those not skilled in "elite" combat training with the IAR-5 use the *Robot Basic Combat Training* stats.

One extra melee action per round, plus those of the pilot at level one. Add one at levels three, six, and twelve. Remember, all bonuses are in addition to the pilot's own hand to hand combat training and attribute bonuses. They do *not* apply to the pilot's physical abilities outside the robot.

Critical strike is the same as the pilot's.
+3 to roll with impact, punch or fall.
+3 on initiative
+2 to strike in hand to hand combat/kicks.
+2 to dodge standing, +4 to dodge running and leaping.
No bonus to parry
No Punch attack
Kick Attack: 2D6 M.D.
Power Kick: 3D6 M.D, but counts as two melee attacks.
Leap Kick: 3D6 M.D.
Running Leap Kick: 6D6 M.D.! This attack must be used at the beginning of a melee round and uses up all but one melee attack. In addition, there's a 01-35% chance of knocking giant-sized opponents to the ground. The victim loses two melee actions and initiative as well as suffers damage.
Body Block/Ram: 2D6 M.D.
Full Speed Running Ram: 1D4×10 M.D. This attack uses up three attacks, but inflicts excellent damage.
Stomp: 1D6 M.D.; effective only against objects smaller than five feet (1.5 m) tall.

6. Special Sensory System of Note: Same as the IAR-2.

CR-004 Scout Spider-Skull Walker

The CR-004 Spider-Skull Walker, better known as the Spider Scout, is a frightening looking, all-terrain, robot vehicle that walks on six insect like legs (**Editor's Note:** Yes, we know spiders have eight legs). It has a lower profile than the tall CR-003 Spider-Skull Walker which enables it to hide, prowl and leap. It is also faster.

The manned bot is designed to be a reconnaissance scout and light infantry combat vehicle. Four Scouts are typically dispatched to escort every one CR-003, creating the eerie appearance of a large mother spider with four of her young. Spider Scouts are frequently sent ahead of troops and armored companies to reconnoiter the area. They can be dispatched as lone individuals, pairs, squads (4-10) or entire platoons. They can easily amble over the debris of ruined cities and are good climbers as long as the terrain is not too steep; 90 degree incline, maximum. Its weapon systems make the Scout only a bit less deadly than its giant predecessor.

Coalition Spider Scout Robot

Model Type: CR-004 Scout Spider-Skull Walker
Nickname: Spider Scout
Class: Multi-purpose, All-Terrain Assault Robot
Crew: Two: a pilot and a gunner, with room for two passengers or prisoners.
M.D.C. by Location:

Triple-Barreled Rail Guns (2) — 100 each
Laser Turret (1; undercarriage) — 80
Mini-Missile Launchers (2; side) — 100 each
Legs (6) — 100 each
Leg Lights (6) — 5 each
Rear Jet Thrusters (2) — 50 each
* Eye Searchlights (2) — 20 each
* Eyebrow Cameras (4; two above each eye) — 5 each
* Sensor Clusters (6; rear) — 25 each
*** Main Body/Skull — 280
Reinforced Crew Compartment — 150

* A single asterisk indicates a small and difficult target to strike, requiring the attacker to make a "called shot," but even then the attacker is -4 to strike.

*** Depleting the M.D.C. of the main body will shut the robot down completely, rendering it useless.

Note: The CR-004 doesn't have a head. The large skull-like head is the main body.
Sensor Note: It is virtually impossible to blind or knockout all the sensors of the Spider Scout.
Leg Note: The robot can lose one leg on each side and not be unbalanced, but speed is reduced by 15%.
Speed

Running: 100 mph (160.5 km) maximum.

Leaping: 10 feet (3 m) high or 20 feet (6 m) lengthwise.

Underwater Capabilities: The Spider Scout is adequately suited for underwater operations. It can walk along the bottom of the sea at about 25% its normal running speed or engage its thrusters to travel at a sluggish speed of 10 mph (16 km/8.5 knots); roughly the same for water surface speed.

Maximum Ocean Depth: One mile (1.6 km).
Statistical Data
Height: 12 feet (3.6 m); the skull is about six feet (1.8 m) tall.
Width: The skull is 7 feet wide (2.1 m), but the legs extend to about 17 feet wide (5.1 m).
Length: The overall length with legs extended is about 17 feet (5.1 m) long, while the body of the skull is 12 feet (3.6 m).
Weight: 12 tons fully loaded.
Physical Strength: Not applicable.
Cargo: Storage space of about 4×4×4 feet (1.2 m) for additional clothing, weapons, supplies, and specimens. This is in addition to a weapons locker that contains six CP-40 laser rifles, two C-50 Dragonfire rifles, 24 standard E-Clips, and two smoke grenades.
Power System: Nuclear, average life is 25 years.
CS Cost: 22 million credits for a new, fully loaded Spider Scout. These bots are not available on the Black Market — exclusive to the CS.

Weapon Systems

1. **C-104 Spider Tri-Barrel Rail Guns (2):** Mounted in the rear, on both sides, are a pair of long-barrelled rail guns. They can turn side to side and up and down in a 75 degree arc and make excellent anti-missile and anti-aircraft weapons.
Primary Purpose: Assault
Secondary Purpose: Defense
Mega-Damage: A burst is 60 rounds and inflicts 1D4×10 M.D. from one gun or 2D4×10 M.D. from both simultaneously.
Rate of Fire: Equal to number of combined hand to hand attacks (usually 4-6).
Maximum Effective Range: 6000 feet (1828 m)
Payload: 10,000 rounds per drum, that's 166 bursts each or 332 total. Reloading a Spider Scout's rail gun requires special equipment or another giant-sized robot. It will take about 30 minutes for those not trained, but a mere 15 minutes by somebody trained in robot mechanics (or who is an Operator O.C.C.).

2. **CR-2T Laser Turret (1):** Mounted under the chin of the Spider Scout is a double-barrelled, medium-range laser turret. It is capable of 360 degree rotation and a 60 degree angle of fire up and down.
Primary Purpose: Anti-Personnel
Secondary Purpose: Defense
Mega-Damage: 5D6 M.D. per dual blast.
Range: 2000 feet (610 m)
Rate of Fire: Equal to the combined number of hand to hand attacks per melee (usually 4 to 6).
Payload: Effectively unlimited.

3. **Mini-Missile Launchers (2):** Located in what might be considered the cheek on each side of the skull head are mini-missile launchers.
Primary Purpose: Anti-Missile and Anti-Aircraft.
Secondary Purpose: Anti-Personnel.
Missile Type: Any type of mini-missile can be used, but standard issue is fragmentation (anti-personnel, 5D6 M.D.) and plasma (1D6×10).
Mega-Damage: Varies with missile type.
Range: About one mile.
Rate of Fire: One at a time or in volleys of two, three, or four.
Payload: 20 total; ten per each of the two launchers.

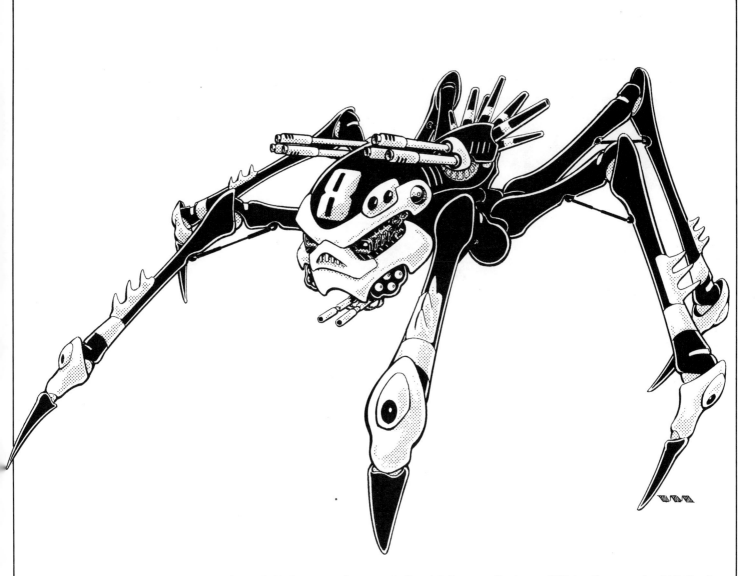

4. Smoke Dispenser: A smoke dispensing unit in the rear under-carriage can release a dense cloud of smoke that will cover a 60 foot (18.3 m) diameter behind it. It can also release tear gas as an alternative, anti-personnel weapon.

Payload: Eight total. The usual mix is four smoke and four tear gas.

5. Hand to Hand Combat: The Spider-Skull Walker is a robot vehicle that is not particularly designed for hand to hand type combat. However, it can strike with one or two of its legs equal to the hand to hand attacks of the pilot, perform a head butt, and leaping body blocks/rams; all such attacks are most effective against opponents that are twice the size of a human or bigger.

Leg Strike — 2D4 M.D.

Stomp —1D6 M.D.

Head Butt — 1D6 M.D.

Leaping Body Block/Ram — 3D6 M.D. with a 01-40% chance of knocking its opponent to the ground. The victim loses initiative and two melee attacks/actions.

6. Special Sensory Systems of Note: Same as the IAR-2, plus all optical enhancements, sonar and radar, sound and audio recording system and molecular analyzer (a larger, heavy-duty version of the bionic system; can recognize and identify 3000 different airborne substances). The mechanical eyes of the Spider Scout are multi-optic cameras with light amplification and telescopic capabilities. Typically, whatever the eyes see, the crew can see on their monitors (effective range: 1200 feet/610 m). If they want to record (sound and image) they can do so with the press of a button. Also note that the two circular indentations in the robot vehicle's eye-brows/ridges are secondary, low light video cameras (effective range: 300 feet/91.5 m).

Special Bonuses and Abilities:

+1 on initiative

+1 to dodge

Prowl/hide at 44% +2% per level of the pilot.

CR-005
Scorpion-Skull Walker

The CR-005 Scorpion-Skull Walker, better known simply as Scorpion, is an experimental all-terrain, robot vehicle that walks on six insect like legs and sports a pair of large, mega-damage pincers (**Editor's Note:** Yes, we know scorpions have eight legs). Its design was inspired by the CR-003 Spider-Skull Walker in an effort to create an incredibly low profile, all environment vehicle that might evade visual detection in light forests and city ruins, and which could make itself prone to lay in wait for the enemy undetected. Thus, the Scorpion Walker can crawl along with its weapon tail completely straight at a maximum height of five feet! Even the pilot and crew sit in a backward reclined position, with control panels directly in front and to the sides on movable, flat panels. Most data is presented on the Heads Up Display system of the crew's helmet visors and "jacked" directly to the crew through cybernetic headjacks connecting them directly to the computer and combat systems.

The manned bot is designed primarily as an assault unit that either sneaks up on its prey and attacks or lays in wait to attack when the enemy comes within striking range. Light weapons are built into the front, head section, which includes a pair of lasers and the huge pincer claws. To strike with its main guns, the robot must raise its tail into position above its head like a real scorpion and fire.

The Scorpion-Skull Walker can also be used as a reconnaissance scout and light infantry combat vehicle. Only 640 (one battalion) are currently operating in the field of combat. Of those, 360 are being deployed in the Tolkeen conflict, 140 along the north and western borders of the Coalition States, and 140 have been sent to participate in the Quebec Campaign.

Coalition Scorpion-Skull Walker

Model Type: CR-005 Scorpion-Skull Walker

Nickname: The Scorpion

Class: Multi-purpose, All-Terrain Assault Robot

Crew: Two: a pilot and a gunner, with room for one passenger.

M.D.C. by Location:

Gatling Rail Guns (3; tail) — 80 each

* Tail Lasers (2; tail) — 40 each

Multiple Mini-Missile Launcher (1; tail) — 100

Secondary Mini-Missile Launchers (2; tail) — 40 each

* Double-Barrelled Head Lasers (2 pair; head) — 40 each

Giant Pincers (2) — 120 each

Legs (4) — 120 each

* Eye Searchlights (2) — 20 each

* Smoke Dispenser (1; grille/teeth of head) — 20

* Eyebrow Cameras (4; two above each eye) — 5 each

* Sensor Cluster (1; nose) — 35

Tail Segments (3, including weapon segment) — 180 each

** Head (crew area) — 180

*** Main Body/Skull — 200

Reinforced Crew Compartment — 150

* A single asterisk indicates a small and difficult target to strike, requiring the attacker to make a "called shot," but even then the attacker is -5 to strike.

** Destroying the head of the robot will destroy all sensor and optic systems and exposes the inner crew compartment — making the crew vulnerable to further attack. Furthermore, all robot combat bonuses are lost; reduce the number of attacks per melee round and speed by half!

*** Depleting the M.D.C. of the main body will shut the robot down completely, rendering it useless.

Leg Note: The robot can lose one or two legs and not be unbalanced, but speed is reduced by 15%. Losing three legs reduces the speed by 50%.

Speed

Running: 50 mph (80.4 km) maximum.

Leaping: Not possible

Underwater Capabilities: Minimal. The Scorpion can walk along the bottom of the sea at about 25% its normal running speed.

Maximum Ocean Depth: 2000 feet (610 m).

Statistical Data

Height: Five feet (1.5 m); the legs protrude an additional three feet (0.9 m) when running.

Width: The skull is six feet wide (1.8 m), but the legs extend to about 18 feet wide (5.4 m).

Length: The overall length with tail extended completely flat is about 25 feet (7.6 m) long, while the body of the skull is eight feet (2.4 m) long.

Weight: 14 tons fully loaded.

Physical Strength: 45

Cargo: None

Power System: Nuclear, average life is 25 years.

CS Cost: 26 million credits for a new, fully loaded Spider Scout. These bots are not available on the Black Market — exclusive to the CS.

Weapon Systems

1. Tail Rail Guns (3): Mounted in the tip of the tail are three rapid-fire, gatling-gun styled rail guns. They are fixed forward, but the weapon segment of the tail can point 180 degrees in all directions, except backwards. The tail can be made to lay flat or at a low angle to fire at enemies from behind.

Primary Purpose: Anti-Armor and Robots

Secondary Purpose: Anti-Personnel

Mega-Damage: A burst is 40 rounds and inflicts 1D4×10 M.D. from one gun, 2D4×10 M.D. from two firing simultaneously or 3D4×10 from all three firing simultaneously. Simultaneous attacks count as one melee action.

Rate of Fire: Equal to number of combined hand to hand attacks (usually 4-6) of the gunner.

Maximum Effective Range: 4000 feet (1200 m)

Payload: 8,000 rounds per each weapon, that's 200 bursts each or 600 total. Reloading the Scorpion's tail requires special equipment or another giant-sized robot and takes about an hour for those not trained or 25 minutes by somebody trained in robot mechanics (or who is an Operator O.C.C.).

2. Tail Lasers (2): Mounted in the tail below the rail guns are two lasers. They are locked in a fixed position, so the tail or weapon segment of the tail must be moved to aim at a target.

Primary Purpose: Anti-Personnel

Secondary Purpose: Defense

Mega-Damage: 3D6 M.D. per single blast or 6D6 per simultaneous double blast.

Range: 2000 feet (610 m)

Rate of Fire: Equal to the combined number of hand to hand attacks per melee of the gunner (usually 3-6).

Payload: Effectively unlimited.

3. Tail Multiple Mini-Missile Launcher (1): Located on top of the tail is a multi-launch mini-missile system.

Primary Purpose: Anti-Missile and Anti-Aircraft.

Secondary Purpose: Anti-Armor

Missile Type: Any type of mini-missile can be used, but standard issue is fragmentation (anti-personnel, 5D6 M.D.) and plasma (1D6×10).

Mega-Damage: Varies with missile type.

Range: About one mile

Rate of Fire: One at a time or in volleys of two, three, or four.

Payload: 18 total.

4. Tail Mini-Missile Launcher (2): A pair of back-up launchers.

Primary Purpose: Anti-Missile and Anti-Aircraft.

Secondary Purpose: Anti-Armor

Missile Type: Any type of mini-missile can be used, but standard issue is fragmentation (anti-personnel, 5D6 M.D.) and plasma (1D6×10).

Mega-Damage: Varies with missile type.

Range: About one mile

Rate of Fire: One at a time or in volleys of two, three, or four.

Payload: 10 total; five per each of the two launchers.

5. Skull, Double-Barreled Lasers (2): Mounted in the front of the head are a pair of lasers. They can move up and down in a 45 degree arc of fire, plus the head can turn 30 degrees from side to side.

Primary Purpose: Anti-Personnel

Secondary Purpose: Defense

Mega-Damage: 4D6 M.D. per single pair of laser blasts (two blasts from one pair of lasers) or 8D6 per simultaneous double blast from both pairs of lasers.

Range: 2000 feet (610 m)

Rate of Fire: Equal to the combined number of hand to hand attacks per melee of the pilot (usually 3-6).

Payload: Effectively unlimited.

6. **Smoke Dispenser:** A smoke dispensing unit is built into the mouth area of the skull. It can release a dense cloud of smoke that will cover a 60 foot (18.3 m) diameter behind it. It can also release tear gas as an alternative, anti-personnel weapon.

Payload: Eight total. The usual mix is four smoke and four tear gas.

7. **Hand to Hand Combat:** The Scorpion-Skull Walker can strike with its pincer claws or use its tail as a club; all such attacks are most effective against opponents that are twice the size of a human or bigger.

Tail Strike — 2D4 M.D.

Pincer Strike/Punch — 2D6 M.D.

Pincer Scissor Cut — 4D6 M.D.

Power Punch, Kick, and Body Block attacks are not applicable.

8. **Special Sensory Systems of Note:** Same as the IAR-2.

Special Bonuses and Abilities:

+1 on initiative.

Prowl/hide at 48% +2% per level of the pilot.

CS Combat Vehicles

Coalition Ground Vechiles

CS Mark V APC (Armored Personnel Carrier; see **Rifts® RPG**)

CS Mark VII Slayer APC

CS Mark IX EPC

CS Tank: Line Backer

CS Tank: Sky Sweeper

CS Fire Storm Mobile Fortress

Coalition Aircraft

CS APC Death Bringer

CS APC Sky Lifter

CS Command Car (Hover Jeep)

CS "Scarab" Officer's Command Car

CS Skull Patrol Car

CS Scout Rocket Cycle

CS Warbird Rocket Cycle

CS Wind Jammer Sky Cycle

Combat Helicopter: Black Lightning

Combat Helicopter: Demon Locust

CS "Talon" Stealth Fighter Jet

Ground Vehicles

CS Mark VII "Slayer"

Armored Personnel Carrier

The Coalition Mark VII armored personnel carrier (APC) is a deadly front-line combat unit with excellent firepower and good mobility. It is heavily armored and with the Death's Head facing, resembles a rushing train engine. The reinforced and heavily armored Death's Head front section allows the driver to ram into other vehicles and robots, as well as structures, with minimal damage. The eight, 12 foot (3.6 m) tall and six foot (1.8 m) wide, puncture proof tires (compliments of Triax) on the vehicle can plow through and ride over power armor and enemy troops!

A 12 foot (3.6 m) tall, heavy, airlock-hatch style door (one outer and one inner doors) is located on both sides and rear (3 total) for the exit of troops. A concealed exit hatch is also located in the ceiling of the crew compartment and in the weapon turret.

Coalition Mark VII "Slayer" APC

Model Type: APC

Class: Infantry Assault and Transport Vehicle

Crew: Eight: One pilot, a co-pilot, communications officer, intelligence officer, and four gunners.

APC Troop Payload: Just about any mix of troops is feasible; whatever is required is done. Some common infantry force include:

50-60 Foot Soldiers all in combat armor.

20 Foot Soldiers and 10 Terror Troopers or Maulers.

40 SAMAS (any) or similar, light power armor.

20 SAMAS (any) and 10 Super SAMAS.

20 troops on Scout Rocket Cycles with 10 SAMAS or 6 Terror.

Troopers or Super SAMAS.

10-15 Glitter Boy Killers, or Hellraisers, or Hellfires.

M.D.C. by Location:

Weapon Turret Housing — 300

Main Laser Cannon (1; turret) — 150

Plasma Mini-Turret (1; atop main turret) — 100

Vertical Mini-Missile Launchers (2; turret) — 50 each

Dual Mini-Missile Launchers (2; turret) — 50 each

Side Laser Turrets (4) — 60 each

Smoke/Gas Dispensers (2; rear) — 15 each

* Sensors (4; two front, two rear) — 30 each

* Eye Windshields (2) — 80 each

* Eye Sliding Metal Coverings (2; as needed) — 100

Main Outer Hatches (3; sides and rear) — 140 each

Main Inner Hatches (3; sides and rear) — 80 each

Concealed Escape Hatches (2) — 80 each

Puncture Proof Wheels (8) — 8 each

Forward Headlights (6; top front) — 5 each

Reinforced Crew Compartment — 100

Forward Death's Head Fronting (1) — 400

** Main Body — 500

* Every item marked by a single asterisk is small and/or difficult to strike. An attacker must make a "called shot" to hit and even then he is -3 to strike.

Destroying the four sensor bubbles (two front, two back) means the pilot must rely on his own vision and instruments; radar and targeting (and accompanying bonuses) are lost.

** Depleting the M.D.C. of the main body will shut the APC down completely, rendering it useless.

Destroying the Death's Head plating in the front reveals the inner reinforced crew compartment and makes it vulnerable to attack.

Destroying two wheels reduces speed by 20%. Destroying three on one side reduces speed by 40% and induces a penalty of -40% to the piloting skill. Destroying four wheels on one side reduces speed by 60%; same penalty.

Speed
Land: 80 mph (128.7 km) maximum.
Water: None
Flying: None

Statistical Data
Height: 28 feet (5.5 m) overall; the body of the APC is 18 feet (5.4 m) tall, but the top weapon turret adds 10 feet (3 m) to the overall height.
Width: 15 feet (4.6 m)
Length: 44 feet (13.4 m)
Weight: 42 tons unloaded.
Cargo: Troops, power armor, robots, small vehicles and/or supplies can be carried inside the 34 foot (10.3 m) long troop bay area; roughly 400 square feet of cargo space with a ceiling height of 17 feet (5.2 m).
Color: Typically blue-black.
Power System: Nuclear, average energy life is 20 years.
CS Cost: 28 million credits. It is exclusive to the CS military and is not available on the Black Market.

Weapon Systems

1. C-T60 High-Powered Laser Cannon (1): The big gun on the main weapon turret is a high-powered, long-range laser cannon. The cannon itself can move up and down in a 45 degree arc of fire; the entire turret can rotate a full 360 degrees. As usual, all the weapon systems are powered from the vehicle's nuclear power supply.
Primary Purpose: Anti-Aircraft and Anti-Armor
Secondary Purpose: Defense
Mega-Damage: 1D6×10 M.D. per blast.
Rate of Fire: Equal to the number of combined hand to hand attacks of the gunner (usually 3-6).
Maximum Effective Range: 6000 feet (1828 m)
Payload: Effectively unlimited

2. C-PT36 Plasma Mini-Turret (1): A mini-turret is located on top of the main turret. It has its own gunner and operates independent of the main laser cannon. This weapon is a plasma cannon and the barrel of the plasma cannon can rotate in all directions in a 30 degree arc.
Primary Purpose: Anti-Armor
Secondary Purpose: Anti-Personnel
Mega-Damage: 6D6 M.D. per dual blast.
Range: 2000 feet (610 m)
Rate of Fire: Equal to the number of hand to hand attacks of the gunner (usually 3-6).
Payload: Effectively unlimited.

3. C-MV12 Vertical Mini-Missile Launchers (2): Part of the mini-turret are two "stacked" vertical mini-missile launchers.
Primary Purpose: Anti-Aircraft and Anti-Armor.

Secondary Purpose: Anti-Personnel

Missile Type: Any type of mini-missile can be used, but standard issue is fragmentation (anti-personnel, 5D6 M.D.) and plasma (1D6×10).

Mega-Damage: Varies with missile type.

Range: About one mile

Rate of Fire: One at a time, or in volleys of two, three, or four.

Payload: 24 total; 12 per each launcher.

4. C-M6 Dual Mini-Missile Launchers (2): A two-shot, self-loading mini-missile launcher is mounted on the two sides of the main weapon turret.

Primary Purpose: Anti-Aircraft and Anti-Armor.

Secondary Purpose: Anti-Personnel

Missile Type: Any type of mini-missile can be used, but standard issue is fragmentation (anti-personnel, 5D6 M.D.) and plasma (1D6×10).

Mega-Damage: Varies with missile type.

Range: About one mile

Rate of Fire: One at a time, or in volleys of two, three, or four.

Payload: 24 total, 12 per each launcher; each has an internal storage and feed mechanism inside the main turret.

5. C-4T Dual Laser Turrets (4): A pair of heavy laser turrets are located on both sides, toward the rear of the APC. These are usually operated by a gunner against enemy troops and approaching vehicles. Each has full 360 degree rotation and a 90 degree arc of fire cup (up and down).

Primary Purpose: Anti-Personnel

Secondary Purpose: Defense

Mega-Damage: 4D6 M.D. per single blast or 1D4×10+8 per simultaneous dual blast. A simultaneous double blast counts as one melee attack.

Range: 4000 feet (1200 m)

Rate of Fire: Equal to number of combined hand to hand attacks (usually 4-6) of the gunner.

Payload: Effectively unlimited.

6. Smoke Dispensers (2): A pair of smoke dispensing units are mounted on the rear of the APC. The unit can release a dense cloud of smoke that will cover an 80 foot (24 m) area behind it, or cover the APC if it is stationary. It can also release tear gas.

Payload: Twenty total, ten each. The usual mix is 14 smoke and six tear gas.

7. Hand to Hand Combat: The Slayer is infamous for driving at full speed and ramming into and knocking over giant robots, vehicles and small structures, as well as plowing through enemy lines and running over any enemy troops that get in the way. The impact from a half speed ram is 1D6×10 M.D. or 2D4×10 M.D from a full speed ram. A ram attack against humans, even in body armor or man-sized power armor, inflicts 1D4×10 M.D. and hurls the character 4D6 yards/meters (victim loses initiative and three melee attacks). Human-sized characters who get run-over suffer 1D6×10+20 M.D.

In addition, the combat troops being transported can be released from the APC to engage the enemy.

8. Sensor System Note: The Mark-VII APC has all the basic features as the robot vehicles. Plus:

A. Eight high impact, puncture proof tires, designed and imported from Triax.

B. Automatic locking hatches opened by voice recognition and/or by number code punched in on an eight digit key pad.

C. Homing beacon and long-range radio communication.

D. Standard field equipment includes portable long-range radio, portable short-range radar, medical kit, ten signal flares, ten C-29 Hellfire plasma rifles and CP-30 energy pistol, three E-Clips for each and a two week supply of dehydrated food and water to supply ten troops.

Coalition Mark IX EPC

Exploratory Personnel Carrier

By Julius Rosenstein

The Coalition Mark IX Exploratory Personnel Carrier (EPC) is a less deadly version of the Mark V APC. Unlike the Mark V, the Mark IX is not designed as a front-line combat unit, but as a transport vehicle for long-range reconnaissance and exploration expeditions. It does provide adequate firepower and protection for its crew and passengers under heavy fire, so if the player characters encounter something too powerful for them to handle, they can survive long enough to call for reinforcements and try to make an escape. The land vehicle can transport 10 people comfortably. SAMAS troops will take up two places. This vehicle is commonly used by Rift Containment Study Group (RCSG) teams, field scientists and the occassional reconniassance team.

Exploratory Personnel Carrier

Model Type: EPC

Class: Infantry and Scientific Transport Vehicle

Crew: Three: pilot, copilot, and gunner.

Transport Capabilities: Standard is 10 troops (including crew)

M.D.C. by Location:

Center Laser Turret — 50

Forward Mini-Missile Launcher — 20

Forward Headlights (2) — 2 each

Smoke/Gas Dispenser — 6

** Main Body — 220

Reinforced Crew Compartment — 60

Treads (2) — 100 each

** Depleting the M.D.C. of the main body will shut the EPC down completely, rendering it useless.

Speed: 110 mph (176 km) maximum on land. In water, speed is about 20 mph (32 km). (The EPC is not designed for major water travel).

Statistical Data:

Height: 10 feet, 7 inches (3.16 m)

Width: 7 feet (2.1 m)

Length: 15 feet, 8 inches (4.75 m)

Weight: 7 1/2 tons fully loaded.

Cargo: Storage space of about four feet (1.2 m) for extra clothing, supplies, weapons, specimens, and personal items; 2 C-14 assault rifles, 4 C-12 laser rifles, 1 C-27 plasma rifle, 1 rocket launcher and 8 fragmentation grenades.

Power System: Nuclear, average energy life is 10 years.

Black Market Cost: Six million credits, and up, for a new, undamaged, fully powered Coalition EPC complete with arma-

ments. As low as one million rebuilt and without any weapon systems. Limited availability, still being tested.

Weapon Systems
1. **CR-2T Laser Turret (2)**: A double-barreled laser turret mounted on top of the EPC that can rotate 360 degrees and has a 70 degree angle of fire (up and down).

Primary Purpose: Anti-Personnel

Secondary Purpose: Defense

Mega-Damage: 4D6 per dual blast.

Range: 4000 feet (1200 m)

Rate of Fire: Equal to the total number of hand to hand attacks per melee (usually 4 to 6).

Payload: Effectively unlimited.

2. **CR-10 Forward Mini-Missile Launcher**: Located in the front of the EPC is a rapid-fire mini-missile launcher. The missiles are usually fired by the pilot.

Primary Purpose: Anti-Personnel

Secondary Purpose: Defense

Missile Type: Any type of mini-missile can be used, but standard issue is fragmentation (anti-personnel, 5D6 M.D.).

Range: One mile (1.6 km).

Rate of Fire: One at a time, or in volleys of 2, 3, 5, or 10.

Payload: Twenty (20)

Note: Less expensive to build than the Mark V APC, the EPC is fairly scarce in Chi-town (because of the many SAMAS troops) and Free Quebec (who prefer the use of Glitter Boys), but is finding increasing usage in Iron Heart (who need relatively inexpensive vehicles for exploration of their territories).

CTX-50 "Line Backer" Coalition Heavy Assault Tank

The CTX-50 "Line Backer" is a very compact, fast and powerful front-line hover tank bristling with armaments. The tank gets its speed and mobility from a triple tier hover jet system. Three large hover jets are built into each side. These can be moved and positioned to best suit the needs of the pilot and maneuvers being attempted. They also provide incredible stability and a smooth ride. The second tier of the hover system covers the entire undercarriage of the tank providing excellent and even lift. The third element of the propulsion system is a set of three huge jets in the rear section. This is what gives the "Line Backer" its extra oomph and speed. Without the rear thrusters (250 M.D.C. each) the tank's speed is reduced by half.

To confound the enemy, there is only one apparent hatch on top of the tank where the gunner sits. Actually, the entire Death's Head face lifts up to reveal the inner, reinforced crew compartment.

Coalition CTX-50 "Line Backer"
Heavy Assault Tank
Model Type: CTX-50

Class: Infantry Hover Tank

Crew: Eight: One pilot, a co-pilot, communications officer, intelligence officer, and four gunners. Two additional passengers can also be accommodated.

M.D.C. by Location:
Weapon Turret Housing — 300
Main Laser Cannons (2; front) — 150 each
* Forward Rail Guns (2; front) — 70 each

Rear Medium-Range Missile Launchers (2) —150 each
Rear Double-Barrel Laser Turret (1) — 80
* Turret Gun (1; any) — 50 to 100
Smoke/Gas Dispensers (2; rear) — 15 each
* Eye Windshields (2) — 80 each
* Eye Sliding Metal Coverings (2; as needed) — 100
Main Hatch (1; Death's Head face) — 300
Gunner's Hatch (1) — 150
Concealed Escape Hatch (1; underbelly) — 100
Side Hover Jets (6) — 150 each
Rear Jet Thrusters (3) — 300 each
Forward Headlights (2; small) — 5 each
Reinforced Crew Compartment — 200
** Main Body — 790

* Every item marked by a single asterisk is small and/or difficult to strike. An attacker must make a "called shot" to hit and even then he is -3 to strike.

** Depleting the M.D.C. of the main body will shut the tank down completely, rendering it useless.

Destroying the Death's Head plating in the front reveals the inner, reinforced crew compartment and makes it vulnerable to attack.

Destroying two of the side hover jets only reduces speed by 10%, but makes sharp turns -5% on the piloting skill. Destroying all six reduces the speed by 25% and inflicts a -20% skill piloting skill penalty when making sharp turns or special maneuvers. Destroying all three rear jets will reduce speed by 50%.

Speed

Land: An astonishing 150 mph (240 km), tremendous speed for a tank! It can also make tight turns and stop on a dime. The vehicle typically hovers three to four feet (0.9 to 1.2 m) above the ground, but can raise as high as 10 feet (3 m) and make jumps up to 60 feet (18.3 m) in length.

Water: The "Line Backer" can also hover across the surface of water at a speed of 100 mph (160 km) and even submerge itself underwater up to an ocean depth of 2000 feet (610 m) and travel at about 25 miles (40 km/21 knots) an hour underwater. However, it cannot open its bay doors underwater without flooding and sinking.

Flying: None

Range: The nuclear power supply gives the transport years of life. The air-cooled hover jets can function continuously for 24 hours before starting to overheat (requires a two hour cooling period).

Statistical Data

Height: 14 feet (4.2 m)

Width: 15 feet (4.6 m)

Length: 20 feet (6 m)

Weight: 40 tons unloaded.

Cargo: None

Color: Typically blue-black or camouflage.

Power System: Nuclear, average energy life is 20 years.

CS Cost: 32 million credits. It is exclusive to the CS military and is not available on the Black Market.

Weapon Systems

1. C-T60 High-Powered Laser Cannons (2): The big guns of the "Line Backer" are a pair of C-T60 high-powered, long-range laser cannons. The guns are built into a ball turret system that offers a 360 degree arc of fire and allows each gunner to operate his cannon independent of the other. As usual, all the weapon systems are powered from the vehicle's nuclear power supply.

Primary Purpose: Anti-Aircraft and Anti-Armor

Secondary Purpose: Defense

Mega-Damage: 1D6×10 M.D. per single blast. The two cannons cannot fire in tandem, although each can be fired independently at the same target by each gunner for a coordinated attack.

Rate of Fire: Equal to the number of combined hand to hand attacks of each gunner (usually 3-6 each, for a total of 6-12 shots per melee round between the two).

Maximum Effective Range: 6000 feet (1828 m)

Payload: Effectively unlimited.

2. C-20R Rail Gun: Designed to be a general purpose gun, it is suitable for assault, anti-armor attacks and cover fire in the support of infantry.

Primary Purpose: Assault

Mega-Damage: A full damage burst is 40 rounds and inflicts 1D6×10 M.D. At the flip of a switch the weapon can fire 10 shot bursts which inflict 3D6 M.D.

Maximum Effective Range: 4000 feet (1220 m)

Rate of Fire: Equal to the combined hand to hand attacks of the gunner (usually 4-6).

Payload: 6000 round drum feed for 150 bursts per each rail gun; 12,000 rounds total! Reloading a drum will take about 15 minutes for those not trained, but a mere five minutes by characters with engineering or field armorer skills.

3. C-20L Laser Turret (1): A mini-turret is located in the rear of the tank. It gets its own gunner and operates independent of the other weapon systems. The turret can rotate 360 degrees and has a 45 degree arc of fire (up and down).

Primary Purpose: Anti-Armor

Secondary Purpose: Anti-Personnel

Mega-Damage: 3D6 M.D. per single blast, or 6D6 M.D. per simultaneous double blast. A simultaneous double blast counts as one melee action.

Range: 4000 feet (1200 m)

Rate of Fire: Equal to the number of combined hand to hand attacks (usually 3-6) of the gunner.

Payload: Effectively unlimited.

4. CR-8 Medium-Range Missile Launchers (2): Located in the rear are a pair of CR-8 missile launchers, capable of firing short or medium-range missiles (medium are standard issue).

Primary Purpose: Anti-Aircraft and Anti-Armor.

Secondary Purpose: Anti-Personnel

Missile Type: Any type of medium-range (or in an emergency, short-range) missile can be used, but heavy missiles are standard.

Mega-Damage: Varies with missile type.

Range: 40-60 miles (64.3 to 96.9 km) for medium-range missiles.

Rate of Fire: One at a time, or in volleys of two or four.

Payload: 16 total; eight per each launcher.

5. Concealed Mini-Missile Launchers (2): A pair of mini-missile launchers are recessed in the front, under the teeth of the Death's Head.

Primary Purpose: Anti-Aircraft and Anti-Armor.

Secondary Purpose: Anti-Personnel

Missile Type: Any type of mini-missile can be used, but standard issue is fragmentation (anti-personnel, 5D6 M.D.) and plasma (1D6×10).

Mega-Damage: Varies with missile type.

Range: About one mile

Rate of Fire: One at a time, or in volleys of two, three, or four.

Payload: 24 total; 12 per each launcher.

6. Smoke Dispensers (2): A pair of smoke dispensing units are mounted on the rear of the tank. The unit can release a dense cloud of smoke that will cover an 80 foot (24 m) area behind it, or cover the tank if it is stationary. It can also release tear gas.

Payload: Twenty total, ten each. The usual mix is 14 smoke and six tear gas.

7. Hand to Hand Combat: Like the Slayer APC, the "Line Backer" can ram into and knock over giant robots, vehicles and small structures, as well as plow through enemy lines. However, being run over by the hover tank only knocks the character to the ground, unable to move due to the pounding jets of air (2D4×10 S.D.C. damage) until the vehicle passes overhead, but is otherwise uninjured. The impact from a half speed ram is 1D4×10 M.D. or 2D4×10 M.D from a full speed ram. A ram attack against humans, even in body armor or man-sized power armor, inflicts 6D6 M.D. and hurls the character 4D6 yards/meters (victim loses initiative and three melee attacks). A deliberate ram attack counts as two melee actions.

8. Sensor Systems Note: All the basic features as the robot vehicles. Plus: standard field equipment includes portable long-range radio, portable short-range radar, medical kit, ten signal flares, ten C-50 Dragonfire rifles and CP-30 energy pistols, four E-Clips for each, and either a light rail gun or a CTT-M20 or CTT-P40 as the top turret gun, as well as a three week supply of dehydrated food and water to supply ten troops.

CTX-52   "Sky Sweeper" Anti-Aircraft Tank

The "Sky Sweeper" anti-aircraft tank is another relatively small and speedy combat vehicle. Unlike the CTX-50, the "Sky Sweeper" is a tread driven ground vehicle. It has a low profile, making it a less conspicuous target, easy to conceal and easy to transport — it can fit inside the Death's Head Transport, Death Bringer Transport and the Fire Storm Mobile Fortress. It has a four man crew and is so easy to operate that it's said a child could do it.

The heavily armored turret can turn 360 degrees and contains two heavy, long-range lasers and a medium laser turret. A soldier (one of the crew or an additional person) can sit in the center of the small turret and use it as a gunner's nest to snipe or rail gun ground troops. The forward rail guns on the lower, main body are suitable for attacks against light aircraft, vehicles, power armor and ground troops. The missiles are guided, so even though launched from a forward facing position, they can be fired at enemies in any direction, on the ground or in the air. A pair of mini-missile launch tubes are also tucked away on the underside of the turret toward the rear.

"Sky Sweeper" Light Anti-Aircraft Tank

Model Type: CTX-52

Class: Infantry Hover Tank

Crew: Five: One pilot, a co-pilot-gunner, two gunners and a communications officer, field scientist or intelligence officer. One additional passenger can squeeze into the crew compartment but quarters are cramped.

M.D.C. by Location:

Cannon Turret Housing — 300

Main Laser Cannons (2; front) — 150 each

* Forward Heavy Rail Guns (2; front) — 90 each

* Rear Double-Barrel Laser Turret (1) — 80

Medium-Range Missile Launchers (2; sides) —130 each

* Mini-Missile Launch Tubes (4; two per side) — 15 each

Smoke/Gas Dispensers (2; rear) — 15 each

* Eye Windshields (2) — 80 each

* Eye Sliding Metal Coverings (2; as needed) — 100

* Main Hatch (2; top of main body in front) — 150 each

Gunner's Hatch (1; top of turret) — 150

Concealed Escape Hatch (1; underbelly) — 100

Armor Covered Treads (2) — 100 each

Reinforced Crew Compartment — 200

** Main Body — 400

    * Every item marked by a single asterisk is small and/or difficult to strike. An attacker must make a "called shot" to hit and even then he is -3 to strike.

    ** Depleting the M.D.C. of the main body will shut the tank down completely, rendering it useless. It also exposes the inner, reinforced crew compartment.

    Destroying one of the treads reduces the tank's speed by 50% and inflicts a -20% skill piloting skill penalty when making sharp turns or special maneuvers. Destroying both treads immobilizes the vehicle.

Speed

Land: 90 mph (144.8 km); excellent speed for a tread-driven tank.

Water: None; the "Sky Sweeper" is not amphibious although it can slosh through water up to its turret (roughly six feet/1.8 m) without trouble.

Flying: None

Range: The nuclear power supply gives the tank years of life and indefinite mileage without fear of overheating.

Statistical Data

Height: 10 feet (3 m) overall; the lower main body is only five feet, six inches tall (1.65 m) tall, but the turret adds another four feet, six inches (1.35 m).

Width: 11 feet (3.3 m)

Length: 16 feet (4.87 m)

Weight: 21 tons unloaded.

Cargo: None

Color: Typically blue-black or camouflage.

Power System: Nuclear, average energy life is 20 years.

CS Cost: 25 million credits. It is exclusive to the CS military and is not available on the Black Market.

Weapon Systems

1. C-T60 High-Powered Laser Cannons (2): The big guns of the "Sky Sweeper" are a pair of C-T60 high-powered, long-range laser cannons. The guns are built into a swivel housing that offers a 180 degree arc of fire, but are forward facing which means the entire turret must move to point in a different direction. Each cannon is operated by its own gunner, although the two usually try to coordinate their attacks. All cannons and all the weapon systems are powered from the vehicle's nuclear power supply.

Primary Purpose: Anti-Aircraft and Anti-Armor

Secondary Purpose: Defense

Mega-Damage: 1D6×10 M.D. per single blast. The two cannons cannot fire in tandem, although each can be fired independently at the same target by each gunner in a coordinated attack.

Rate of Fire: Equal to the number of combined hand to hand attacks of each gunner (usually 3-6 each, for a total of 6-12 shots per melee round between the two).

Maximum Effective Range: 6000 feet (1828 m)

Payload: Effectively unlimited

2. C-44R Rail Gun Turrets: A pair of high-powered, double-barreled rail gun turrets are located in the front of the tank. One is operated by the pilot, the other by the co-pilot. They are designed to be general purpose weapons suitable for assault, anti-armor, cover fire in the support of infantry and self-defense, as well as anti-aircraft.

Primary Purpose: Anti-Aircraft

Secondary Purpose: Anti-Personnel and Defense.

Mega-Damage: A full damage burst is 80 rounds and inflicts 2D6×10 M.D. At the flip of a switch the weapon can fire 40 round bursts which inflict 1D6×10 M.D.

Maximum Effective Range: 4000 feet (1220 m)

Rate of Fire: Equal to the combined hand to hand attacks of the gunner (usually 4-6).

Payload: 12,000 round drum feed for 150 full bursts per each rail gun; 24,000 rounds total! Reloading a drum will take about 20 minutes for those not trained, but a mere five minutes by characters with engineering or field armorer skills.

3. C-20L Double-Barrel Laser Turret (1): A mini-turret is located in the rear of the tank. It gets its own gunner and operates independent of the other weapon systems. The turret can rotate 360 degrees and has a 45 degree arc of fire.

Primary Purpose: Anti-Armor

Secondary Purpose: Anti-Personnel

Mega-Damage: 3D6 M.D. per single blast, or 6D6 M.D. per simultaneous double blast. A simultaneous double blast counts as one melee action.

Range: 4000 feet (1200 m)

Rate of Fire: Equal to number of combined hand to hand attacks (usually 3-6) of the gunner.

Payload: Effectively unlimited.

4. CR-8 Medium-Range Missile Launchers (2): Located in the rear are a pair of CR-8 missile launchers, capable of firing short or medium-range missiles (medium are standard issue). Typically operated by one of the cannon gunners.

Primary Purpose: Anti-Aircraft and Anti-Armor.

Secondary Purpose: Anti-Personnel

Missile Type: Any type of medium-range (or in an emergency, short-range) missile can be used, but heavy missiles are standard.

Mega-Damage: Varies with missile type.

Range: 40-60 miles (64.3 to 96.9 km) for medium-range missiles.

Rate of Fire: One at a time, or in volleys of two, or four.

Payload: 10 total; five per each launcher.

5. Concealed Mini-Missile Launch Tubes (4): A pair of mini-missile launch tubes are located under the back hood of the turret. Operated by one of the gunners.

Primary Purpose: Anti-Aircraft and Anti-Armor.

Secondary Purpose: Anti-Personnel

Missile Type: Any type of mini-missile can be used, but standard issue is fragmentation (anti-personnel, 5D6 M.D.) and plasma (1D6×10).

Mega-Damage: Varies with missile type.

Range: About one mile

Rate of Fire: One at a time, or in volleys of two, three, or four.

Payload: Eight total; two per each of the four launch tubes.

6. Smoke Dispensers (2): A pair of smoke dispensing units are mounted on the rear of the tank. The unit can release a dense cloud of smoke that will cover an 80 foot (24 m) area behind it, or cover the tank if it is stationary. It can also release tear gas.

Payload: Ten total; five each. The usual mix is eight smoke and two tear gas.

7. Hand to Hand Combat: The "Sky Sweeper" avoids running into or over enemy troops and seldom sees front-line combat; tends to be used as a tactical support weapon behind the line and at military outposts, or as a strategic, mobile anti-aircraft and anti-missile weapon that keeps changing its location to confound and confuse the enemy.

8. Sensor System Note: All the basic features as the robot vehicles. Plus enhanced radar and communications.

CTX-54 "Fire Storm" Mobile Fortress — Super Tank

Inspired by art by Wayne Breaux

The Fire Storm Mobile Fortress is a juggernaut of Coalition technology and tenacity. It is a low ground hover vehicle that is effectively the equivalent of two Death's Head Transports with a command tower connecting them. Unlike the Transports, the Fire Storm hovers three to ten feet (0.3 to 3 m) above the ground and moves at a comparatively slow 60 mph (96.5 m) as its maximum speed (typically travels at about half that). However, the massive assault fortress can rise up to 300 feet (91.5 m) to hover and fly over forests, towns or small cities to rain down its destructive force upon them. In addition to a maelstrom of missiles and energy beams, the flying fortress holds hundreds of troops, including SAMAS, Super SAMAS, a company of Hellraisers, other robots, vehicles and aircraft. Power armor and light robots are the primary armored force because their comparatively small size allows for the greatest number and maximum firepower.

The Fire Storm flying fortress is designed to be a mobile Command Center and headquarters for ground and power armor troops. So far, only 12 are in service with another 12 being prepped and tested for combat duty and six more under construction. Eventually, the plan is to have at least one Fire Storm Mo-

bile Fortress for every Field Army (four divisions: 23,000-30,000 troops).

The Fire Storm *is* a huge flying Command Post, with medical, communications, strategic operations, and support capabilities as well as armored troop transport. It is not a flying city, meaning that living quarters (except for officers and crew) are limited and cramped. Consequently, when a base site has been chosen, the Fortress usually lands and rests on the ground. While "grounded," the Fire Storm serves as the center of a temporary field base (temporary being as little as a few days or as much as a few years; typically 2D4 months). Approximately half of its armored troop complement establishs a perimeter camp in the immediate area around the Fortress. A larger base camp or field army(s) of 5000 to 30,000 troops is sprawled out around that. The Fire Storm serves as the mobile army's HQ and main support unit. It can pick up and go whenever necessary, whether it is to relocate to a different position, fall back to a safer position, or to establish a new front elsewhere. It *may* engage in actual infantry assaults against opposing armies or when laying siege to an enemy base or city, but is usually held back until the enemy is ready to fall or when CS troops get into trouble. The Fire Storm is too important as a strategic HQ, Command Center and troop support unit to jeopardize in foolish or unnecessary field operations — not to mention extremely expensive.

Fire Storm Mobile Fortress

Nicknames: Super Fortress and Fire Storm Command Center.

Model Type: AFC-500

Class: Air and Ground Super Fortress and Command Center

Crew: The crew is the minimum number of soldiers and technicians needed to maintain the basic operation of the juggernaut.

Command Center: Division Commanders (2-4), 30 combat officers, 20 communications officers, and 60 crew.

Death's Head Transports (2): 34 total: 17 per each transport; one pilot, two co-pilots, two communication engineers, two technical officers and 10 crew.

Troop Payload: Just about any mix of troops is feasible, but the following is the typical combat force carried within the Fire Storm; whatever is required is done. Some common infantry forces include:

- One Squad (6) of Skull Smashers
- One Squad (6) of Spider-Skull Walkers.
- One Squad (10) of Glitter Boy Killers.
- One Platoon (40) of Scout Spider-Skull Walkers.
- One Platoon (40) of Hellraisers.
- One Platoon (40) of Hellfires *or* CS Cyborg Strike Troopers.
- One Platoon (40) of Terror Trooper Commandos *or* CS Juicers.
- One Platoon (40 troops) of Scout Rocket Cycles and/or Warbird Rocket Cycle *or* other small aircraft.
- Two Platoons of Special Forces (80 troops: 60 in Striker SAMAS and 20 in Terror Troopers or power armor of choice).
- One Company of Light Assault SAMAS (160 troops; old or new style).
- One Company of Super SAMAS (160 troops)
- One Company of Infantry Soldiers (160 troops; most support crew).

Total: 782 combat troops (894 including the basic crew). Plus several dozen small vehicles like trucks, jeeps and hovercycles. An additional Company of man-sized troops can be squeezed in if necessary, and another company or two of power armor troops could ride on the outer hull.

M.D.C. by Location:

Forward Observation Windows (6; eye shaped) — 100 each
Eye Sliding Metal Coverings (6; as needed) — 200 each
C-2000 Super Rail Cannons (2) — 800 each
C-300DH Rail Gun Turrets (2; sides) — 350 each
Command Deck Laser Turret (1; forward) — 300
* Light Laser Turrets (24; two per bay door) — 70 each
Main Cargo Bay Doors (8; three front, five back) — 300 each
Secondary Bay Doors (4; side and top back) — 150 each
* Concealed Escape Hatches (6; bottom) — 150 each
* Missile Hatches (16; front) — 120 each
Loading Ramps (6) — 150 each
* Undercarriage Hover Jets (24) — 120 each
Rear Jets (4; transports) — 200 each
Forward Spotlights (3) — 30 each
Rear Spotlights (3) — 30 each
* Small landing lights (48) — 2 each
Reinforced Crew Compartment of Transports — 200
Reinforced Crew Compartment of Command Deck — 350
Main Body Sub-Sections: Medium Transports (2) — 1000 each
Main Body of Command Deck (1) — 2000
* Main Body: Command Center (1) — 5000

* Every item marked by a single asterisk is small and/or difficult to strike. An attacker must make a "called shot" to hit and even then he is -3 to strike.

** Depleting the M.D.C. of the main body of each section will destroy that particular section. Depleting the 5000 points of the Command Center destroys the heart of the Fire Storm Fortress, shutting down all its weapon systems, life support, communications, sensors, hover systems and the Command Deck — the two transports can detach and abandon the shattered center of the mobile fortress complex.

Speed

Driving on the ground: Not possible.

Flying: One of the most interesting design elements is the ability of the fortress to divide into three separate components, two medium-sized Death's Head Transports and the Command Center. The transports can fly at 180 mph (288 km) and attain an altitude of 1000 feet (305 m), but have only a pair of concealed lasers in the forehead above the eyebrow ridge of the Death's Head (1D4×10 M.D. per double blast; 2000 ft/610 m range). Without the assistance of the two transports, the Command Center's maximum speed is reduced to 30 mph (48 km) with a maximum altitude of 100 feet (30.5 m), but has all the weapons at its disposal, plus troops. The three can reattach at will and rarely separate unless there is a tactical advantage to do so, or when the Command Center is being overrun and the fortress is under evacuation.

Range: The Command Center contains a small nuclear power plant, plus secondary power systems that provide the Fire Storm with an estimated 50 years of life. It can hover for days at a time, land on the ground, and fly when necessary. Take-off from a ground position takes about 15 minutes; 3D4 minutes in an emergency.

Statistical Data

Height: 76 feet (23.2 m)

Width: 104 feet (32. 7 m)

Length: 240 feet (73 m)

Weight: Approximately 1250 tons fully loaded.

Cargo: See troop complements.

Power System: Nuclear, average energy life is 50 years.

CS Cost: Top secret, but estimated to be over a billion credits.

Weapon Systems

1. **C-2000 Super Rail Cannons (2):** An *experimental* weapon designed specifically for the Fire Storm Fortress. The two long barrels that run along the neck of the Command Deck are a pair of giant rail guns that fire super-charged rounds that can punch holes in tanks and aircraft like they were made of cardboard! The super rail cannon points forward, but its angle of fire can be adjusted 25 degrees up and down.

Primary Purpose: Anti-Armor and Aircraft.

Secondary Purpose: Bombardment of enemy installations.

Mega-Damage: 1D4×100 M.D. per single blast or 2D8×100 M.D. per double blast. However, for both rail cannons to be used simultaneously, the target must be wider than 60 feet (18.3 m). Both barrels are often fired at targets over a mile (1.6 km) away to insure that one of the two hits (-1 to strike).

Range: Two miles (3.2 km).

Rate of Fire: Eight blasts per melee round, four per rail cannon; each is operated by a gunner and a communications officer.

Payload: 2000 blasts; 1000 per each rail cannon.

2. C-300DH Rail Gun Turrets (2): A large dual cannon turret is mounted on the top of the Command Center on either side of the Command Deck. The turrets draw their power from independent nuclear power supplies. Each turret can rotate 360 degrees and can tilt up and down at a 80 degree sweep. Two gunners and a communications officer are assigned to each turret.

Primary Purpose: Anti-Aircraft and Anti-Power Armor.

Secondary Purpose: Anti-Armor (tanks, robots, dragons, etc.)

Mega-Damage: A burst is 100 rounds and inflicts 3D4×10 M.D.

Rate of Fire: Equal to number of combined hand to hand attacks of the gunner (usually 4-6 per melee round).

Maximum Effective Range: Two miles (3.2 km).

Payload: 100,000 rounds per each gun, that's 1000 bursts without reloading. Reloading a rail gun requires special equipment and takes about an hour.

Missile Note: The side of the turret has ten ports from which *mini-missiles* can be fired. Standard range and damage per type, payload is 20 per turret, and can be fired one at a time or in volleys of two, four, six or ten.

3. C-60T Command Deck Laser Turret (1): A heavy, double-barrel, laser cannon turret is built into the chin of the Command Deck's Death's Head. It can rotate 180 degrees and has a 90 degree arc of fire, up and down.

Primary Purpose: Anti-Armor

Secondary Purpose: Anti-Personnel and Defense.

Mega-Damage: 2D4×10 M.D. per simultaneous double blast.

Range: 6000 feet (1828 m)

Rate of Fire: Eight blast per melee round; operated by two gunners and a communications officer.

Payload: Effectively unlimited.

4. Long-Range Missile Battery: In the front of the Command Center, on either side of the Command Deck, are eight sliding hatches. Behind each is a missile launcher able to fire two missiles at a time. The *top* four on both sides (8 total) are long-range missile launchers.

Primary Purpose: Anti-Armor and Aircraft.

Secondary Purpose: Bombardment of enemy installations.

Missile Type: Any type of long-range missile can be used, but standard issue is high explosive and plasma (2D6×10 M.D.) and/or multi-warhead smart bomb (2D4×10 and +5 to strike).

Mega-Damage: Varies with missile type.

Range: Over 500 miles (800 km).

Rate of Fire: One at a time, or in volleys of two or four.

Payload: 32 total.

5. Medium-Range Missile Battery: In the front of the Command Center, on either side of the Command Deck, are eight sliding hatches. Behind each is a missile launcher capable of firing two missiles at a time. The *bottom* four on both sides (8 total) are medium-range missile launchers (short-range missiles can be fired in case medium-range are not available).

Primary Purpose: Anti-Armor and Aircraft.

Secondary Purpose: Bombardment of enemy installations.

Missile Type: Any type of medium-range missile can be used, but standard issue is high explosive and plasma (2D6×10 M.D.) and/or multi-warhead smart bomb (2D4×10 and +5 to strike).

Mega-Damage: Varies with missile type.

Range: Over 40 miles (64 km).

Rate of Fire: One at a time, or in volleys of two or four.

Payload: 64 total.

6. C-2T Dual Laser Turrets (24): A pair of these light laser turrets are located at or hang over every bay door. Each pair is assigned a gunner to operate it, but if manpower is low, can be set to fire at enemies identified by a small targeting computer and sensor system. Each has full 360 degree rotation and a 90 degree arc of fire.

Primary Purpose: Anti-Personnel

Secondary Purpose: Defense

Mega-Damage: 4D6 M.D. per dual blast.

Range: 4000 feet (1200 m)

Rate of Fire: Can shoot up to six times per melee when operated by a gunner, or four times per melee when automated without a gunner.

Payload: Effectively unlimited.

7. Hand to Hand Combat: None. See troops.

8. Sensor System Note: All the most advanced sensors and communications systems and technology at the Coalition's disposal circa 105 PA.

Coalition Aircraft

Death Bringer APC

The Death Bringer Transport is a heavily armored, flying, Armored Personnel Carrier (APC) used to transport combat troops. Power armor and small manned robots and troops on small flying vehicles are typically its cargo. In such cases, the Death Bringer may not even have to land. Instead, it slows down, opens its doors and lets its troops leap into action — it is a particularly frightening sight to see a swarm of SAMAS, Super SAMAS or small flyers rocket out of the Death Bringer's bays and into action. When land troops are transported, a ramp slides out from the five bay doors to allow quick disembarkment of troops, small bots and small vehicles (hovercycles, jeeps, etc.). The large, side Death's Head with the laser turret crowning its forehead is actually a reinforced bay door that slides up to let the somewhat large power armor, bots and vehicles to exit.

A pair of laser ball turrets are located at the front and rear of the APC. A single turret is also located above the Death's Head bay door. The main gun is a high-powered cannon that fires powerful plasma shells equal to the mini-missile but without any special guidance system — the cannon points and fires.

Death Bringer APC

Model Type: AFC-151 Death Bringer Death's Head Transport

Class: Air Armored Troop Carrier and Assault Vehicle

Crew: Eight: One pilot, a co-pilot, communications officer, intelligence officer, and four gunners.

APC Troop Payload: Just about any mix of troops is feasible; whatever is required is done. Some common infantry forces include:

60-80 Foot Soldiers (with or without jet packs).

40 Foot Soldiers and 20 Terror Troopers or Maulers.

60 SAMAS (any) or similar, light power armor.

30 SAMAS (any) and 20 Super SAMAS.

20-30 troops on Scout Rocket Cycles with 6-10 SAMAS escorts.

25-30 Glitter Boy Killers, or Hellraisers, or Hellfires.

M.D.C. by Location:

Main Gun: Cannon Turret (1) — 300

* Laser Turrets (6) — 130 each

* Forward, Rear & Side Lights (24) — 5 each

* Searchlight (1; front, bottom) — 20

* Main Combat Sensor (1; on top of cannon turret) — 20

* Eye Windshields (2) — 80 each

* Eye Sliding Metal Coverings (2; as needed) — 100

Hover Jet Banks (4; lower body) — 400 each

Rear Jet Thrusters (3; small) — 70 each

Bay Doors (5; two per side and one rear) — 150 each

Death's Head Doors (2; sides) — 250 each

Extendable Ramps (5) — 30 each

Reinforced Crew Compartment — 200

** Main Body — 900

    * Every item marked by a single asterisk is small and/or difficult to strike. An attacker must make a "called shot" to hit and even then he is -3 to strike.

    Destroying the sensor unit means the pilot must rely on his own vision and instruments; radar and targeting (and accompanying bonuses) are lost.

    Destroying one bank of hover jets reduces speed by 25%.

    ** Depleting the M.D.C. of the main body completely destroys the vehicle.

Speed

    Land: Unlike the Giant Death's Head Transport, the Death Bringer can hover above the ground as low as four feet (1.2 m), but when that close to the ground, maximum speed is 200 mph (320 km).

    Water: The Death Bringer can also hover across the surface of water at a speed of 100 mph (160 km) and even submerge itself underwater up to an ocean depth of 2000 feet (610 m) and travel at about 25 miles (40 km/21 knots) an hour. However, it cannot open its bay doors underwater without flooding and sinking.

    Flying: Four huge banks of jet thrusters are located on the sides of the transport. Three small thrusters are also located in the rear, center section. Flying speed is a respectable 400 mph (643.6 km), but maximum altitude is limited to 6000 feet (1828 m).

    Flying Range: The nuclear power supply gives the transport years of life. The air cooled hover jets can function continuously for 24 hours before starting to get overheated. With a half hour to an hour cooling off period every 8-10 hours, the vehicle can be operated constantly without fear of overheating and damage to the propulsion system.

Statistical Data

Height: 36 feet (11 m) overall; the body of the APC is 26 feet (7.9 m) tall, but the top cannon turret adds 10 feet (3 m) to the overall height.

Width: 35 feet (10.7 m)

Length: 86 feet (26.2 m)

Weight: 123 tons unloaded.

Cargo: Troops, power armor, robots, small vehicles and/or supplies can be carried inside the 70 foot (21.3 m) long troop bay area; 2100 square feet of cargo space with a ceiling height of 20 feet (6 m).

Color: Typically blue-black.

Power System: Nuclear, average energy life is 20 years.

CS Cost: Top Secret, but estimated to be 80-100 million credits. It is exclusive to the CS military and is not available on the Black Market.

Weapon Systems

1. **CPC-100 High-Powered Cannon Turret (1):** The main gun is a cannon that fires plasma rocket shells. The entire turret, which includes a sensor disk and antenna, can turn 360 degrees. The cannon itself can be raised in a 45 degree arc of fire. The main gun is typically controlled by an independent gunner.

Primary Purpose: Assault/Anti-Armor/Anti-Monster

Secondary Purpose: Defense

Mega-Damage: 1D6×10 M.D. per round.

Rate of Fire: Equal to the gunner's hand to hand attacks per melee round +1 (usually 3 to 6).

Maximum Effective Range: 8000 feet (2438.4 m)

Payload: 100 rounds.

Bonus: +1 to strike.

2. **Laser Turrets (6):** A pair of turrets are mounted on the forward and back sections of the vehicle. Another one is mounted above the sliding Death's Head Bay door on both sides of the APC. Each can rotate 360 degrees in all directions and the weapon barrels can be raised and lowered in a 180 degree arc of fire. Typically the co-pilot and/or pilot operates the two forward turrets, while the two rear turrets are operated by one gunner and each of the side turrets by another (and the main cannon is operated by the fourth gunner).

Primary Purpose: Assault

Secondary Purpose: Anti-Missile

Mega-Damage: 3D6 M.D. per single blast or 6D6 simultaneous double blast. Note that the individual turrets are not keyed to fire in tandem, but each (except the two rear guns) has a separate gunner.

Rate of Fire: Equal to the pilot's or gunners hand to hand attacks/actions per melee round (typically 3-6).

Maximum Effective Range: 4000 feet (1200 m)

Payload: Effectively unlimited.

3. **Sensor Systems Note:** Has all the standard robot sensors and systems as well as the following.

1. Thermo-Imager: A special optical heat sensor that allows the infrared radiation of warm objects to be converted into a visible image. Enables the pilot to see in the dark, in shadows, and through smoke. Range: 2000 feet (610 m).

2. Infrared and Ultraviolet Optics: This optical system projects a beam of infrared light that is invisible to the normal eye. The infrared beam enables the pilot to see in the dark and to see other infrared beams. The ultraviolet system enables the pilot to see into the ultraviolet spectrum of light and is mostly used to detect the light beams of ultraviolet detection systems. **Note:** The infrared light beam can be seen by anybody who also has infrared optics, and the beam can be traced back to its source. Smoke impairs the infrared beam, making it impossible to see.

3. Lights: Built into the mouth area of the face of the Death's Head is one large searchlight that can rotate in a 45 degree arc.

On the front of the hover system housings and bottom of the large bay doors are four lights used for landing and disembarkment as well as visual searches, that also serve as infrared searchlights. The lights can be used to scan an area at night using the invisible light to avoid detection. Only somebody who can also see infrared light will see the beams. Range: 300 feet (91.5 m), 1000 feet (305 m) for the searchlight.

4. Enhanced Radar: Can identify and simultaneously track up to 96 different targets. Range: 200 miles.

5. Special Bonuses: +1 to dodge when flying at cruising speeds and +2 to dodge when flying over 300 mph. Trained CS pilots get an additional +10% to pilot the Coalition transport.

CS APC Sky Lifter

The Sky Lifter is another one of the Coalition's giant Death's Head Transports. It is designed as a robot and vehicle transport with minimal weapon systems and a huge cargo bay. The Sky Lifter is typically part of a larger convoy and/or escorted by a squadron of Sky Cycles, Rocket Cycles or SAMAS. Its only weapon systems are a powerful, concealed rail gun and concealed medium-range missile launchers.

The four, side, bay doors are 22 feet (6.7 m) tall and 18 feet (5.4 m) wide with sliding ramps for loading. Larger vehicles and cargo must use the rear cargo door which is 50 feet (15.2 m) tall by 40 feet (12.2 m) wide.

Sky Lifter Death's Head Transport

Model Type: AFC-060

Class: Air Armored Troop Carrier

Crew: 20; one pilot, one co-pilot, two gunners, two communication engineers, and 14 crew to handle and secure cargo — six use the Mauler power armor to lift, carry and stow heavy equipment.

Cargo/Troop Capability: The Sky Lifter can accommodate the following combinations:

As many as 18 *thirty* foot (9 m) robot vehicles, or ...

40 Hellraisers, or Hellfires, or G.B. Killers, or ...

12 Spider-Skull Walkers, or ...

40 Spider Scouts, or ...

12 ground APCs or tanks, plus the crews to pilot them and the troops transported with them, or ...

Approximately 80 Warbirds or Scout Rocket Cycles or similar small vehicles and their pilots.

If transporting human-sized troops, the Sky Lifter can accommodate roughly one battalion — 640 troops in full combat gear plus a half dozen small to medium-sized vehicles or a dozen Super SAMAS or Terror Troopers.

M.D.C. by Location:

Forward Observation Windows (2; eye shaped) — 200 each

Eye Sliding Metal Coverings (2; as needed) — 300 each

Concealed Forward Cannon Turret (1) — 350

Concealed Mini-Missile Launchers (4; two per side) — 150 each

Tail Fin — 300

Lower Saucer Hover Jets (3) — 400 each

Rear Jets (2) — 200 each

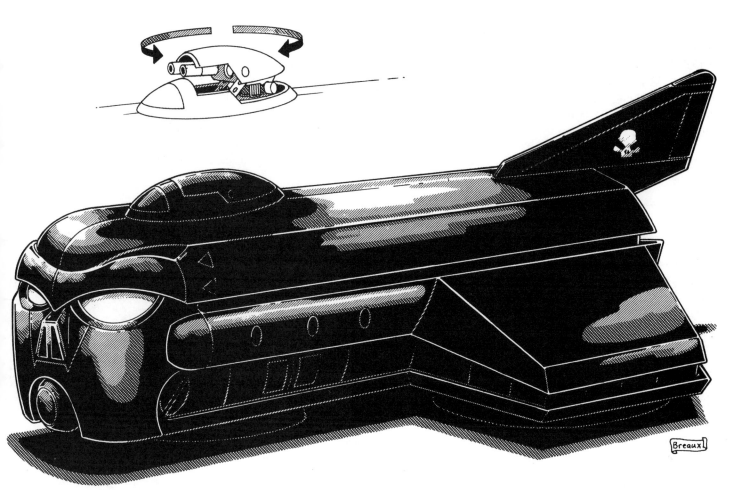

* Side Bay Doors (4; two per side) — 150 each
Giant Bay Door (1; rear) — 300
Extendable Ramps (5) — 50 each
Reinforced Pilot's Crew Compartment — 200
** Main Body — 2300

    * Every item marked by a single asterisk is small and/or difficult to strike. An attacker must make a "called shot" to hit and even then he is -3 to strike.

    Destroying the sensor unit means the pilot must rely on his own vision and instruments; radar and targeting (and accompanying bonuses) are lost. The sensor cluster is the front quarter of the housing for the concealed rail gun.

    Destroying one of the saucer hover platforms reduces speed by 30%.

    ** Depleting the M.D.C. of the main body completely destroys the vehicle.

Speed

Land: Unlike the Giant Death's Head Transport, the Sky Lifter can hover above the ground as low as four feet (1.2 m).

Water: The Sky Lifter can hover across the surface of water at a speed of 100 mph (160 km) and even submerge itself underwater up to an ocean depth of one mile (1.6 km). Speed underwater is 35 mph (56 km/30 knots). However, it cannot open its bay doors underwater without flooding and sinking.

Flying: Three saucer-shaped propulsion systems on the underbelly and a pair of jet thrusters in the rear section provide the giant vehicle's lift and speed. Flying speed is 400 mph (643.6 km), but maximum altitude is limited to 6000 feet (1828 m).

Flying Range: The nuclear power supply gives the transport years of life. The hover jets can function continuously for 24 hours before starting to overheat (requires a two hour cooling period; to push beyond this is to risk burning out one of the saucers).

Statistical Data

Height: 88 feet (26.8 m); the tail adds another 30 feet (9 m) for an overall height of 118 feet (35.9 m).

Width: 100 feet (30.5 m) for the main body, but the wedge-like wings add another 100 feet for an overall width of 200 feet (61 m).

Length: 240 feet (73 m)

Weight: Approximately 1900 tons

Cargo: See above.

Color: Typically blue-black.

Power System: Nuclear, average energy life is 20 years.

CS Cost: Top secret, but estimated to be 200 million credits. A Death's Head transport has never been available on the Black Market.

Weapon Systems

1. **The CPC-200 Double-Barrel High-Powered Cannon Turret (1):** The main gun is a concealed cannon that fires plasma rocket shells. The weapon portion of the turret raises to fire — the front stationary section of the weapon housing is the sensor unit. Once in an up position, the cannon can turn 360 degrees and tilt up and down at a 45 degree angle. The gun is typically controlled by a gunner.

Primary Purpose: Assault/Anti-Armor/Anti-Monster

Secondary Purpose: Defense

Mega-Damage: 1D6×10 M.D. per single round or 2D6×10 per double round.

Rate of Fire: Equal to the gunner's hand to hand attacks per melee round +1 (usually 3 to 6).

Maximum Effective Range: 8000 feet (2438.4 m)

Payload: 300 rounds.

Bonus: +1 to strike.

2. **Concealed Mini-Missile Launchers (4):** The triangular markings toward the front of the transport are mini-missile launchers. Each pair is operated by a gunner.

Primary Purpose: Anti-Aircraft and Anti-Armor.

Secondary Purpose: Anti-Personnel

Missile Type: Any type of mini-missile can be used, but standard issue is fragmentation (anti-personnel, 5D6 M.D.) and plasma (1D6×10).

Mega-Damage: Varies with missile type.

Range: About one mile

Rate of Fire: One at a time, or in volleys of two, four or eight.

Payload: 400 total! Each triangular launch unit has a massive payload of 100 each!!

3. **Sensors:** Same as the other Death's Head Transports.

CS Command Car

The Command Car is basically a versatile hover jeep that is used by officers, field commanders and combat troops as a means of transportation. The vehicle is an open-top convertible that can be covered with a light, semi-transparent covering (15 M.D.C.). Since most combat troops wear body armor, the cover is rarely used — special drains and light M.D.C. materials protect the interior from weather damage. A light rail gun is located in the back, along with a seat for a tail gunner. The weapon folds up, back and down when the canopy is used to enclose the interior of the vehicle. The windshield is made of a tough, mega-damage glass that is as tough as steel. The eyes of the Death's Head are high-intensity searchlights. The three small circular items on each side are infrared headlights for stealth night driving.

The Command Car is reliable and quiet. It can hover as close to the ground as two feet (0.6 m) or as high as 500 feet (152 m). A pair of jet thrusters in the rear gives it extra speed. It is frequently used by Commandos, Special Forces and commissioned field officers, as well as for parades and troop inspections.

Flying Command Car

Nickname: "The Platform"

Model Type: AFC-101
Class: Military Transport
Crew: One, a pilot; tail gunner optional. Can accommodate four passengers comfortably, a fifth can be squeezed in with the tail gunner.

M.D.C. by Location:
* Rear Rail Gun (1; manned) — 50
  Windshield (1) — 30
  Doors (4) — 40 each
  Eye Searchlights (2) — 15 each
* Infrared Headlights (6) — 2 each
* Bottom Hover Jets (6) — 50 each
  Rear Jets (2) — 50 each
  Retractable Canopy/Cover — 15
** Main Body — 180

   * Every item marked by a single asterisk is small and/or difficult to strike. An attacker must make a "called shot" to hit and even then he is -3 to strike.

   Destroying one of the bottom hover jets reduces speed by 10%. Destroying one of the rear jets reduces speed by 20%.

   ** Depleting the M.D.C. of the main body completely destroys the vehicle.

Speed

   Flying: 200 mph (321.8 km), but cruising speed is considered to range between 80 and 150 mph (128 and 240 km). VTOL capable, can hover stationary; retractable landing gear. Maximum altitude is limited to about 500 feet (152 m).

   Water: The Command Car can also skim across the surface of water at a speed of 100 mph (160 km/85 knots). It is not a submersible and will sink like a rock if the hover jets are turned off.

Flying Range: The nuclear power supply gives the vehicle decades of life. The command car is a workhorse that can be flown continuously for 96 hours without fear of overheating.

Statistical Data
Height: 4 feet (1.2 m)
Width: 5 feet, 6 inches (1.7 m)
Length: 11 feet (3.3 m)
Weight: 2.1 tons
Cargo: Minimal storage space, about three feet (0.9 m) behind seats for extra clothing, weapons, and personal items.
Power System: Nuclear, average energy life is 20 years.
CS Cost: 650,000 credits. The Black Market, Northern Gun and other manufacturers sell "knock-offs" (copies), complete with a light rail gun, for 850,000 credits; 450,000 for a rebuilt. Good availability.

Weapon Systems

1. **C-30R Light Rail Gun:** Located on a retractable weapon mounting.
Primary Purpose: Anti-Personnel
Secondary Purpose: Defense
Weight: 90 lbs (40.8 kg; ammo compartment inside vehicle).
Mega-Damage: A Burst is 30 rounds and inflicts 6D6 M.D.; one round does 1D4 M.D.
Rate of Fire: Equal to number of combined hand to hand attacks (usually 4-6).
Maximum Effective Range: Two miles (3.2 km).
Payload: 2400 rounds, that's 80 bursts.
2. **Sensors:** Long and short-range radio, infrared optics, and short-range radar.

CS "Scarab" Officer's Car

The "Scarab" is a completely enclosed flying hover car that is assigned to commanding officers, government officials, and visiting dignitaries. A pilot and gunner usually come with the vehicle. The "Scarab" has proven to be a tough and combat worthy vehicle and is sometimes used by Special Forces, Commandos and members of the Rifts Containment Studies Group.

For defense, four ball turret lasers are located where the wheels would be on a normal car. The pilot typically operates the forward turrets and the gunner, the rear turrets. A concealed pair of mini-missile launchers can also be extended to fire a volley of missiles.

The enclosed vehicle offers maximum protection with mega-damage steel and glass. The eyes of the Death's Head are high-intensity searchlights, with a pair of infrared headlights for stealth night driving located beneath them. It can hover as close to the ground as two feet (0.6 m) or as high as 1500 feet (457.2 m). The Scarab is aerodynamic, with its sleek, rounded body frame, and a pair of jet thrusters in the rear provide extra speed.

Scarab Officer's Car
Model Type: AFC-103
Class: Military Transport

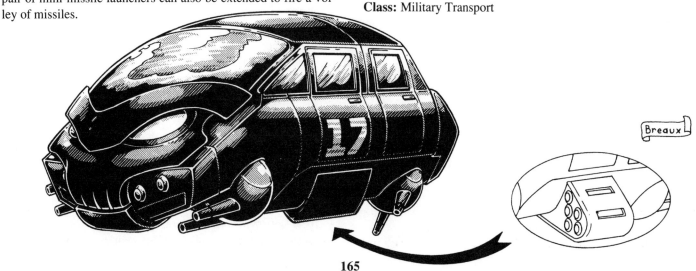

Crew: Two, a pilot and gunner. Can accommodate four passengers comfortably, a fifth or sixth can be squeezed in, but makes for cramped, uncomfortable conditions.

M.D.C. by Location:

* Laser Turrets (4; bottom) — 50 each
Concealed Mini-Missile Launchers (2) — 150 each
* Mini-Missile Launchers (2) — 50 each
Front Windshield (1) — 40
Side Windows (6) — 20 each
Doors (4) — 50 each
Eye Searchlights (2) — 15 each
* Infrared Headlights (4) — 2 each
* Bottom Hover Jets (5) — 50 each
Rear Jets (3) — 50 each
** Main Body — 240

 * Every item marked by a single asterisk is small and/or difficult to strike. An attacker must make a "called shot" to hit and even then he is -3 to strike.

 Destroying one of the bottom hover jets reduces speed by 10%. Destroying one of the rear jets reduces speed by 20%.

 ** Depleting the M.D.C. of the main body completely destroys the vehicle.

Speed

Flying: 220 mph (352 km), but cruising speed is considered to range between 80 and 150 mph (128 and 240 km). VTOL capable, can hover stationary; retractable landing gear. Maximum altitude is limited to about 1500 feet (457.2 m).

Water: The Scarab can also skim across the surface of water at a speed of 110 mph (160 km/93.5 knots). It is submersible, with an underwater speed of 50 mph (80.4 km/42.5 knots), but a maximum ocean depth of only 300 feet (91.5 m).

Flying Range: The nuclear power supply gives the vehicle decades of life. The Scarab can be flown continuously for 48 hours without fear of overheating.

Statistical Data

Height: 7 feet (2.1 m)
Width: 5 feet, 6 inches (1.7 m)
Length: 20 feet (5.4 m)
Weight: 2.4 tons.
Cargo: Minimal storage space, about three feet (0.9 m) behind seats for extra clothing, weapons, and personal items.
Power System: Nuclear, average energy life is 20 years.
CS Cost: 1.6 million credits. The Black Market and Northern Gun sell "knock-offs" (copies), complete with weapon systems, for 2.1 million credits; 1.3 million for a rebuilt. Fair availability.

Weapon Systems

1. **C-40BT Laser Turrets (4):** Four double-barrel lasers built into ball turrets are located in each corner of the car. Each is capable of 180 degree rotation and arc of fire.

Primary Purpose: Anti-personnel
Secondary Purpose: Defense

Mega-Damage: 4D6 per double blast from one turret, or 8D6 M.D. per simultaneous dual blasts from two turrets. All four turrets cannot fire in tandem.
Range: 2000 feet (610 m)
Rate of Fire: Equal to the number of hand to hand attacks per melee round of the pilot or gunner (usually 4 to 6).
Payload: Effectively unlimited.

2. **CR-10 Concealed Mini-Missile Launcher (2):** A pair of mini-missile launchers are mounted on the sides of the vehicle. Each contains a total of ten mini-missiles.

Primary Purpose: Anti-Personnel
Secondary Purpose: Anti-Armor
Missile Type: Any type of mini-missile can be used, but standard issue is fragmentation (anti-personnel, 5D6 M.D.) and plasma (1D6×10).
Mega-Damage: Varies with missile type.
Range: About one mile
Rate of Fire: One at a time or in volleys of two, three, four, or five.
Payload: Twenty, ten missiles in each launcher.

3. **Sensors:** Long and short-range radio, infrared optics, and short-range radar.

CS Skull Patrol Car

The "Skull" patrol car is a smaller, lighter version of the Scarab Command Car. It too is completely enclosed, but has a heavy plasma turret on its roof and a pair of single shot mini-missile launchers on its undercarriage. This vehicle is used by the military and the ISS. Although suitable for combat, the Skull is primarily used by the Army for border patrols, convoy escorts, military police cars, and transportation. A pilot and gunner are usually assigned to each, with seating for two passengers in the back (a mega-damage sheet of transparent material separates prisoners from the police officers when used for policing). The Skull is sometimes used by wilderness scouts, reconnaissance teams and members of the Rifts Containment Studies Group.

It can hover as close to the ground as two feet (0.6 m) or as high as 1200 feet (365 m). The Skull is not as aerodynamic or fast as the Scarab, but a good, reliable vehicle. Jet thrusters are located on the undercarriage and in the rear.

Flying Patrol Car

Model Type: AFC-105
Class: Military Transport
Crew: Two, a pilot and gunner. Can accommodate two passenger comfortably, a third can be squeezed in, but makes for cramped, uncomfortable conditions.

M.D.C. by Location:

* Plasma Turret (1; roof) — 70
* Mini-Missile Launchers (2) — 25 each
Front Windshields (2) — 30 each
Side Windows (6) — 20 each
Doors (4) — 50 each
Headlights (2) — 5 each
* Infrared Headlights (2, small) — 2 each
* Bottom Hover Jets (5) — 50 each
Rear Jets (3) — 50 each
** Main Body — 200

 * Every item marked by a single asterisk is small and/or difficult to strike. An attacker must make a "called shot" to hit and even then he is -3 to strike.

 Destroying one of the bottom hover jets reduces speed by 10%. Destroying one of the rear jets reduces speed by 20%.

 ** Depleting the M.D.C. of the main body completely destroys the vehicle.

Speed

Flying: 150 mph (240 km), but cruising speed is considered to range between 50 and 80 mph (80.4 to 144 km). VTOL capable, can hover stationary; retractable landing gear. Maximum altitude is limited to about 1500 feet (457.2 m).

Water: The patrol car can also skim across the surface of water at a speed of 110 mph (160 km/93.5 knots). It is submersible, with an underwater speed of 40 mph (64.3 km/34 knots), but a maximum ocean depth of only 300 feet (91.5 m).

Flying Range: The nuclear power supply gives the vehicle decades of life. The Skull patrol car is a workhorse that can be flown continuously for 96 hours without fear of overheating.

Statistical Data

Height: 6 feet (1.8 m)
Width: 6 feet (1.8 m)
Length: 11 feet (3.3 m)
Weight: 1.9 tons.
Cargo: Minimal storage space, about three feet (0.9 m) behind seats for extra clothing, weapons, and personal items.
Power System: Nuclear, average energy life is 20 years.
CS Cost: 1.4 million credits. The Black Market and Northern Gun sell "knock-offs" (copies), complete with weapon systems, for 1.8 million credits; 1.1 million for a rebuilt. Good availability.

Weapon Systems

1. **C-40PT Plasma Turret (1):** A plasma turret is on the roof of the car. It is capable of 360 degree rotation and 180 degree arc of fire.

Primary Purpose: Anti-personnel
Secondary Purpose: Defense
Mega-Damage: 6D6 per blast.
Range: 2000 feet (610 m)
Rate of Fire: Equal to the number of hand to hand attacks per melee round of the pilot or gunner (usually 4 to 6).
Payload: Effectively unlimited.

2. **CR-02 Concealed Mini-Missile Launchers (2):** A single shot mini-missile launcher is built into the underside of the vehicle. Each contains a total of eight mini-missiles.

Primary Purpose: Anti-Personnel
Secondary Purpose: Anti-Armor
Missile Type: Any type of mini-missile can be used, but standard issue is fragmentation (anti-personnel, 5D6 M.D.) and plasma (1D6×10).
Mega-Damage: Varies with missile type.
Range: About one mile
Rate of Fire: One at a time or in volleys of two.
Payload: 2; one missile in each launcher.

3. **Sensors:** Long and short-range radio, infrared optics, and short-range radar.

CS Scout Rocket Cycle

Nicknamed the "Slingshot," the Scout Rocket Cycle is a fast, one-man combat vehicle. It has proven to be a favorite of Special Forces, Commandos and RPA "Fly Boy" Aces, particularly those assigned to reconnaissance, search and destroy missions, guerilla warfare, surgical strikes and infiltration behind enemy lines. The rocket cycle is not much bigger than a conventional motorcycle, is amazingly maneuverable and well armed. A squadron (6-10) has been known to rip apart a lone, enemy giant robot, tank or Glitter Boy with relative ease and little, if any, loss of man or vehicle.

Four rapid-fire pulse lasers are located in the front, backed up by a pair of mini-missile launchers. Directional, ball thrusters in the front, side (rear), and bottom help to provide stability at great speeds and for VTOL. The two jet engines in the tail provide dizzying speed. The eyes of the Death's Head are high-intensity headlights. The "Slingshot" rocket bike can hover as close to the ground as one foot (0.3 m) or as high as 2500 feet (762 m).

Scout Rocket Cycle

Nicknames: Slingshot and Rocket Scout.
Model Type: AFC-111
Class: Aerial Military Combat Vehicle
Crew: One

M.D.C. by Location:

* Laser Turrets (4; front) — 20 each
Mini-Missile Launchers (2; sides) — 40 each
Front Windshield (1) — 25
* Eye Headlights (2) — 8 each
* Directional Jets (10) — 15 each
* Tail Fins (4) — 15 each
Rear Jets (2) — 55 each
** Main Body — 150

* Every item marked by a single asterisk is small and/or difficult to strike. An attacker must make a "called shot" to hit and even then he is -4 to strike.

Destroying three or more of the directional jets inflicts a piloting skill penalty of -15%. Destroying one of the rear jets reduces speed by 50% and inflicts a piloting penalty of -30%. Destroying both sends the vehicle crashing to the ground.

** Depleting the M.D.C. of the main body completely destroys the vehicle.

Speed

Flying: 440 mph (704 km), but cruising speed is considered to range between 80 and 150 mph (128 and 240 km). VTOL capable, it can hover stationary; retractable landing gear. Maximum altitude is limited to about 2500 feet (762 m).

Water: The Scout Rocket Cycle can also skim across the surface of water at a speed of 210 mph (336 km/178.5 knots). It is not submersible.

Flying Range: The nuclear power supply provides the vehicle decades of life. The Rocket Scout can be flown continuously for 12 hours without fear of overheating.

Statistical Data

Height: 4 feet (1.2 m)
Width: 4 feet (1.2 m)
Length: 11 feet (3.3 m)
Weight: 1000 pounds (450 kg).
Cargo: Only enough to stow an energy rifle and three E-clips.
Power System: Nuclear, average energy life is 20 years.

CS Cost: 850,000 credits. The Black Market and Northern Gun sell cheap "knock-offs" that have half the speed, but similar weapons and capabilities, for 500,000 credits; 600,000 for a rebuilt CS vehicle. Good availability for the slower knock-offs, poor availability of CS rebuilts.

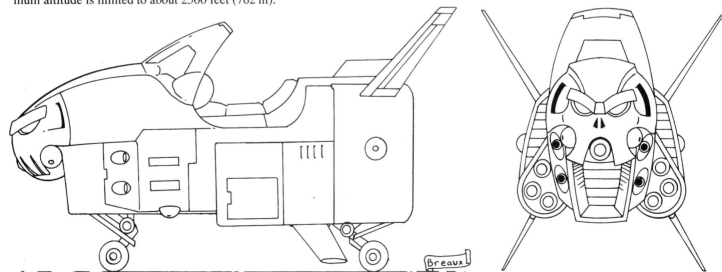

Weapon Systems

1. C-RF4 Rapid-Fire Pulse Lasers (4): Four short-barreled lasers are built into the nose of the cycle. Each can pivot 30 degrees in all directions.

Primary Purpose: Anti-Aircraft and Anti-Armor.

Secondary Purpose: Strafing/Anti-Personnel

Mega-Damage: 2D6 per single blast, 4D6 per double blast, 6D6 per triple blast and 8D6 from a full blast. Simultaneous multiple blasts count as one melee attack.

Range: 1800 feet (548.6 m)

Rate of Fire: Equal to the number of hand to hand attacks of the pilot.

Payload: Effectively unlimited.

2. Modified CR-10 Concealed Mini-Missile Launchers (2): A pair of mini-missile launchers are mounted on the sides of the vehicle. Each contains a total of six mini-missiles.

Primary Purpose: Anti-Armor

Secondary Purpose: Anti-Personnel

Missile Type: Any type of mini-missile can be used, but standard issue is fragmentation (anti-personnel, 5D6 M.D.) and plasma (1D6×10).

Mega-Damage: Varies with missile type.

Range: About one mile

Rate of Fire: One at a time or in volleys of two, three, four, or five.

Payload: 12; six missiles in each launcher.

3. Sensor: Long and short-range radio and short-range radar.

4. Combat Bonus: Elite RPA SAMAS pilots and RPA "Fly Boys" get a bonus of +2 on initiative and two additional attacks per melee round when piloting one of these vehicles.

CS Warbird Rocket Cycle

The Warbird is a cross between the "Slingshot" Scout Rocket Cycle and Sky Cycle and is designed for aerial dog-fighting and heavy combat. As such, it is ideal for combating flying power armor, enemy aircraft and flying monsters, but is also capable of engaging ground troops as well. This fast, maneuverable, one-man combat vehicle is another favorite of Special Forces, Commandos and RPA "Fly Boy" Aces. The Warbird is roughly twice the size of the Rocket Scout but armed to the teeth! A triple-bar-rel rail gun is located in the nose, high-powered lasers and a particle beam weapon above it, mini-missiles on the sides and fusion bombs toward the rear, hence the slogan, "Don't mess with the Warbird."

Concealed, directional thrusters are located in the front, sides, rear and top to help provide stability at great speeds and for VTOL. The two jet engines in the tail provide dizzying speed. The eyes of the Death's Head are high-intensity headlights. The Warbird Rocket Cycle can hover as close to the ground as one foot (0.3 m; although not recommended — four feet/1.2 m is considered safe) or as high as 6000 feet (1828 m).

Warbird Rocket Cycle

Nickname: Warbird
Model Type: AFC-115
Class: Aerial Military Combat Vehicle
Crew: One
M.D.C. by Location:

* Lasers (2; front) — 15 each
* Particle Beam (1) — 25
* Rail Guns (3) — 65 each
  Mini-Missile Launchers (2; sides) — 40 each
* Fusion Bombs (4) — 15 each
  Front Windshield (1) — 35
* Headlights (2; undercarriage) — 4 each
* Directional Jets (12) — 15 each
* Tail Fins (3) — 25 each
  Side/Rear Jets (2) — 100 each
** Main Body — 220

    * Every item marked by a single asterisk is small and/or difficult to strike. An attacker must make a "called shot" to hit and even then he is -4 to strike.

    Destroying three or more of the directional jets inflicts a piloting skill penalty of -15%. Destroying one of the rear jets reduces speed by 50% and inflicts a piloting penalty of -30%. Destroying both sends the vehicle crashing to the ground.

    ** Depleting the M.D.C. of the main body completely destroys the vehicle.

Speed

    <u>Flying</u>: 400 mph (643 km), but cruising speed is considered to range between 80 and 150 mph (128 and 240 km). VTOL capable, it can hover stationary; retractable landing gear. Maximum altitude is limited to about 6000 feet (1828 m).

    <u>Water</u>: The Warbird Rocket Cycle can also skim across the surface of water at a speed of 200 mph (321 km/170 knots). It is not submersible.

    <u>Flying Range</u>: The nuclear power supply provides the vehicle decades of life. The Warbird can be flown continuously for 24 hours without fear of overheating.

Statistical Data

<u>Height</u>: 4 feet (1.2 m); the tail adds three feet (0.9 m) for an overall height of 7 feet (2.1 m).
<u>Width</u>: 10 feet (3 m)
<u>Length</u>: 12 feet (3.6 m)
<u>Weight</u>: 1.2 tons.
<u>Cargo</u>: Only enough to stow an energy rifle and three E-clips.
<u>Power System</u>: Nuclear, average energy life is 20 years.
<u>CS Cost</u>: 1.3 million credits. The Black Market and Northern Gun sell cheap "knock-offs" that have half the speed, two nose rail guns, no particle beam weapon and no fusion bombs, for 900,000 credits; one million for a rebuilt CS Warbird. Fair availability for the slower knock-offs, terrible availability for CS rebuilts.

Weapon Systems

1. C-42 Rail Gun Cluster Housing: Three high-powered, gatling gun style rail guns built into the nose of the rocket jet. One, two or all three can be fired simultaneously at the same target. They are specifically designed to be anti-aircraft and power armor weapons but are suitable for strafing ground assaults, anti-tanks and for providing cover fire to support infantry troops.

<u>Primary Purpose</u>: Anti-Aircraft
<u>Secondary Purpose</u>: Anti-Personnel and Defense.
<u>Mega-Damage</u>: A full damage burst from one rail gun is 40 rounds and inflicts 1D6×10 M.D., two guns 2D6×10 M.D. and three guns, 3D6×10 M.D.
<u>Maximum Effective Range</u>: 4000 feet (1220 m)
<u>Rate of Fire</u>: Equal to the combined hand to hand attacks of the gunner (usually 4-6).
<u>Payload</u>: 4,000 round drum feed for 100 bursts per *each* rail gun; 12,000 rounds total! Reloading a drum will take about 20 minutes for those not trained, but a mere five minutes by characters with engineering or field armorer skills.

2. Forward Lasers (2): Two lasers are built into the nose of the cycle. Each can pivot 45 degrees in all directions.
<u>Primary Purpose</u>: Strafing/Anti-Personnel
<u>Secondary Purpose</u>: Defense
<u>Mega-Damage</u>: 2D6 per single blast or 4D6 per double blast. Simultaneous dual blasts count as one melee attack.
<u>Range</u>: 2000 feet (610 m)
<u>Rate of Fire</u>: Equal to the number of hand to hand attacks of the pilot.
<u>Payload</u>: Effectively unlimited.

3. Forward Particle Beam Weapon (1): Mounted above the two lasers is a P-beam blaster built into the nose of the cycle. It can pivot 45 degrees in all directions. This heavy weapon is used in (comparatively) close-range combat and as an anti-missile weapon.
<u>Primary Purpose</u>: Anti-Aircraft/Armor and Anti-Missile.
<u>Secondary Purpose</u>: Strafing/Anti-Personnel
<u>Mega-Damage</u>: 2D6 per single blast.
<u>Range</u>: 1400 feet (426.7 m)
<u>Rate of Fire</u>: Equal to the number of hand to hand attacks of the pilot.
<u>Payload</u>: Effectively unlimited.

4. Concealed Mini-Missile Launchers (2): A mini-missile launcher is built into the forward sections of the two main jet housings. Each contains a total of ten mini-missiles.
<u>Primary Purpose</u>: Anti-Aircraft/Armor
<u>Secondary Purpose</u>: Anti-Personnel
<u>Missile Type</u>: Any type of mini-missile can be used, but standard issue is fragmentation (anti-personnel, 5D6 M.D.) and plasma (1D6×10).
<u>Mega-Damage</u>: Varies with missile type.
<u>Range</u>: About one mile
<u>Rate of Fire</u>: One at a time or in volleys of two, three, four, or five.
<u>Payload</u>: Twenty; 10 missiles in each launcher.

5. Fusion Mini-Bombs (4): Held in a light containment shielding are four fusion mini-bombs — basically a Type Two or Type Three fusion block in a weighted container. These bombs are typically used against large targets like buildings and bunkers. When the Warbird is over his target, one or more bombs are jettisoned and fall to the earth, exploding on impact.
<u>Mega-Damage</u>: 2D6×10 or 4D6×10 M.D. to a 10 foot (3 m) radius.
<u>Penalty</u>: -2 to strike targets smaller than 20 feet in diameter.

6. Sensor: Long and short-range radio and short-range radar.

7. Combat Bonus: Elite RPA SAMAS pilots and RPA "Fly Boys" get a bonus of +1 on initiative and one additional attack per melee round when piloting one of these vehicles.

CS Wind Jammer
Sky Cycle

The Wind Jammer is an infantry combat version of the AFC-023 that is even faster and more deadly than the original. The Wind Jammer is used to patrol border areas, perform fly-by reconnaissance, rescue, and to bombard enemy ground troops. The front of the Wind Jammer has a concealed, short-range laser for dog-fights, but its main weapon system is contained in its weapon appendage. The appendage looks like a ramp or flip-open hatch for storage or landing gear, but opens to fire a pair of gatling-gun style rail guns and a mini-missile launcher.

The circular depressions are directional thrusters to give the Sky Cycle greater stability and control. The five lower jets in the tail, combined with the one large, central thruster also help to modulate speed and control. The Wind Jammer can hover as close to the ground as one foot (0.3 m; although not recommended — four feet/1.2 m is considered safe) or as high as 6000 feet (1828 m). Like its predecessor, the Wind Jammer also has wheels and can rocket along on the ground.

Note: The AFC-023 Coalition Sky Cycle has been given to the ISS to patrol the cities and neighboring towns.

Coalition Wind Jammer Sky Cycle
Model Type: AFC-033
Class: Air Assault Vehicle
Crew: One. Can possibly seat one passenger, but dangerous and uncomfortable for the passenger.

M.D.C. by Location:
* Rail Guns (2; weapon appendage) — 50 each
Mini-Missile Launcher (1; weapon appendage) — 30
Weapon Appendage (1) — 110
Front Windshield (1) — 35
* Headlights (2; front; small) — 2 each
* Directional Jets (12) — 10 each
Tail Fin (1) — 90
Main Jet Thruster (1) — 150
Lower Rear Jets (5) — 80 each
** Main Body — 220

   * Every item marked by a single asterisk is small and/or difficult to strike. An attacker must make a "called shot" to hit and even then he is -4 to strike.

   Destroying three or more of the directional jets inflicts a piloting skill penalty of -10%. Destroying one of the secondary rear jets reduces speed by 10%. Destroying the main thruster reduces speed by 50% and inflicts a piloting penalty of -30%. Destroying all rear jets sends the vehicle crashing to the ground.

   ** Depleting the M.D.C. of the main body completely destroys the vehicle.

Speed

Driving on the ground: Ground speed is 0-200 mph (321.8 km) maximum; can reach 100 mph (160 km) in three seconds!

171

Flying: 620 mph (992 km, almost the speed of sound), but cruising speed is considered to range between 80 and 150 mph (128 and 240 km). VTOL capable, it can hover stationary; retractable landing gear. Maximum altitude is limited to about 6000 feet (1828 m).

Water: The Wind Jammer can skim across the surface of water at a speed of 200 mph (321 km/170 knots) but tends to skip along the surface and is -20% on the piloting skill to maintain control. It is not submersible.

Flying Range: The nuclear power supply provides the vehicle decades of life. The Wind Jammer can be flown continuously for 24 hours without fear of overheating.

Statistical Data
Height: 10 feet (3 m)
Width: 8 feet (2.4 m)
Length: 16 feet (4.8 m)
Weight: 2.2 tons
Cargo: Minimal storage space; enough to stow a suit of extra clothing, a rifle and handgun, and some personal items.
Power System: Nuclear, average energy life is 20 years.
CS Cost: 1.8 million credits. Exclusive to the CS — nobody has done a "knock-off" of the old or new style Coalition Sky Cycle.

Weapon Systems

1. **CR-33 Mini-Missile Launcher (1):** Concealed in the weapon appendage is a mini-missile launcher. It can only fire when the weapon appendage is open.

Primary Purpose: Anti-Personnel
Secondary Purpose: Anti-Armor (tanks, robots, dragons, etc).
Missile Type: Any type of mini-missile can be used, but standard issue is fragmentation (anti-personnel, 5D6 M.D.) and plasma (1D6×10).
Mega-Damage: Varies with missile type.
Range: About one mile
Rate of Fire: One at a time or in volleys of two, three, or four.
Payload: 24 total.

2. **C-33 Weapon Appendage Rail Guns:** Two high-powered, gatling gun style rail guns built into the weapon appendage. One or both can be fired simultaneously at the same target. They are specifically designed to be anti-aircraft and power armor weapons but are suitable for strafing ground assaults, anti-tanks and for providing cover fire to support infantry troops.

The weapon appendage can be raised and lowered in a 45 degree arc of fire.

Primary Purpose: Anti-Aircraft
Secondary Purpose: Anti-Personnel and Defense.
Mega-Damage: A full damage burst from one rail gun is 40 rounds and inflicts 1D6×10 M.D., two guns 2D6×10 M.D. Simultaneous dual bursts on the same target counts as one melee attack.
Maximum Effective Range: 4000 feet (1220 m)
Rate of Fire: Equal to the combined hand to hand attacks of the gunner (usually 4-6).
Payload: 4,000 round drum feed for 100 bursts per *each* rail gun; 8,000 rounds total! Reloading a drum will take about 20 minutes for those not trained, but a mere five minutes by characters with engineering or field armorer skills.

3. **Concealed Laser (1):** Hidden in the tip of the nose is a light laser. It is fixed forward and can only fire straight ahead.

Primary Purpose: Anti-Personnel
Secondary Purpose: Defense
Mega-Damage: 6D6 M.D. per dual blast.
Range: 2000 feet (610 m)
Rate of Fire: The pilot can operate all weapon systems at a rate equal to his number of hand to hand attacks per melee (usually 4 to 6).
Payload: Effectively unlimited.

4. **Smoke Dispenser:** A smoke dispensing unit in the rear undercarriage can release a dense cloud of smoke that will cover an 80 foot (24 m) area in front of it. It can also release tear gas.

Payload: Six total; usually all smoke.

5. **Hand to Hand Combat:** None.

6. **Sensor Systems Note:** Has all the standard robot sensors and communications capabilities, including radar.

7. **Special Bonuses:** +1 on initiative, +1 attack per melee round, +2 to dodge when flying at cruising speeds and +4 to dodge when flying over 250 mph.

Black Lightning

Coalition Combat Helicopter

The Coalition State of Iron Heart introduced the combat helicopter as a comparatively inexpensive multi-function attack aircraft. Not only are helicopters roughly equivalent to the Sky and Rocket Cycles, but they can be used to transport cargo and haul giant robots (dangling below the Chopper on wires). The Black Lightning is an advanced, multi-purpose combat helicopter that is a workhorse at Iron Heart. It is used for low altitude reconnaissance, rescue, insertion and extraction of ground and sea troops, combat, infantry support, cargo hauling, and defense. The 'copter is reasonably well armored and has impressive firepower and maneuverability. A squadron of four to eight gunships can destroy tanks, ground APCs and small to medium air transports as well as engage enemy power armor, other helicopters, ground troops, stationary targets and giant bots. They are ineffective, however, against squads of power armor troops that outnumber them, the faster Rocket Cycles and the giant, well armed Death's Head Transports.

As a multi-purpose helicopter the Black Lightning has also been used by the fledgling navy (NAC), especially for search and rescue missions and combat support.

Model Type: CH-10
Class: Helicopter Gunship.
Crew: Four: Pilot, co-pilot/gunner, communications officer/gunner and another gunner. It can also carry four human-sized passengers or two power armor troops — the addition of a pair of SAMAS can add to the gunship's combat abilities and element of surprise.
M.D.C. by Location:
*** Four-Blade Top Rotors — 100 (25 each blade)
* Nose Laser (1) — 35
* Nose Rail Gun (1) — 25
* Wing Rail Guns (4; two per wing) — 40 each
* Mini-Missile Tube Launchers (8; four per wing) — 10 each
Sensor Clusters (2; side) — 50 each
Weapon Wings (2; a weapon mount) — 70 each

172

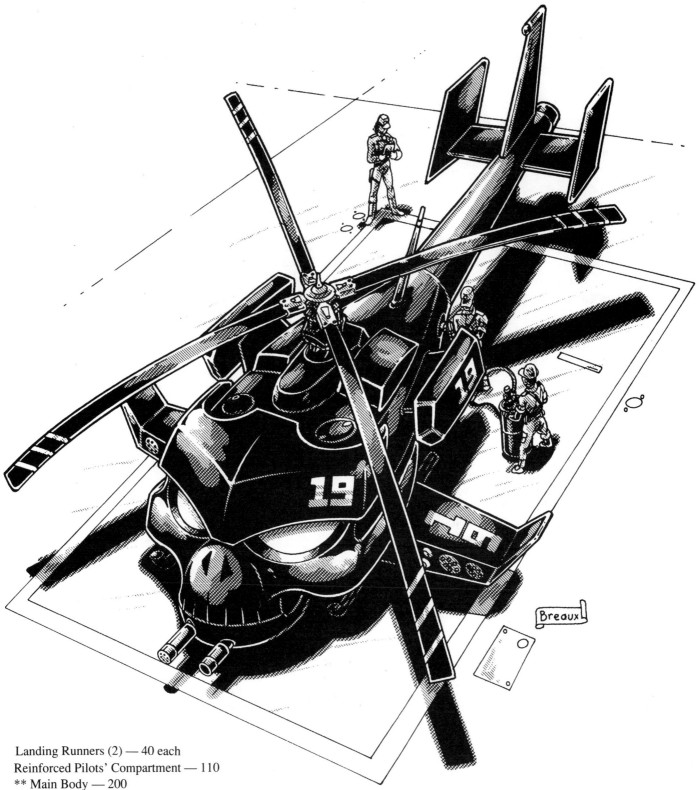

Breaux!

Landing Runners (2) — 40 each
Reinforced Pilots' Compartment — 110
** Main Body — 200

* Every item marked by a single asterisk is small and/or difficult to strike. An attacker must make a "called shot" to hit and even then he is -4 to strike.

** Destroying the main body knocks the helicopter out of the sky and destroys it completely.

***Destroying one of the main rotors will knock the helicopter off course (pilot loses initiative and three melee actions that round, or the next, to maintain control), speed is reduced by 20% and the pilot suffers a -20% on all subsequent piloting skill rolls. Destroying two rotors will knock the bird out of the sky! Roll under piloting skill -40% for a *successful* crash landing —the helicopter doesn't explode or disintegrate on impact. If successful, the chopper is wrecked, but crew and passengers are uninjured and crash damage is half.

A crash will do 4D6×10 M.D. to the helicopter and crew, and 1D6×10 M.D. to a 50 foot (15.2 m) radius from the point of impact from flying debris, etc.

Speed:

Ground: Not possible.

Flying: The Black Lightning can hover stationary, VTOL, and travel at a maximum flight speed of 300 mph (480 km).

Cruising and attack speeds vary, but tend to be between 100 and 200 mph (160 to 329 km) and it has excellent VTOL capabilities.

Altitude: A maximum ceiling (altitude) of 20,000 feet (6096 m). Combat height (the height in which air to ground attacks are possible): 3000 feet (910 m).

Range: Liquid fuel engine with a range of approximately 500 miles (800 km). The absence of a nuclear or other "high-tech" engine and fuel supply makes the helicopter inexpensive.

Statistical Data:

Height: 15 feet (4.6 m)

Width: Body: 10 feet (3 m) wide; wingspan: 17 feet, 2 inches (5.23 m); main rotors have a diameter of 50 feet (15.2 m).

Length: 40 feet (12.2 m)

Weight: 8 tons fully loaded.

Cargo: Limited; it can also carry four human-sized passengers or two power armor troops. However, it can haul up to 20 tons suspended underneath it (reduces maximum speed to 80 mph/128.7 km).

Power System: Liquid fuel engine.

CS Cost: 750,000 credits. Ishpeming and Golden Age Armaments both offer a "knock-off" for one million credits, but getting fuel can be difficult.

Weapon Systems:

1. **Nose Mounted Laser (1):** A laser is mounted in the chin of the Coalition Death's Head. It serves as an additional defense and combat measure against the enemy. Although facing forward, the gun can be positioned up and down 30 degrees. Typically controlled by the co-pilot.

Primary Purpose: Anti-Aircraft and Anti-Missile.
Secondary Purpose: Anti-Personnel and Defense.
Mega-Damage: A single blast is 4D6 M.D.
Rate of Fire: Equal to the co-pilot's number of hand to hand attacks.
Effective Range: 3000 feet (910 m)
Payload: Effectively unlimited.

2. **Nose Rail Gun (1):** Controlled by the pilot or the co-pilot/gunner.

Primary Purpose: Anti-Aircraft
Secondary Purpose: Anti-Personnel and Defense.
Mega-Damage: A full damage burst from the rail gun is 40 rounds and inflicts 6D6 M.D.
Maximum Effective Range: 4000 feet (1220 m)
Rate of Fire: Equal to the combined hand to hand attacks of the pilot (usually 4-6).
Payload: 4,000 round drum feed for 100 bursts.

3. **C-33 Weapon Appendage Rail Guns (2 sets):** Two high-powered, gatling gun style rail guns are built into weapon wing on both sides of helicopter. One or both can be fired simultaneously at the same target, however both weapon wings (4 rail guns) cannot be fired in tandem at the same target. They are specifically designed to be anti-aircraft and power armor weapons but are suitable for strafing ground assaults, anti-tanks and for providing cover fire to support infantry troops. The weapon wings are fixed forward.

Primary Purpose: Anti-Aircraft
Secondary Purpose: Anti-Personnel and Defense.

Mega-Damage: A full damage burst from one rail gun is 40 rounds and inflicts 1D6×10 M.D., two guns 2D6×10 M.D. Simultaneous dual bursts on the same target count as one melee attack.
Maximum Effective Range: 4000 feet (1220 m)
Rate of Fire: Equal to the combined hand to hand attacks of the gunner (usually 4-6).
Payload: 2,000 round drum feed for 50 bursts per *each* rail gun; 8,000 rounds (200 bursts) total! Reloading a drum will take about 20 minutes for those not trained, but a mere five minutes by characters with engineering or field armorer skills.

4. **Tube Mini-Missile Launchers (8) on the Weapon Wings:** They can be controlled by the pilot or the co-pilot/gunner. Helicopters assigned to NAC can fire mini-torpedoes.

Primary Purpose: Anti-Armor and Anti-Personnel.
Secondary Purpose: Defense
Mega-Damage: Varies with missile type.
Rate of Fire: One at a time, or volleys of two, three, five, ten or twenty-four.
Effective Range: About one mile (1.6 km)
Payload: 48 total; 24 mini-missiles per launcher.

5. **Features of Note:** Doppler radar bounces a signal off the surface of water or land and measures the frequency shift produced by the relative movement of source and reflector. It can be used to track storms and to compute the helicopter's position.

A winch and hook is used to raise and lower people (especially in rescue operations) or supplies. It can accommodate a maximum weight of 20 tons.

The helicopter also has all the standard sensors and features of most aircraft, such as radar, long and short-range communications, etc.

Demon Locust

Coalition Combat Helicopter

The Demon Locust is a larger, lethal gunship and troop transport. It too is designed by the Coalition State of Iron Heart and introduced as a comparatively inexpensive, multi-function attack aircraft. It is slower than the Black Lightning but has a larger range of weapons, including a long-range laser cannon, a pair of rail guns, and a battery of missiles. It is used for low altitude reconnaissance, rescue, insertion and extraction of ground and sea troops, combat, infantry support, light cargo hauling, and defense.

Model Type: CH-12
Class: Helicopter Gunship and Troop Transport.
Crew: Four: Pilot, co-pilot/gunner, communications technician and a secondary gunner. It can also carry a full squad (10) of human-sized troops or five power armor soldiers.
M.D.C. by Location:
Four-Blade Top Rotors — 120 (30 each blade)
* Forward Laser Cannon Turret (1) — 100
* Nose Sensors (2) — 25 each
* Wing Rail Guns (2; one per wing) — 40 each
* Mini-Missile Tube Launchers (6; three per wing) — 40 each

Weapon/Missile Wings (2) — 100 each
Retractable Landing Gear (1 set) — 30
Reinforced Pilots' Compartment — 110
** Main Body — 250

Speed:

Ground: Not possible.

Flying: The Demon Locust can hover stationary, VTOL, and travel at a maximum flight speeds of 250 mph (400 km). Cruising and attack speed vary, but tend to be between 100 and 200 mph (160 to 329 km) and it has excellent VTOL capabilities.

Altitude: A maximum ceiling (altitude) of 20,000 feet (6096 m). Combat height (the height in which air to ground attacks are possible): 3000 feet (910 m).

Range: Liquid fuel engine with a range of approximately 700 miles (1120 km; extra large fuel tanks). The absence of a nuclear or other "high-tech" engine and fuel supply makes the helicopter inexpensive.

Statistical Data:

Height: 20 feet (6 m)

Width: Body: 12 feet (3.6 m) wide; wing span: 22 feet (6.7 m); main rotors have a diameter of 60 feet (18.3 m).

Length: 65 feet (19.8 m)

Weight: 19 tons fully loaded

Cargo: Limited; enough room to add ten passengers or equivalent cargo.

Power System: Liquid fuel.

CS Cost: 925,000 credits. Ishpeming and Golden Age Arma-

ments both offer a "knock-off" for 1.3 million credits, but getting fuel can be difficult.

Weapon Systems:

1. Forward Mounted Laser Cannon (1): A laser cannon is mounted in a turret under the Coalition Death's Head. It can rotate 360 degrees and has a 180 degree arc of fire. Typically controlled by the co-pilot.

Primary Purpose: Anti-Aircraft and Anti-Armor.

Secondary Purpose: Anti-Personnel and Defense.

Mega-Damage: A single blast does 1D4×10 M.D.

Rate of Fire: Equal to the co-pilot's number of hand to hand attacks.

Effective Range: 4000 feet (1200 m)

Payload: Effectively unlimited.

2. Nose Rail Gun (1): Controlled by the pilot or the co-pilot/gunner.

Primary Purpose: Anti-Aircraft

Secondary Purpose: Anti-Personnel and Defense.

Mega-Damage: A full damage burst from the rail gun is 40 rounds and inflicts 6D6 M.D.

Maximum Effective Range: 4000 feet (1220 m)

Rate of Fire: Equal to the combined hand to hand attacks of the pilot (usually 4-6).

Payload: 4,000 round drum feed for 100 bursts.

3. Wing Rail Guns (2): Controlled by a gunner.

Primary Purpose: Anti-Aircraft

Secondary Purpose: Anti-Personnel and Defense.

Mega-Damage: A full damage burst from one rail gun is 40 rounds and inflicts 1D4×10 M.D.

Maximum Effective Range: 4000 feet (1220 m)

Rate of Fire: Equal to the combined hand to hand attacks of the pilot (usually 4-6).

Payload: 6,000 round drum feed for 150 bursts per each of the two wing guns; 12,000 rounds and 300 bursts total.

4. Tube Mini-Missile Launchers (6) on the Weapon Wings: They are controlled by a gunner. Helicopters assigned to NAC can fire mini-torpedoes.

Primary Purpose: Anti-Armor and Anti-Personnel.

Secondary Purpose: Defense

Mega-Damage: Varies with missile type.

Rate of Fire: One at a time, or volleys of two, three, four or five.

Effective Range: About one mile (1.6 km)

Payload: 60 total; 10 mini-missiles per each of the six launchers.

5. Medium-Range Missile Launchers (4): Built into the weapon wings are heavy missiles used against tanks, robots, large aircraft and ground targets. They can be launched by the co-pilot/gunner or a gunner. Torpedoes can be substituted for missiles.

Primary Purpose: Anti-Armor and Anti-Ship.

Secondary Purpose: Anti-Aircraft and Defense.

Mega-Damage: Varies with missile type; often cruise missiles.

Rate of Fire: One at a time, or in volleys of two or four.

Effective Range: About 50 miles (80 km).

Payload: Eight; four per wing launch unit.

6. Features of Note: Doppler radar bounces a signal off the surface of water or land and measures the frequency shift produced by the relative movement of source and reflector. It can be used to track storms and to compute the helicopter's position.

A winch and hook is used to raise and lower people (especially in rescue operations) or supplies. It can accommodate a maximum weight of 20 tons.

The helicopter also has all the standard sensors and features of most aircraft, such as radar, long and short-range communications, etc.

SF-7 CS Talon

Stealth VTOL Jet Fighter

The Talon is a pre-Rifts supersonic, stealth jet fighter recently put into manufacture by the Coalition State of Iron Heart. The aircraft's Vertical Take-Off and Landing (VTOL) capabilities makes it ideal for horizontal launching from the roof hangar of a fortified super-city or underground bunker. Since it doesn't need an airstrip to land and take-off, the Talon can land in small clearings, aboard the decks of suitably large ships, and even on the flat rooftops of sturdy buildings. **Note:** There may be a risk of the roof caving in (1-61% chance) unless the building is a large mega-damage structure or built to accommodate helicopters or giant robots. The aircraft can take off and land on any flat surface more than 40 feet (12.2 m) in diameter, but cannot hover and fly at low speeds; it is a jet. Thus, it can only hover when the VTOL system has been engaged, and then only for the purpose of landing or taking off.

The Talon's low profile, shape and stealth systems enables it to slip through enemy radar even at medium to high altitudes. Its cargo of missiles can unleash a deadly barrage against the unsuspecting enemy.

The Talon has a reinforced pilot's compartment and ejection system to protect the pilot and crew or passengers (maximum two human-sized people). The entire compartment can be jettisoned and safely parachute to the ground or water below — the compartment has a flotation device. A distress signal automatically activates four minutes after the pilot has been ejected. The signal device can transmit non-stop for one week — longer if shut off and on at intervals rather than constant transmission. The radio is also likely to remain intact (1-79% chance) and can also transmit for about a week before the battery goes dead (50 mile/80 km range; directional transmitter and receiver). A small first-aid kit, one gallon of drinking water, a survival knife, and a signal flare gun with four flares is stowed under the pilot's seat.

SF-7 CS Talon Stealth VTOL Jet Fighter

Model Type: SF-7 Stealth Combat Aircraft

Class: Fighter Jet

Crew: One, with seats for two additional crew members; typically a bombardier and communications officer.

M.D.C. by Location:

* Concealed Forward Mounted Laser Guns (2; nose) — 40 each

Belly Mounted Long-Range Missile Launcher (1) — 50

Belly Mounted Mini-Missile Launchers (2) — 60 each

* Top Mini-Missile Launchers (4) — 50 each

Bomb Bay Style Belly Hatch (1; for cargo) — 80

Large Wings (2) — 200 each

* Small Tail Fins (2) — 90 each

Main Jets (2; rear) — 150 each

** Main Body — 350

Reinforced Pilot's Compartment — 120

* Every item marked by a single asterisk is small and/or difficult to strike. An attacker must make a "called shot" to hit and even then he is -4 to strike.

** Destroying the main body knocks the aircraft out of the sky and turns it into smoldering wreckage.

Destroying one of the small, tail fins reduces speed by 5% and piloting skill is -10% on all maneuvers. Destroying both small fins reduces speed by 25% and the piloting skill is -20%.

Destroying one of the large, main wings (and one of the VTOL engines) will send the aircraft into a spin and rocketing to earth. VTOL is impossible. The jet will crash and the pilot and passengers killed unless they are ejected. The crash causes 2D4×100 M.D. to a 300 foot (91 m) radius. Nothing is salvageable from the wreckage.

Breaux

Speed:

Driving on the ground: Only possible for conventional take-off and landing, as well as parking/storage.

Flying: The jet propulsion system enables the Talon to reach a maximum speed of Mach 1.5 (1005 mph/1608) and climb to an altitude of 60,000 feet (18,288 m). The jet has a minimum glide-speed of 60 mph (96 km); if it goes any slower, it may stall completely and crash, unless engaged in VTOL. Cruising speed tends to be between 250 mph (400 km) and Mach One (675 mph/1080 km). Attack speed can range from 250 mph (400 km) to Mach 1.5 against ground targets and maximum speed against aerial adversaries. Ground attacks can involve launching missiles or strafing runs.

Range: Nuclear powered, giving it continual energy, but the jet engines begin to overheat after 18 hours of continual use. Occasional rest stops every four to six hours, giving the engines an hour to cool down, will enable the aircraft to fly at intervals for months without trouble.

Statistical Data:

Height: 18 feet (5.48 m) with landing pads out, 14 feet (4.3 m) airborne/with landing gear retracted.

Width: Wingspan is 65 feet (19.8 m)

Length: 30 feet (9 m)

Weight: 16 tons empty, 22 tons fully loaded.

Cargo: None, other than the seating for two behind the pilot, which can be used for storage when not occupied.

Power System: Nuclear with a 20 year life.

Features of Note: Equipped with ejection, parachute and flotation devices (described above), as well as a self-destruct system that can be activated by the pilot or automatically engages five minutes after emergency ejection or impact, whichever comes first.

CS Cost: Top secret, but estimated to be 70-100 million credits. This aircraft has only just been unveiled; there are no knock-offs. Note: The Talon is an experimental aircraft that is being planned for use against Tolkeen and the Xiticix. Only one Air Wing, made up of 30 jets, is in existence and operating out of the state of Chi-Town.

Weapon Systems

1. **Belly Mounted Long-Range Missile Launcher (1):** Recessed in the belly of the Talon is a long-range missile launcher.

Primary Purpose: Strategic strikes against land structures, i.e. enemy bunkers and installations.

Secondary Purpose: Anti-Aircraft and Anti-Armor.

Mega-Damage: Varies with missile type; heavy weapons are standard.

Rate of Fire: One at a time or volleys of two.

Effective Range: Varies with missile type.

Payload: 6 total.

2. **Mini-Missile Launchers (2):** Recessed in the belly of the jet are a pair of mini-missile launchers. Mini-missiles are used because they are much more precise than "dropped" bombs, have good range (one mile/1.6 km), reasonably good damage capacity (especially when launched in volleys of eight or more) and can be used with precision to strike a specific target as small as a man! Furthermore, the jet can carry a much larger payload of these small missiles.

Primary Purpose: Strategic Strikes

Secondary Purpose: Anti-Aircraft and Anti-Personnel.

Mega-Damage: Varies per mini-missile type.

Rate of Fire: Volleys equal to the total number of hand to hand attacks per melee. One volley regardless of the number of missiles, counts as one melee attack. Belly mini-missiles are launched against specific military targets in volleys of 4, 8, 12 or 24

Effective Range: About one mile (1.6 km).

Payload: 150 total; 75 per launcher.

3. **Top Mini-Missile Launchers (4):** The two circular indications on the main body of the jet, located on either side of the jagged fins, are a pair of mini-missile launchers. The cover plate slides away and the missiles are ready to fire. These are primarily used against other aircraft and enemy missiles but can also be used against ground targets when the belly launchers are empty (dangerous because it leaves the jet practically defenseless).

Primary Purpose: Anti-Aircraft and Anti-Missile.

Secondary Purpose: Strategic Strikes

Mega-Damage: Varies per mini-missile type.

Rate of Fire: One at a time or in volleys of two or five.

Effective Range: About one mile (1.6 km).

Payload: 100 total; 25 per each of the four launchers.

4. **Concealed Forward Mounted Lasers (2):** A laser is mounted on each side of the nose. It serves as the last line of defense against enemy planes and missile volleys, although some pilots use it for strafing runs against ground targets. Although facing forward, the guns can be positioned up and down 30 degrees.

Primary Purpose: Anti-Aircraft and Anti-Missile.

Secondary Purpose: Anti-Personnel and Defense.

Mega-Damage: A single blast is 3D6 M.D., or a simultaneous dual blast does 6D6 M.D.

Rate of Fire: Equal the pilot's number of hand to hand attacks.

Effective Range: 4000 feet (1220 m)

Payload: Effectively unlimited.

5. **Sensors:** Has all the standard robot sensors and systems as well as enhanced Doppler radar (can identify and simultaneously track up to 96 different targets. Range: 200 miles).

Special Bonuses: +2 to dodge when flying at cruising speeds and +4 to dodge when flying at or over Mach One.

Coalition Police & Law Enforcement

By Kevin Siembieda with ideas and text by Julius Rosenstein and Patrick Nowak.

The ISS Organization

Internal Security Specialists (ISS)

ISS Division:

ISS Inspectors: Effectively a combination Police & FBI.

Net-Set (NTSET): Monster hunters and exterminators.

Psi-Net (PRP): Enforcers of the PRP laws and control of psychic activities.

Law enforcement and internal security for the cities, towns and communities of the Coalition States rest in the capable hands of well-trained and highly motivated individuals known as *ISS Inspectors*. They operate under the auspices of the organization known as **Internal Security Specialists (ISS)**, or the ISS subdivisions: *NTSET* or *Psi-Net*. These lawmen have the formal title of "inspector," but on the street they are often referred to as "specters," as in superhuman ghosts who step out of the darkness to apprehend their prey. The term "specter" is especially common among LL's/Low Levelers, Grungers (the lowliest LL's), City Rats, street gangs, criminals, and "Rejects" (the inhabitants of the 'Burbs). ISS Inspectors actually like the moody and fear inspiring name, and have cultivated the image of being tough, shadowy figures lurking in the background and appearing from nowhere to deal out justice to wrongdoers.

The operations of the ISS include civilian police and internal city security. They are not the military, although they function under a military structure of command and wear the old CS "Dead Boy" armor. The ISS differs from the military in a few regards. First, the military is largely a reactionary force — meaning they respond accordingly to any immediate danger from outside the Coalition Territories. Second, the military deals primarily with "foreign" enemies and military objectives outside the allied States. They are not involved in the day to day routine of urban life or law enforcement. The military becomes involved in internal, domestic/city affairs only when called upon to *assist* in serious crisis situations beyond the range of the ISS. Such a crisis can include an attack leveled against a city from invading forces, unusual or extreme acts of terrorism, dimensional raiders who have penetrated the city (a rarity), or a legion of supernatural creatures (or one mega-powerful one) that the ISS, NTSET or Psi-Net has been unable to handle and continue to wreak havoc in the city (also a rarity).

Unless clearly a military situation, like an all-out attack, or enemy encroachment of its border, a city must *invite* the military to participate in peacekeeping or internal security. Military forces can only be called into a city by Emperor Prosek (for any

ISS Inspectors in the Coalition States are found primarily at large established towns, cities and fortified super-cities, like Chi-Town. The military handles most matters in the surrounding villages, small towns, farms, outlying wilderness and border communities, as well as military duty beyond the Coalition States. The CS military and the ISS both have a presence in the no-man's zones known as the 'Burbs.

The official duties of the ISS Inspectors are enforcing the law and protecting the citizens from criminals, terrorists, magic, non-humans and the supernatural. They also engage in "preventative measures" against insurrection and unrest among the populace. Thus, they are ever vigilant for rogue scholars, rogue scientists, practitioners of magic, subversives, terrorists, cyber-snatchers, and criminals of all kind.

"Preventative measures" usually involve covert surveillance and investigations of suspected spies and criminals, including citizens and visitors *suspected* of being subversives, magic users or inhuman, or involved with *Enemies of the State* — a broad range of felons from unauthorized educators, historians and rogue scientists, to practitioners of magic, D-Bees and super-natural monsters. In order to do their job, they are given the authority to engage in surveillance, tailing, and wiretaps, freedom of search and seizure of property, freedom to secretly enter and search a citizen's home or business, and to hold and question suspects for 72 hours without hard evidence — suspicion or pure malice are frequently enough to warrant any of these things. Often, the techniques and tactics used by ISS Specters border on the level of "James Bond" or "Mission Impossible." Police brutality and harassment are common.

Despite its fascist mentality and harsh practices, the ISS uses astonishing restraint, common sense, and hospitality when dealing with the *average citizen*. Those known to be criminals or traitors suffer the brunt of their ire. This is due in part to the fact that most ISS Inspectors believe the endless propaganda and hype that paint them as the people's champions. However, it is due in larger part to the ISS Inspectors' genuine and sincere dedication to protecting and defending the *human citizens*, and humans in general. Most of the men, women and Dog Packs serving the ISS, NTSET and PRP are public servants who routinely lay down their lives to protect John Q Citizen. In fact, the average citizen, even the poorest on the lowest levels of the great walled cities, regard the ISS Inspectors and their Psi-Division sister branch (PRP) as courageous and trustworthy heroes! The average CS citizen does not hesitate to turn to them for protection or comfort in any matters dealing with crime or security. Furthermore, most are quick to cooperate and eager to help defend against demonic monsters, insane wizards and dangerous minds (rogue scholars and other "subversives"). They do so not out of fear, but loyalty to their protectors and the government who preserves their (comparatively) idyllic life.

The ISS value human life above all else, but can be particularly harsh with humans they believe are involved in the most heinous crimes. These include *murder* of a fellow human, *cyber-snatching* (gang members that attack people with cybernetic or bionic body parts and chop them out of the still living victim; maiming or killing their victims for the valuable hardware), *the practice/teaching/smuggling/use of magic or magic items, acts of terrorism, dissident activities* (those who speak out or act against the CS, ISS or Emperor Prosek), *humans who consort with* the

reason), the regional head of the ISS, the regional Governor, or the city High-Mayor, but the latter three can only do so under an emergency petition in response to a clear and present danger. The military has no "official" jurisdiction in the cities or any domestic affairs.

supernatural/demonic, magic users, D-bees and outlaws/subversives and those branded as criminals of the State, like Erin Tarn.

Non-humans and humans involved with D-bees, the supernatural/demonic, and magic, especially those caught illegally inside the city, are treated with extreme prejudice and suffer terrible beatings, physical and psychological torture, harassment, endangerment, and murder. The ISS and all branches of CS law enforcement and the military are authorized to use whatever level of force the individual officer(s) believes necessary in dealing with these dangerous criminals.

Practitioners of magic, psychics without Identification Coding (IC) and registration, and **unregistered cyborgs** (partial and full conversion, including Headhunters), **Crazies,** and **Juicers** are *always* considered "armed and dangerous" regardless of the circumstances; even if the character lays down his weapons and surrenders. Consequently, "deadly force" is not only recommended but strongly encouraged, particularly in an urban setting where innocent human lives may be in jeopardy. This policy, often referred to as the "better safe than sorry" policy, may seem like an excuse to commit murder and typical of the extreme measures taken by the CS, but it is actually reasonable and sound. The perpetrators listed above possess powers and abilities that are not evident from just looking at them. Often these superhuman abilities and/or concealed weapons are incredibly powerful and deadly. As a result, an adversary may seem completely docile or even helpless one instant and become a murderous dynamo the next. Thus, it is wise to view such augmented and magical beings as "armed and dangerous," even when they appear to be cooperative or incapacitated. Many an ISS inspector, Net Set and PRP officer has been attacked, injured and slain by a magic wielding or augmented human who seemed helpless.

Supernatural and demonic beings (including many monstrous *looking* D-bees) are regarded with even greater concern and levels of lethality. When dealing with these menaces, the ISS, NTSET, PRP and the military usually take a "shoot first, kill it, and ask questions later" policy. Considering how humancentric and alien-phobic the CS authorities are (and citizens in general), this is one policy eagerly accepted by all of its police and armed forces. "Better dead than breathing," "too much force is never enough," and "atomize it to be sure," are three common cliches used by front-line troops and ISS Inspectors specializing in dealing with magic and the supernatural. Every veteran who has faced the supernatural or magically empowered has stories about the seemingly dead, near dead and occasionally, even the obliterated, coming back to life and retaliating with bloody vengeance. "Sometimes you can't be sure these things are dead unless you've sprayed their atoms to the winds."

The ISS are well trained and specially equipped for dealing with superhumans (Juicers, Crazies, 'Borgs, etc.), psychics, D-bees, demons and supernatural monsters. However, it is the **NTSET** and sometimes the **PRP Psi-Net Divisions,** that are usually assigned the task of hunting down, sniffing out and destroying psionic, magic and/or supernatural horrors. Meanwhile, the ISS Inspector deals with the more routine affairs and criminals of urban life. In addition to their crime-busting and law enforcement activities they spend a lot of time searching out rebels, criminals, traitors, and other threats to the survival of the Coalition States, and thus to the survival of the human race.

Specters are not restricted in the methods that they may use to deal with enemies of the Coalition. Indeed, they are highly rewarded for creativity in their pursuit of dangerous criminals. This attitude, in turn, fuels the mystique that the inspectors have established for themselves.

There are three major functions in the operation of the Internal Security Specialists:

1. Peacekeeping (ISS Police)
2. Civil law enforcement (ISS Specter/Detective)
3. Intelligence & Internal Security (ISS Intelligence/FBI)

NTSET and Psi-Net/PRP fall under number three.

All ISS officers get solid, basic training to enable them to perform all three functions, but in addition to the special training of the NTSET and Psi-Net officers, there are some distinctions within the ISS as well.

Law & Order within the ISS

Specters who transgress against ISS regulations are subject to arrest and the not so tender mercies of a full investigation by the ISS, including a psionic scan and possible interrogation by a Psi-Net operative. As a rule, first-time offenders and those with otherwise good records who are accused of minor infractions are generally returned to their own units to face punishment within their own unit; which is usually lenient (dock a day or two wages, a desk job for a week, etc.). Major infractions and/or perennial offenders are dealt with more severely, and criminal action could be taken against them, leading to a dishonorable discharge from all public service, imprisonment and even execution. The ISS can be extremely tough on those who tarnish their good name and reputation, or consort with monstrous nonhumans. Many such characters fall victim to ISS "street justice" before any court gets them. Such extreme justice dealt out to "their own" results in a mysterious disappearance (killed) or a lethal accident, ideally set up to redeem his name (such as running into a burning building or the jaws of a monster to save a fellow officer or citizen). ISS officers have no tolerance for traitors within their ranks.

ISS Peacekeeper O.C.C.

Peacekeepers are the tough, streetwise beat cops and city defenders. ISS police clad in old style, "Dead Boy" body armor or SAMAS power armor who have a regular presence on the street and in the community. They break up fights, direct traffic, keep an eye out for crooks and monsters, rush to the rescue on a Sky Cycle and diligently protect people and institutions from the criminal element and monsters. They are highly visible and provide a show of strength to give the people a sense of security and keep the peace on a day to day basis. Their skills focus on combat, riot control and public relations. When the commission of a crime requires extensive investigation, that task goes to the Inspectors. This relationship is analogous to the police departments of pre-Rifts times where undercover officers and plainclothes detectives ("Inspectors") would handle the assignments that the uniformed officers ("Peacekeepers") could not.

Attribute Requirements: I.Q. and M.E. 9, and P.S. 10 or higher. High physical attributes or psionics are desirable but not mandatory.

O.C.C. Bonuses: +1 on initiative at levels 1, 3, 7, 10 and 14. +1 to save vs magic illusion and mind control and +2 to save vs horror factor at levels 2, 4, 7, 10, 12 and 15.

Investigation (Special): This is the training in techniques, principles, and theories of investigation, such as how to look for and recognize clues by systematically examining details with care and accuracy, observation, and research. Investigative techniques can be applied to environments, events, evidence, the spoken word, and body language. A character with this skill is more likely to remember details and locate hidden compartments. **Base skill:** 25%+5%/level. **Note:** Adds a bonus of +5% to the following skills: forensics, pathology and *recognizing* forgeries.

O.C.C. Skills:

Mathematics: Basic (+20%)
Radio: Basic (+15%)
Streetwise (+20%)
Find Contraband, Weapons & Cybernetics (+10%)
Interrogation Techniques (+10%)
Intelligence (+15%)
Recognize Weapon Quality (+12%)
Literacy (+10%)
Lore: Demon & Monsters (+10%)
Lore: Magic (+10%)
Pilot Hovercraft (+10%)
Pilot: Robots & Power Armor: Basic
Pilot: Robot Combat Elite: SAMAS
Wrestling or Boxing (player's choice)
W.P. Blunt
W.P. Energy Pistol
W.P. Energy Rifle
Hand to Hand: Expert
Hand to hand: expert can be changed to martial arts (or assassin if evil) at the cost of one O.C.C. Related Skill.

O.C.C. Related Skills: Select four skills from one of the following areas of special training: Communications, Electronics, Mechanical, Military, Piloting, Rogue or Technical — all of these special MOS-type skills are areas of specialty and get a +10% skill bonus. Three other skills can also be selected from any of the available categories at level one, and two additional skills at levels four, eight and twelve.

Communications: Any (+10%)
Domestic: Any
Electrical: Any
Espionage: Any
Mechanical: None unless selected as an MOS.
Medical: Paramedic (+5%) only, unless selected as an MOS.
Military: None, other than O.C.C. skills.
 Physical: Any
Pilot: Any (+5%)
Pilot Related: Any
Rogue: Any (+4%)
Science: Advanced Math only (+15%), unless selected as an MOS.
Technical: Any (+10%; all human Specters are Literate)
W.P.: Any

Wilderness: None

Secondary Skills: The character gets four secondary skills at level one, and one additional at levels three, seven, and ten. These are additional areas of knowledge that do not get the advantage of the bonus listed in parentheses. All secondary skills start at the base skill level. Also, skills are limited (any, only, none) as previously indicated in the list.

Standard Equipment: Old style Coalition "Dead Boy" body armor, energy rifle and energy sidearm of choice, four extra E-clips for each, neuro-mace, vibro-knife or saber, silver plated survival knife, nightstick, four tear gas grenades, two flash grenades, two flares, silver cross, six wooden stakes and a small mallet, robot medical kit, pocket laser distancer, portable language translator, two sets of handcuffs, utility belt, air filter & gas mask, uniform, dress uniform.

Equipment Available Upon Assignment: Special body armor including military issue (special request for extraordinary circumstances), access to explosive ordnance (rifle grenades, mini-missiles, hand grenades, etc.) if necessary for the mission, any types of weapon, extra ammunition, optical enhancements, sensory equipment, camera, recording and surveillance equipment, electro-adhesive pads, automatic lock pin release gun, and other items. Non-regulation (including military) weapons, armor, equipment and vehicles may also be issued depending on the situation. Plus the Peacekeeper has access to ISS computers and data files, department offices, shooting range, and other facilities.

Vehicles are usually limited to a simple motorcycle, hover cycle, or hover patrol car. Occasionally, power armor and robot vehicles. **Note:** Due to their special status, peacekeepers may commandeer virtually anything that aids in the pursuit of criminals/terrorists. Also, many peacekeepers on undercover or infiltration assignments may be issued special equipment for that specific assignment.

Most human ISS Peacekeepers have medium to high level security clearances while experienced and trusted veterans will have top clearance.

Money: The ISS Peacekeeper is *provided* with a nice, five room apartment (on levels 12-20 in the fortified super-cities; no charge), full medical benefits (including cybernetic prosthetics and bio-systems), as well as access to ISS, NTSET and PRP facilities. His monthly salary is 4200 credits. The character starts off with 3D4x1000 credits.

Cybernetics: Clock calendar to start with, but implantation of cybernetic and bionics may be awarded for exemplary service and heroics or when necessary to fix an injury. 25% of the human Peacekeepers have had necessary cybernetic corrective surgery or minor implants. **Note:** Many city law enforcers will have the letters "CPD," which means City Police Department, stenciled on their armor, jackets, or on the pocket of their shirt. The letters "ISS" are also likely to appear someplace on the armor or uniform, and occasionally in place of "CPD."

ISS Specter O.C.C.

ISS Inspectors or "Specters" are basically *police detectives* responsible for the investigation and prevention of crimes, and activity involving nonhumans and magic. They examine the crime

gal operations, body-chop-shops, cyber-snatchers, and investigate subversives and bring to justice the perpetrators of robbery, murder, extortion, kidnapping, smuggling, and other crimes. They are streetwise and constantly keep an eye out for trouble and suspicious activity, especially evidence of "unnatural" activity. When engaging in an investigation that might involve magic, psionics or the supernatural, they may consult or work jointly with a NTSET operative or Psi-Net Inspector. NTSET and Psi-Net are all members of the ISS umbrella organization and work well together, sharing information and resources.

Attribute Requirements: I.Q. and M.E. 11 or higher. High physical attributes or psionics are desirable but not mandatory.

O.C.C. Bonuses: +1 on initiative at levels 1, 3, 8, and 12. +1 to save vs magic illusion and mind control, +1 to save vs possession, +1 to save vs horror factor at levels 2, 4, 7, 10, 12 and 15.

Investigation (Special): This is the training in techniques, principles, and theories of investigation, such as how to look for and recognize clues by systematically examining details with care and accuracy, observation, and research. Investigative techniques can be applied to environments, events, evidence, the spoken word, and body language. A character with this skill is more likely to remember details and locate hidden compartments. **Base skill:** 40%+5%/level. **Note:** Adds a bonus of +5% to the following skills: forensics, pathology and *recognizing* forgeries.

O.C.C. Skills:

Mathematics: Basic (+20%)
Radio: Basic (+15%)
Streetwise (+14%)
Find Contraband, Weapons & Cybernetics (+14%)
Interrogation Techniques (+20%)
Intelligence (+15%)
Surveillance Systems (+15%)
Recognize Weapon Quality (+10%)
Literacy (+20%)
Lore: Demon & Monsters (+15%)
Lore: Magic (+10%)
Pilot Hovercraft (+5%)
Pilot: Robots & Power Armor: Basic
Escape Artist (+15%)
Wrestling
W.P. Blunt
W.P. Energy Pistol
W.P. Energy Rifle
Hand to Hand: Martial Arts (or Assassin if evil)

O.C.C. Related Skills: Select four skills from one of the following areas of special training: Communications, Electronics, Espionage, Mechanical, Medical (typically crime sciences), Piloting, Science or Technical — all of these special MOS-type skills are areas of specialty and get a +15% skill bonus. Four other skills can also be selected from any of the available categories at level one, and two additional skills at levels four, eight and twelve.

Communications: Any (+10%)
Domestic: Any
Electrical: Any
Espionage: Any
Mechanical: None unless selected as an MOS
Medical: Paramedic (+5%) only, unless selected as an MOS.

scene, interrogate witnesses, gather evidence and do all the other things expected from a detective. They may do their duty in full armor, uniform, or undercover in plain clothes. The Specters are also usually the law officers who go undercover to break up ille-

Military: None, other than O.C.C. skills.
 Physical: Any
Pilot: Any (+5%)
Pilot Related: Any
Rogue: Any
Science: Advanced Math only (+15%), unless selected as an MOS.
Technical: Any (+10%; all human Specters are Literate)
W.P.: Any   Wilderness: None

Secondary Skills: The character gets four secondary skills at level one, and one additional at levels three, seven, and ten. These are additional areas of knowledge that do not get the advantage of the bonus listed in parentheses. All secondary skills start at the base skill level. Also, skills are limited (any, only, none) as previously indicated in the list.

Standard Equipment: Old style Coalition "Dead Boy" body armor, energy rifle and energy sidearm of choice, four extra E-clips for each, neuro-mace, vibro-knife or saber, silver plated survival knife, nightstick, four tear gas grenades, two flash grenades, two flares, silver cross, six wooden stakes and a small mallet, robot medical kit, pocket laser distancer, portable language translator, two sets of handcuffs, utility belt, air filter & gas mask, uniform, dress uniform.

Equipment Available Upon Assignment: Special body armor, including military issue (special request for extraordinary circumstances), access to explosive ordnance (rifle grenades, mini-missiles, hand grenades, etc.) if necessary for the mission, any types of weapon, extra ammunition, optical enhancements, sensory equipment, camera, recording and surveillance equipment, electro-adhesive pads, automatic lock pin release gun, and other items. Non-regulation (including military) weapons, armor, equipment and vehicles may also be issued depending on the situation. Plus the Inspector has access to ISS computers and data files, department offices, shooting range, and other facilities.

Vehicles are usually limited to a simple motorcycle, hover cycle, or hover patrol car, occasionally, power armor and robot vehicles. **Note:** Due to their special status, inspectors may commandeer virtually anything that aids in the pursuit of criminals/terrorists. Also, many inspectors on undercover or infiltration assignments may be issued special equipment for that specific assignment.

Most human ISS Inspectors have medium to high level security clearances while experienced and trusted veterans will have top clearance.

Money: The ISS Specter is *provided* with a nice, five room apartment (on levels 12-20 in the fortified super-cities; no charge), full medical benefits (including cybernetic prosthetics and bio-systems), as well as access to ISS, NTSET and PRP facilities. His monthly salary is 4200 credits. The character starts off with 3D4x1000 credits.

Cybernetics: Clock calendar to start with, but implantation of cybernetic and bionics may be awarded for exemplary service and heroics or when necessary to fix an injury. 25% of the human Specters have had necessary cybernetic corrective surgery or minor implants. **Note:** Many city law enforcers will have the letters "CPD," which means City Police Department, stenciled on their armor, jackets, or on the pocket of their shirt. The letters "ISS" are also likely to appear someplace on the armor or uniform, and occasionally in place of "CPD."

Intel Specter

ISS Intelligence Officer

The Department of Intelligence and Internal Security handles most of the espionage and counter-espionage duties for the ISS; they can be thought of as the equivalent to the FBI of 21st Century Earth. Whereas a military specialist will often be assigned to spy outside CS territory, an Intel Specter deals with spying inside the cities and towns, as well as special operations to ferret out, respond and counter underground dissidents, assassins, smugglers, traitors, spies, Black Market operations, terrorism, extortion, kidnapping, and similar. They also keep a sharp eye out for "unnatural" occurrences that suggest the involvement of psionics, magic, alien technology, contraband and the supernatural. The Intel Specter also engages in surveillance operations, sniffing out criminal and subversive groups, rogues and magic users, as well as engaging in sting operations, undercover work and infiltration and spying.

Attribute Requirements: I.Q. and M.E. 14 or higher. High physical attributes or psionics are desirable but not mandatory.

O.C.C. Bonuses: +1 on initiative at levels 1, 4 and 9. +1 to save vs magic illusion and mind control, +1 to save vs possession and 12. +2 to save vs horror factor at levels 2, 4, 7, 10, 12 and 15.

Investigation (Special): This is the training in techniques, principles, and theories of investigation, such as how to look for and recognize clues by systematically examining details with care and accuracy, observation, and research. Investigative techniques can be applied to environments, events, evidence, the spoken word, and body language. A character with this skill is more likely to remember details and locate hidden compartments. **Base skill:** 45%+5%/level. **Note:** Adds a bonus of +5% to the following skills: forensics, pathology and *recognizing* forgeries.

O.C.C. Skills:
Mathematics: Basic (+20%)
Radio: Basic (+15%)
Optic Systems (+20%)
TV & Video (+20%)
Surveillance Systems (+20%)
Disguise (+15%)
Forgery (+10% to recognize forgery)
Streetwise (+16%)
Find Contraband, Weapons & Cybernetics (+16%)
Interrogation Techniques (+20%)
Intelligence (+20%)
Literacy (+20%)
Lore: Demon & Monsters (+10%)
Lore: Magic (+10%)
Pilot: Robots & Power Armor: Basic
Pilot Hovercraft (+5%)
W.P. Blunt
W.P. Energy Pistol
W.P. Energy Rifle
Hand to Hand: Martial Arts (or Assassin if evil)

O.C.C. Related Skills: Select four skills from one of the following areas of special training: Communications, Electronics,

Espionage, Mechanical, Medical (typically crime sciences), Military, Piloting, Science, Technical, Rogue — all of these special MOS-type skills are areas of specialty and get a +15% skill bonus. Four other skills can also be selected from any of the available categories at level one, and two additional skills at levels four, eight and twelve.

Communications: Any (+10%)
Domestic: Any
Electrical: Any
Espionage: Any
Mechanical: None unless selected as an MOS
Medical: Paramedic (+5%) only, unless selected as an MOS.
Military: None, other than O.C.C. skills.
 Physical: Any
Pilot: Any (+10%)
Pilot Related: Any
Rogue: Any
Science: Advanced Math only (+15%), unless selected as an MOS.
Technical: Any (+10%; all human Specters are Literate)
W.P.: Any
Wilderness: None

Secondary Skills: The character gets four secondary skills at level one, and one additional at levels three, seven, and ten. These are additional areas of knowledge that do not get the advantage of the bonus listed in parentheses. All secondary skills start at the base skill level. Also, skills are limited (any, only, none) as previously indicated in the list.

Standard Equipment: Plain clothes, old style Coalition "Dead Boy" body armor, energy rifle and energy sidearm of choice, four extra E-clips for each, neuro-mace, vibro-knife or saber, silver plated survival knife, nightstick, four tear gas grenades, two flash grenades, two flares, silver cross, six wooden stakes and a small mallet, robot medical kit, pocket laser distancer, portable language translator, two sets of handcuffs, utility belt, air filter & gas mask, uniform, dress uniform.

Equipment Available Upon Assignment: Special body armor including military issue (special request for extraordinary circumstances), access to explosive ordnance (rifle grenades, mini-missiles, hand grenades, etc.) if necessary for the mission, any types of weapons, extra ammunition, disguises, optical enhancements, sensory equipment, camera, recording and surveillance equipment, electro-adhesive pads, automatic lock pin release gun, and other items. Non-regulation (including military) weapons, armor, equipment and vehicles may also be issued depending on the situation. Plus the Inspector has access to ISS computers and data files, department offices, shooting range, and other facilities.

Vehicles are usually limited to a simple motorcycle, hover cycle, or hover patrol car. Occasionally, power armor and robot vehicles. **Note:** Due to their special status, inspectors may commandeer virtually anything that aids in the pursuit of criminals/terrorists. Also, many inspectors on undercover or infiltration assignments may be issued special equipment for that specific assignment.

Most human ISS Inspectors have medium to high level security clearances while experienced and trusted veterans will have top clearance.

Money: The ISS Specter is *provided* with a nice, five room apartment (on levels 12-20 in the fortified super-cities; no charge), full medical benefits (including cybernetic prosthetics and bio-systems), as well as access to ISS, NTSET and PRP facilities. His monthly salary is 4200 credits. The character starts off with 3D4x1000 credits.

Cybernetics: Clock calendar and headjack with augmented hearing to start with, but implantation of cybernetic and bionics may be awarded for exemplary service and heroics or when necessary to fix an injury. 25% of the human Specters have had necessary cybernetic corrective surgery or minor implants. 30% have a Type AB-2 or AA-1 cyber-disguise (player's choice if allowed by G.M.). **Note:** Many city law enforcers will have the letters "CPD," which means City Police Department, stenciled on their armor, jackets, or on the pocket of their shirt. The letters "ISS" are also likely to appear someplace on the armor or uniform, and occasionally in place of "CPD."

"Net Set" Operatives

"Crazy Cavanaugh" made his way silently through the maze of pipes that lined the passageway. The smell of mildew, mold and corroding metal mixed with something alien. He knew he and his team were closing in on their quarry.

Lt. Cavanaugh was a Chi-Town "city cop" who loved his work. As a specialist in the **Nonhuman Tactical Strike and Eradication Team (NTSET;** a.k.a. "Net Set" — LL's/Downsiders, Rejects, Grungers and City Rats called them the "Nut Set," or "Nut Set Specters"). His job was simple, to protect the city and its people.

As a cop charged with keeping the city safe from monsters, he wasn't faced with the moral ambiguity of troops in the field of combat. He knew his enemies and eradicated them without doubt or hesitation. If they weren't human, they were the enemy. Nonhumans weren't allowed (didn't belong) in the city. Crazy Cavanaugh didn't really make the distinction between the subtleies ascribed to them by titles like D-bee, alien, mutant, demon, shapechanger, werebeast, and supernatural being. They were all just "monsters" to him. An inhuman enemy, invader, predator or destroyer that didn't belong in "his" city.

Sure, Chi-Town had its share of human kooks, hoodlums, gang-bangers and criminals, but all and all, the fortified city was a safe place — a good place to live. The real danger (to his thinking) came from sorcerers and monsters. Tracking and eliminating the inhuman threat was his specialty. Even with the incredible security measures, scanners, psychics and Dog Packs, sorcerers, D-bees, mutants and supernatural monstrosities still manage to find their way into the city. Not surprising, really. Rifts and magic made just about anything possible. No place in the world was completely safe or impregnable. In fact, Chi-Town and the other CS super-cities were about as safe and secure as humanly possible. He chuckled to himself about his choice of words, "humanly possible"; yeah, humans weren't the problem.

Crazy Cavanaugh had seen it all. Psionic masters who used their mind powers to make Sentries "see" identification codes, documents and sensor readings that didn't really exist. Practitioners of magic who could teleport or Rift themselves inside the city, bypassing the company of soldiers and security systems at all entrances. Dragons, D-bees and demons who were *shapechangers* were among the boldest and most difficult infiltrators to catch and terminate. But some of the worst were demonic predators, entities, and slobbering hellspawned creatures — horrific things — who used their magic or dimension warping powers to "pop" in past the defenses, hide in the shadows and sewers, and prey on men, women and children for food and pleasure. He'd also seen his fair share of trouble from psychotic Juicers, Crazies, 'Borgs, Wild Psi-Stalkers, and terrorists, too.

Lt. Cavanaugh stepped into a shadow, checked his weapons, and paused to give his two Psi-Hound partners time to move into position. He loved working Dog Boys. They were the best at sniffing out nonhumans, especially supernatural nightmares. And loyal! He could never admit it publicly, but he trusted Dog Boys, any Dog Boy, more than humans or Psi-Stalkers. In his 12 years on the force he had seen Psi-hounds leap in front of him to take a bullet or claw meant for him, and stand at his side in fire-fights where fellow humans turned and fled. They weren't afraid to take chances to save lives, and they were willing to follow him into hell and back if he led the way. He liked that.

Seventeen of his Dog Boy squad members had died in the line of duty, three times as many had suffered serious injury, but none had ever gone "rogue" on him. Each and every one a damn national hero in his book. You don't see that kind of unswerving dedication and loyalty to duty in the average human. Oh, there were lots of good "men" too. Tough warhorses like Lieber, Thomas, Kirby, Williamson, Sinnot and Rosen, but a lot of the rookies, and even some of the veterans, didn't have what it took to sludge through the filth of the lower levels, hunting monsters and madmen day in and day out. Not that he blamed them. It was a tough job that sent a lot of otherwise good, loyal, ISS Specters off the deep end. That's why the Grungers and LL's called the NTSET division the "Nut Set."

He caught himself before he chuckled aloud. Even among his fellow "nuts" he was considered the craziest. He had been dubbed "Crazy Cavanaugh" years ago. Hell, he'd seen rookies wet themselves at the very thought of being assigned to his tactical squad of "Monster Stompers" — except for the Psi-Hounds, of course. They were ready, loyal and, if he was crazy, they were just as crazy as he was. Crazy? Hell, if he was so crazy, why was he and his squad the most decorated on the force? The CS wouldn't have spent the money on the replacement bio-systems, cybernetics, and bionics that now comprised 60% of his body if he was really a crazy man. No, he and his Dog Boys knew how to get the job done. He and they leapt into situations that were so dangerous or frightening that a only a crazy man would do it. Yep, crazy like a fox.

Lieutenant Cavanaugh's musings vanished the instant the sound of a whimpering child reached his bionic ear. It was time to get down to business. Six Low Leveler children had disappeared in as many days.

Some snob-cops and elitist Lofties don't have much regard for LL's (Low Levelers), but in Cavanaugh's book, human was human, Lowly or Lofty, it didn't matter. He fought to protect every citizen of Chi-Town, it just seemed that most every damn monster, D-bee and lunatic sought refuge in the sewers, service tunnels and slums of the lower levels. There were probably lots

of reasons for this, but it didn't matter to Cavanaugh, he went where the trail took him.

Another whimper. The veteran Lieutenant activated his bionic multi-optic eye with a thought. Moving as silent as a ghost, he peered into the darkness around the corner. He smiled. This was his lucky day, the boys at the office were betting that the perp was a vampire, but he knew better. The problems on Level Eight were vampire related, but this was the handiwork of a two-bit ghoul or a sleazy demonic predator snatching kids off the street because they were easy prey. Not only would he win the office betting pool, but the latest victim was still alive. In the distance, he heard the hunting cries of his two Dog Boy partners, Aldo and Boris. Their howls told him they were in hot pursuit of the fiend responsible. Probably herding it to the rest of the team. If they didn't have him in their sights at the very moment, it would only be a minute or so.

This was an easy one, for a change.

After doing a quick scan of the frightened child, Crazy Cavanaugh knelt on one knee, flicked on his flashlight and announced, "It's all right, honey. You're safe, now. Ain't nobody gonna hurt you while me and my Dog Pack are here." The six year old boy ran to him, sobbing. He cradled the trembling child in his arms and whispered comforting words as he surveyed the area more closely, while shielding the boy's eyes from the carnage that laid around them. Cavanaugh mentally thanked god for making the monster's lair pitch black, so the child couldn't see the skeletal remains of the less fortunate victims that came before him. Cavanaugh counted nine skeletons — the damned thing had been hunting longer than they had suspected. He hoped his "Boys" would tear the bastard to pieces when they caught him.

The NTSET Organization

An elite Division of the ISS

NTSET is an elite, anti-supernatural Police Division that functions under the auspices of the ISS. Its operatives never leave the city, not even to visit the 'Burbs. Their mission is simple and direct, to hunt down and exterminate inhuman menaces before they can hurt innocent humans. Their jurisdiction: the cities and towns of the Coalition States. More than the "Specters," the "Nut Set," as they are called by most Low Levelers, don't particularly care about what may be transpiring *beyond* the boundary of their city. Their focus is the protection of "their" city and the people in it from the supernatural and unnatural.

Erin Tarn once referred to the "Nut Set" as "anti-paranormal super-troopers — fanatics dedicated to keeping the supernatural and magic from invading their turf." Although simplistic and amusing, Erin's assessment is fundamentally correct. The "Nut Set" specializes in tracking, locating and exterminating all beings having to do with magic and the supernatural, including demons, dragons, faeries, practitioners of magic and most D-bees.

In addition to basic combat training, police investigative procedures and intense training in counter-insurgence and counter-terrorism, they are knowledgeable in lore about magic, demons, and monsters and how to best subdue and destroy such beings. NTSET teams usually operate like a precision machine, working in concert as an elite strike force, using coordinated attacks and exploiting the strengths of each team member. Such teams engage in surgical strikes against "nests" of monsters and dangerous D-bees, search and destroy missions, rescue, and patrols of the slums, sewers and areas of the city where supernatural predators and inhuman refugees are most likely to hide.

The NTSET may also assist the ISS in more mundane matters. They can work any type of case from vandalism and robbery to murder, but are most likely to be asked to assist in the investigation of homicides, kidnappings, and extortion, as well as participate in raids against criminal operations — particularly those that might involve superhumans (Juicers, Crazies, 'Borgs, psychics and mutants), nonhumans, or practitioners of magic. In an emergency, they will do whatever is necessary to maintain the peace and protect lives.

The "Nut Set" are daring and bold champions of the people who willingly put their lives on the line to make their world a better, safer place for humans. However, even the human citizens they so fiercely protect regard them with fear as much as respect. The stories about the NTSET's daring, often seemingly insane measures to get their foes are legendary. Most veterans are so jaded by the supernatural that nothing phases them, so they accept and respond to the fantastic and terrifying as if it were an everyday occurrence — and for most NTSET, it is. Furthermore, their association with Psi-Stalkers, Dog Boys and Mind Melters make them seem a bit "inhuman" themselves. All of this has set the NTSET agents apart even from the ISS Specters, and has earned them the nickname, "Nut Set." **Note:** Most NTSET, other than some raw recruits, take no offense by the name and accept it in good humor. Many take pride in it, admitting that "you'd have to be *nuts* to take this job and do what we do." Many even refer to themselves and their fellow NTSET agents as the "Nut Set," without the slightest derogatory intent. "Facts is facts," as Crazy Cavanaugh would say.

Nonhumans Among the NTSET

Over 50% of the NTSET operatives are nonhumans! More nonhumans than in any other branch of the Military or Internal Security forces.

40% Psi-Hounds/Dog Boys

10% Psi-Stalkers

5% Psionics: Mind Melters, Bursters and others.

45% Human (25% of which have bionic and cybernetic replacement limbs and implants).

Some Lofties and extreme human supremacists have questioned the wisdom of an internal security force "overrun by mutants and psychics," but the NTSET has performed so diligently and heroically that nobody can find fault with the organization. The "Nut Set" are among the most loyal, dedicated and honorable of all the branches of the Coalition Army and Civil Defenders. Less than 2% are found to be (or even suspected of) corrupt or guilty of negligent conduct. The Dog Boys and Psi-Stalkers are absolutely crucial in sensing, locating and destroying the supernatural and magic empowered enemies of humankind.

NTSET Psi-Hound O.C.C.

Race: Mutant Dog

Attribute Requirements: I.Q. 10, M.E. 12 or higher. The higher one's M.E., the better and high physical attributes are also recommended but not required. Of course, all Dog Pack members have special *mutant* powers that enable them to sense magic and the supernatural. Some also have additional abilities or aptitudes based on their breed. See the **Rifts® RPG** and the soon to be released **Rifts® Lone Star** for complete details.

O.C.C. Bonuses: +1 on initiative at levels 1, 4 and 9. +1 to save vs magic illusion and mind control, +1 to save vs psionic attack and +1 to save vs magic of all kinds. +1 to save vs possession at levels 1, 3, 6, 10, and 13. +2 to save vs horror factor at levels 2, 4, 7, 10, 12 and 15.

O.C.C. Skills:
Language: American at 98%
Land Navigation (+20%)
Math: Basic (+20%)
Radio: Basic (+15%)
Tracking (humanoids; +15%)
Intelligence (+10%)
Surveillance Systems (+10%)
Streetwise (+10%)
Lore: Demons & Monsters (+20%)
Lore: Magic (+20%)
Climbing (+10%)
Running
W.P. Blunt
W.P. Energy Pistol
W.P. of Choice
Hand to Hand: Martial Arts; this skill cannot be changed.

Note: Only 10% of the Dog Boys assigned to NTSET have had previous duty in the military or ISS, most are hand-picked (or genetically bred) for service in NTSET.

O.C.C. Related Skills: Select four other skills from any of the available categories at levels one, four, eight and twelve.
Communications: Scrambler, TV & Video only (+10%)
Domestic: Any (+5%)
Electrical: Basic only (+5%)
Espionage: None
Mechanical: None
Medical: First Aid only (+10%)
Military: Etiquette and Recognize Weapon Quality only (+10%)
Physical: Any
Pilot: None
Pilot Related: None
Rogue: Any (+5%)
Science: None
Technical: Any (+10%)
W.P.: Any
Wilderness: Any

Secondary Skills: The character gets four secondary skills at level one, and one additional at levels three, seven, and ten. These are additional areas of knowledge that do not get the advantage of the bonus listed in parentheses. All secondary skills start at the base skill level. Also, skills are limited (any, only, none) as previously indicated in the list.

Standard Equipment: Dog Pack NTSET operatives are allowed to wear full suits of the old style "Dead Boy" armor. The shapes of the different breeds of dog prevents them from wearing the standard environmental helmet, so they are given a skull cap, goggles and air filter to protect the head. In the alternative, Dog Pack DPM light riot armor can be worn.

Energy pistol of choice, four extra E-clips, neuro-mace, one or two vibro-knives and/or saber, survival knife, silver cross, squirt gun, nightstick, two flash grenades, two flares, robot medical kit, pocket laser distancer, portable language translator, two sets of handcuffs, utility belt, air filter & gas mask, uniform, dress uniform.

Equipment Available Upon Assignment: Additional weapons, extra ammunition, optical enhancements, camera or surveillance equipment, electro-adhesive pads, automatic lock pin release gun, and other items. Dog Boys are seldom issued a vehicle. Most NTSET Dog Boys have low to medium level security clearances, but can escort a human squad leader or commander to any level that he has clearance to.

Money: The NTSET Dog Boy is *provided* with all of his or her needs, a nice two room apartment (levels 4-10 in the fortified super-cities; no charge), food (delivered or served at NTSET Squad Buildings), clothing, equipment, full medical benefits (including cybernetic prosthetics and bio-systems), as well as access to ISS, NTSET and PRP facilities. A modest allowance of 150 credits a month is provided for personal items. The character starts off with 3D4x10 credits.

Cybernetics: None to start with, but implantation of cybernetics and bionics may be awarded for exemplary service and heroics or when necessary to fix an injury.

NTSET Protector O.C.C.

Race: Human or Psi-Stalker
Attribute Requirements: I.Q. 10, M.E. 12, and P.P. 14 or higher. The higher one's M.E., the better and high physical attributes are recommended but not required.

O.C.C. Bonuses: +1 on initiative at levels 1, 4 and 9. +1 to save vs magic illusion and mind control, and +1 to save vs magic of all kinds. +1 to save vs possession at levels 1, 4, 9, and 12. +2 to save vs horror factor at levels 2, 4, 7, 10, 12 and 15.

O.C.C. Skills:
Language: American at 98%
Land Navigation (+10%)
Math: Basic (+20%)
Radio: Basic (+15%)
Surveillance Systems (+10%)
Tracking (humanoids; +15%)
Intelligence (+10%)
Streetwise (+20%)
Pilot: One of choice (+10%)
Read Sensory Equipment (+10%)
Lore: Demons & Monsters (+20%)
Lore: Magic (+20%)
Climbing (+10%)
Running
W.P. Energy Pistol
W.P. Energy Rifle
W.P. Blunt
W.P. of Choice
Hand to Hand: Martial Arts; this skill cannot be changed.

Note: 10% of the NTSET have served in the Coalition Military as Commandos or Special Forces, thus they have those areas of special training, including hand to hand Commando.

O.C.C. Related Skills: Select four skills from one of the following areas of special training: Espionage, Mechanical, Medical

Electrical: Basic only (+5%)

Espionage: Any (+5%)

Mechanical: Automotive, Basic Mechanics, or Locksmith only Medical: Any (+5%; +10% to Crime Sciences and Pathology)

Military: Limited to Recognize Weapon Quality, and Demolitions (all three) only (+10%).

Physical: Any

Pilot: Any (+5%)

Pilot Related: Any

Rogue: Any (+4%)

Science: Any

Technical: Any (+10%; 25% of all human NTSET are Literate)

W.P.: Any

Wilderness: None

Secondary Skills: The character gets three secondary skills at level one, and one additional at levels three, seven, and ten. These are additional areas of knowledge that do not get the advantage of the bonus listed in parentheses. All secondary skills start at the base skill level. Also, skills are limited (any, only, none) as previously indicated in the list.

Standard Equipment: Old style Coalition "Dead Boy" body armor, energy rifle and energy sidearm of choice, four extra E-clips for each, neuro-mace, vibro-knife or saber, silver plated survival knife, nightstick, four tear gas grenades, two flash grenades, two flares, silver cross, six wooden stakes and a small mallet, robot medical kit, pocket laser distancer, portable language translator, two sets of handcuffs, utility belt, air filter & gas mask, uniform, dress uniform.

Equipment Available Upon Assignment: Special body armor, including military issue (special request for extraordinary circumstances), access to explosive ordnance (rifle grenades, mini-missiles, hand grenades, etc.) if necessary for the mission, any types of weapon, extra ammunition, optical enhancements, sensory equipment, camera or surveillance equipment, electro-adhesive pads, automatic lock pin release gun, and other items. Non-regulation (including military) weapons, armor, equipment and vehicles may also be issued depending on the situation.

Vehicles are usually limited to a simple motorcycle, hover cycle, jet pack or hover patrol car and occasionally, power armor and robot vehicles. Most NTSET humans have medium level security clearances while experienced and trusted veterans will have top clearance.

Money: The NTSET agent is *provided* with a nice, four room apartment (on levels 8-18 in the fortified super-cities; no charge), full medical benefits (including cybernetic prosthetics and bio-systems), as well as access to ISS, NTSET and PRP facilities. His monthly salary is 4,500 credits; veterans get 5000 credits and high ranking officers (captain and up) get an extra 400 credits a month per level of rank. The character starts off with 3D6x1000 credits.

Cybernetics: None to start with, but implantation of cybernetic and bionics may be awarded for exemplary service and heroics or when necessary to fix an injury. 25% of the human NTSET operatives have had necessary cybernetic corrective surgery.

(typically crime sciences), Physical, Piloting, Science or Rogue —all of these special MOS skills get a +10% skill bonus. Two other skills can also be selected from any of the available categories at levels one, four, eight and twelve.

Communications: Any (+10%)

Domestic: Any

Lt. Jack "Crazy" Cavanaugh
NTSET Specialist — Quick Stats

Crazy Jack is one of the most notorious and decorated NTSET agents in the Division. He is a crafty, streetwise veteran of 12 years. He commands a squad of six Dog Boys; Aldo and Boris are his favorites (they've been partners for five years). In a crisis, he can be assigned as many as 40 police officers, human or Dog Boy, and occasionally coordinates efforts with the ISS or the military for massive, city-wide operations and manhunts. He has security clearance in Chi-Town for city levels 1-30, but spends most of his time on levels 1-8. There was never a more dedicated member of the "Nut Set."

Race: Human

Alignment: Scrupulous

Attributes: I.Q. 14, M.E. 22, M.A. 14, P.S. 20 (cybernetic), P.P. 18 (cybernetic), P.E. 13, P.B. 9, Spd 80 (bionic).

Hit Points: 44; **S.D.C.:** 32

Weight: 155 lbs (69.75 kg); **Height:** 5 ft, 11 inches (1.79 m)

Age: 32

P.P.E.: 7

Level of Experience: 8th Level NTSET Inspector.

Disposition: Cagey, clever, resourceful, honest and loyal. Jack is fanatically dedicated to protecting humans from nonhumans, monsters and other dangers. Over the years he's come to trust Dog Boys over most others and even prefers their company over others — in his eyes, they are honest, straightforward and loyal (like him). Lieutenant Cavanaugh would sacrifice his life to save another without hesitation (and probably will). He is well liked by his peers and loved by the men and Psi-Hounds under his command.

Magic Knowledge: Lore and personal experience only.

Psionic Powers: None

Attacks per Melee Round: Four; paired weapons.

Bonuses of Note: +2 on initiative, +4 to strike, +7 to parry and dodge, +3 to pull punch, +4 to roll with punch or impact, +5 to damage, +1 to save vs magic, +4 to save vs psionic attack, +2 to save vs possession, and +6 to save vs horror factor.

Skills of Note: Hand to hand martial arts, boxing, climbing 98/98%, running, all O.C.C. skills at around 90%, plus find contraband 54%, lore: D-bee 70%, lore: psychic 70%, computer operation 85%, pilot hovercycle, literacy: American 75%, and W.P. knife.

Weapons of Note: Vibro-knife in left boot, neural mace, TX-26 Triax Particle Beam pistol (used with permission from ISS Command; 5D6 M.D., 400 ft/122 range, 15 shots), 9 mm pistol with silver rounds, and C-27 Plasma cannon for "big jobs."

Cybernetics of Note: Both legs are bionic and look mechanical; arms, skin grafts, and many internal organs are bio-systems and look completely human. Multi-optic eye (left), amplified hearing and sound filtration system.

Psi-Net

By Patrick Nowak and Kevin Siembieda

The leaders of Chi-Town and the Coalition States have utilized psychic humans and mutants like the Dog Pack and Psi-Stalkers for decades, but it wasn't until the last 30 or so years that they agreed to establish a military and civilian psychic monitoring and law enforcement division. After due consideration, they decided that not only would the units be responsible for the identification and registration of psychics, but also for recruiting, training and policing them. In the year 85 P.A., the Coalition government, in cooperation with the Military, authorized the establishment of a program to study, contain and utilize psionic abilities in human beings. Thus were born *Psi-Net and Psi-Battalion*.

The current Commander of **Psi-Battalion** is *Lieutenant Colonel Carol Black*, an accomplished officer who possesses minor, sensitive psi-powers herself. Colonel Black has successfully headed Psi-Bat for 20 years, worked on the committee that developed the Psychic Registration Program (PRP) and helped to establish the framework for Psi-Net. She has also lobbied for scientific studies and humane laws regarding psychics and the use of psionic powers. Psi-Bat is a Special Branch of the Coalition Army that functions primarily as a Special Forces team that include spies and assassins.

Psi-Net became the civilian institution, an organization dedicated to all matters concerning registered CS psychics. The network is not really a military or normal police/ISS unit, but a regulatory body that handles the operation of the **Psychic Registration Program** and **Identification Coding (IC)**. This entails the identification of individuals with psionic abilities, evaluations of all registered psychics every five years, apprehension of psionic criminals, operation of the psychic rehabilitation/incarceration facility, research into psionic abilities and phenomena, public awareness campaigns (propaganda to promote psychics), and recruitment of psychics for military and ISS training.

It is safe to say that Psi-Net is involved in every activity concerning psychics in the Coalition States, but their duty does not end there. Psi-Net Inspectors also participate in the scanning and evaluation of visitors at the ports of entry at all Coalition cities where their powers help to identify (and interrogate) other psychics, shapechangers, supernatural beings, creatures of magic, practitioners of magic, spies and criminals who might be trying to enter the city illegally or with *thoughts* of evil intent. The psychics' involvement in this area of city-wide internal security is invaluable. Psi-Net agents are also involved in criminal investigations of all kinds, interrogations and "scans" of prisoners, the detection of psionics in others, and sensing the presence of, identifying, tracking and apprehending practitioners of magic and the supernatural — often in cooperation with NTSET or the ISS, but individually as well. However, Psi-Net's area of specialty is dealing with matters involving psionics and mind control.

Note: Psionic individuals can also find investigative, police, defense and combat oriented work in the Coalition Army, particularly in *Psi-Battalion*, and in the private sector as consult-

ants, private detectives, bodyguards, and researchers, as well as adventurers. Of course, not all psychics use their psionic powers to make a living. Some prefer to pursue other areas of interest as their chosen career and either use their "special" abilities as it is appropriate for that line of work or ignore them entirely (tries not to use them).

After more than two decades of operation, the organization is fairly well received by the population of the Coalition at large. The unit has an excellent record of success and has earned the confidence of the ISS, military, politicians and the average citizen. A carefully engineered propaganda campaign designed to promote the members of Psi-Net and Army psychics has worked masterfully. The public loves the Dog Packs and trust most psychics and Psi-Stalkers who operate within Psi-Net and Net-Set. Non-Coalition psychics are on the other hand, still generally feared by CS citizens, and seen as dangerous mutants with questionable motives. This is in part due to the same propaganda that has promoted the "honest psychics" of Psi-Net "dedicated to making the Coalition States a safe place."

Psychics serving under any of the ISS branches are generally considered to be loyal patriots in the service of the State. Still, there is a bit of apprehension and concern about Psi-Stalkers and psychics within Coalition Society, even those employed by the ISS, NTSET and Psi-Net. The most extreme human supremacists (roughly 5% of the population) fear and distrust all psychics, asking the question how can anyone feel relaxed or safe around somebody who can read your mind, sense your emotions, hypnotize or possess you, or worse? They are even more alarmed that the CS government has put psychics in charge of regulating psychics, claiming that they cannot be trusted to respond unbiasedly and with due diligence toward their "own kind."

Psi-Net has also taken steps to protect its members from persecution and strives for greater understanding and acceptance of psychics. Colonel Black, the head of the Psi-Battalion of the Army, and Psi-Net agents have lobbied for laws to protect psychics from unwarranted acts of racism, cruelty or violence by regular CS citizens and soldiers. Emperor Prosek has been surprisingly cooperative, and Joseph Prosek II has a small group of Mind Melters and psi-sensitives on his propaganda staff. The position of the Proseks seems to be one of, "you scratch our back and we'll scratch yours." Meaning, psychics who obey the law, willingly participate in the Psychic Registration Program (PRP) and serve the Coalition States to the best of their ability (which often means accepting a position within the ISS, its sister branches, the military or government) can expect their support and a good life. The psychic is no longer an outsider but a respected member of society whom others value and trust. Many psychics find working for the ISS, military or government appealing because it places them in positions of prestige and power, although a bit (sometimes extremely) dangerous. Those who aren't enamored with the idea of becoming a psychic policeman, spy or regulator usually keep a low profile for fear of being targeted as a subversive, spy or criminal.

The idea of having psychics police their own kind has worked surprisingly well. Regulation of psychics within the Coalition States is the major service of Psi-Net. Individuals, including children as young as five years old, who possess major or master psi-abilities are submitted to Identification Coding and tattooed with a scannable IC bar code. Psi-Net enforcement officers keep close track of psychics registered in the Coalition States, monitoring their lives including changes of address, career choices, political associations, hobbies, and suspicious activities. Every psychic is required to undergo evaluation every five years at a Psi-Net facility within 30 days of their birth date. This examination lasts 1D4 hours, during which the individual is tested for any signs of depression, mental instability/insanity, anti-social tendencies, and unhealthy or dissident beliefs. Psychics who pass the examination are free to leave and return to their normal routine for another five years (92%). If the Psi-Net examiner determines that the individual represents a potential danger to society, however, that person is politely asked to enroll in a social conformity program. Those who willingly agree undergo psychiatric observation, evaluation and therapy (if needed). The program can last one week to several months depending on whether or not the person is reasonably well adjusted or having trouble dealing with his/her powers and fitting in to society as a productive citizen.

Those who refuse are placed under secret surveillance by Psi-Net and considered potential rogues, criminals or sociopaths. Any behavior that is considered dangerously aberrant is sufficient cause for forcible apprehension and subjection to an intense conformity program. While confined in this high-security institution (some would call it a prison), attempts are made to rehabilitate the person through extensive therapy, including psychic surgery! At the end of six months, a review board evaluates each subject to decide whether rehabilitation is a realistic solution. In the cases where the board concludes that reform is not possible, the subject is declared a menace to society and terminated without trial or appeal, all in the name of public safety!

All psychic criminals in the Coalition States are sent to the psychic cell block of the *Chi-Town Penitentiary* — a prison city located some distance for the city of Chi-Town, staffed by Psi-Battalion personnel. Most criminals gifted with master psionic abilities are terminated upon conviction due to their considerable powers. Even so, there are still numerous inmates with telekinesis, mind control and similar dangerous powers who must be carefully guarded by psionic-resistant or psychic prison guards! Such duty typically falls to Dog Boys and Psi-Stalkers. The cell blocks at the Chi-Town prison can hold two thousand inmates, but the population is usually less than five hundred because serious criminals are executed. Fugitive retrieval also goes hand in hand with the operation of the prison and Psi-Battalion is expected to apprehend psychic criminals in Coalition territory. If the escapee makes it to a CS city, he becomes the jurisdiction of Psi-Net.

Recruiting Psychics

Psi-Net, and to a lesser degree, Psi-Battalion, provides the ISS and Coalition Army with a steady stream of psychic recruits. They encourage young psychics to consider the Internal Security Specialists or Military as the best way to serve their people and earn respect; possibly money and fame too. Both Psi-Net and Psi-Battalion can help psychic recruits to learn to develop and control their powers by Mind Melters and psi-sensitive instructors. Individual training is provided to each psychic who shows exceptional aptitude or a willingness to learn and follow orders. Often, this specialized coaching, especially at an early age (as young as 9 years old), means a psionic individual can direct their mental energy to develop a specific area of psionic emphasis (healing, sensitive, physical, Eruptor, Dominator, Nullifier, etc.).

The psionic classification and majority of psi-abilities in most older recruits (20 years old and up) are usually firmly established, leaving little room for redirection or further development. Such training can hone one's psionic powers to perfection. Many psychics, especially the young, are frightened by their own "sixth sense" and "inhuman powers." Many are afraid they'll be seen as monsters and imprisoned or killed. Others panic whenever a power manifests itself and lose control or try to force it back and never develop them. For these poor souls, Psi-Net means redemption and salvation by helping them to understand, control and develop their powers for the *benefit* of humankind. They are provided guidance, counseling and, when needed, psychiatric care. Recruits are taught to first understand themselves, their unique powers and how they can use them to help others (e.g. the CS). They are also taught meditation techniques, mind block and psychic lore. Being a member of Psi-Net also means enjoying the camaraderie of other psychics and not having to hide or worry about their "special" powers. Furthermore, many are glad to be able to hone and use their powers to help defend humankind — any feelings of shame are transformed into feelings of self-worth, purpose and patriotism.

Psionic Research

Research into psychic phenomena and understanding, controlling and developing countermeasures for psionic abilities is a vital mission of Psi-Net and the Psi-Battalion, although it ranks comparatively low on the military's priority list; defense, combat, and control are priorities number one, two and three respectively. Colonel Black of Psi-Battalion has emphasized the need to understand psychic abilities and to learn the full extent of the power of the human mind. To this end, she has lobbied for additional research and has managed to establish a special department within Psi-Battalion where psychics and scientists conduct comprehensive studies of psionic powers and the people who wield them. She and others would like to see more done in this area. **Note:** Psi-Net has no such research program and focuses entirely on the maintenance of the PRP and city security.

This ongoing research project is the most extensive study of psionics in human history including the period before the Great Cataclysm! In the few short years that the battalion has existed, there has been considerable progress in the study relative to existing human knowledge. Before the study, human knowledge concerning psionics was limited to innuendo, rumors and speculation. By studying and training a large number of psychics varying in age from early childhood to late adulthood, several discoveries and leads have been made. General knowledge remains fairly limited and why psionics is strong in some (roughly 30% of all humans) but not others, is still unclear, and more questions have been raised than answered. One thing they have learned is that psionics is something that a person is born with, it cannot be learned — either one possesses psionics or he doesn't. This would suggest the power is genetic and may be a human mutation, yet the appearance of this (presumably) recessive trait may skip entire generations, or manifest itself as minor abilities in one family member and as major or master psionics in a sibling.

Among humans and most (not all) D-bees, researchers have been able to classify master psychics into five major classifications: **Psychic Sensitive, Nullifiers, Eruptors, Dominators,** and **Mind Melters.** Scientists have discovered that if training and focus begins at an early age, the raw talents of these master psychics can be fine tuned and directed towards a desired effect in most cases.

The largest group of master psychics are **Psychic Sensitive,** individuals who are *sensitive* to powerful psychic emanations, energy and supernatural forces. Of the master psychics registered under the PRP, 63% are reactive or psi-sensitive. These psychic individuals who feel or sense things around them (psychic or magic energy, ley lines, the supernatural, evil, good, the emotions of others, danger, etc.) sometimes without even trying. These *psychic sensitives* feel the presence of outside energy and stimuli and respond to impending danger, the presence of powerful entities, supernatural beings and forces of magic. Sensitive commonly have the ability to feel the emotions of other beings, read psychic images imprinted on objects and communicate telepathically. Dog Pack and Psi-Stalker mutants are the most common psi-sensitive psychics in the Coalition States. Healers are usually considered psychic sensitive.

Nearly a fifth of the master psychics registered as residents of the Coalition States fall into the second category of **Eruptors.** These psychic individuals are born with extreme amounts of mental energy that is narrowly focused to produce terrifying displays of psionic power, especially in the magic-rich environment of Rifts Earth! Unlike the sensitive/reactive psychic, the Eruptor can control their outbursts to a certain degree, but they still lack finely-tuned control over their mental energy once it is released. Eruptors are instinctive masters of a particular energy, including pyrokinesis, electrokinesis, hydrokinesis and telekinesis, but lack sensitive and other psionic abilities. Furthermore, they often lack full control over their power and may literally *erupt* with devastating energy when angry or scared. It's as if all of their psionic potential became narrowly focused into one explosive power with a handful of secondary and comparatively minor powers. The *Burster* is an example of an Eruptor. Psychics whose major powers are *physical,* even though they may also possess some sensitive or other powers, are considered a sub-set of the Eruptor classification because they create physical phenomena through psionics.

Dominators are the least numerous and most dangerous group of master psionics. These psychics tend to be supremely confident, forceful and manipulative. Their powers are almost entirely focused in areas the enable them to control others. By concentrating, the individual can accomplish incredible mental feats that can include telekinesis, hypnotic control of others, mind reading and even the ability to create swords of pure psionic energy. These individuals are extremely dangerous in the world of **Rifts.** As soon as a Dominator shows any signs of criminal activity or little regard for human life, they are executed without trial.

Mind Melters are the most powerful, known, class of psychic. These psychics seem to have no limit to the power available to them and can manifest any range of psi-powers from sensitive and healer abilities to physical and super-psionics. They are the second rarest of all psychic classifications.

Nullifiers are psychics whose powers seem to be a reflex reaction to potential psychic energy (P.P.E.) that negates, weakens or discharges this ambient psionic energy. Such characters are typically resistant or even impervious to magic, psionics, possession, and the supernatural. Nobody, not even the psychic nullifier, has any idea how they do it. These are the rarest of the psychics.

Important Note: See **Rifts® World Book 12: Psyscape** for complete information about these and other psionic character classes and abilities.

PRP/Psi-Net Agent

Psi-Net agents can be thought of as "psychic police" who specialize in every activity concerning psychics in the Coalition States. They monitor PRP registrants, enforce PRP laws, and participate in the scanning and evaluation of visitors at the ports of entry, city-wide security, as well as criminal investigations of all kinds, particularly those involving psionics, psychics and mind control. A Psi-Net agent is often assigned to assist in ISS and NTSET investigations.

Psi-Net Unit Information:

25% Non-Psychic humans (equal to ISS Peacekeeper or Spectcr).

40% Sensitive, including Psi-Stalkers (20%), Dog Pack (50%) and human sensitive (30%).

15% Eruptors: Bursters, Zappers, etc. (humans)

11% Dominators (humans)

6% Mind Melters (humans)

3% Nullifiers (humans)

Attribute Requirements: I.Q. 11 and M.E. 15 or higher. High physical attributes are desirable but not mandatory. Remember, only 25% of Psi-Net agents possess no psionic powers whatsoever. 10% have minor psionics, 50% major and 40% master psionics.

O.C.C. Bonuses: +1 to save vs psionic attack and most forms of mind control, +2 to save vs magic illusion, and +1 to save vs possession. +1 to save vs horror factor at levels 1, 4, 8, 12 and 15.

Investigation (Special Skill for all Psi-Net agents): This is the training in techniques, principles, and theories of investigation, such as how to look for and recognize clues by systematically examining details with care and accuracy, observation, and research. Investigative techniques can be applied to environments, events, evidence, the spoken word, and body language. A character with this skill is more likely to remember details and locate hidden compartments. **Base skill:** 30%+5% per level; add a +5% bonus when investigating matters involving psychics, psionics or the supernatural.

Special MOS Selection:

Psi-Net "Tracker" (optional MOS): Psychic characters who can sense and locate the source of supernatural, magic or psionic emanations are trained to "sniff out" and "track down" rogue psychics, fugitives and supernatural monsters. This is done through a combination of psionic powers and learned tracking skills. Dog Boys and Psi-Stalkers are frequently used in this capacity.

Most also have the following skills and bonuses in addition to their standard training (use in place of MOS skills):

Sniper

Track (humanoids; +20%)

Track Animals (+10%)

Escape Artist (+10%)

Disguise (+15%)

+1 to save vs horror factor and +5% to investigation skill.

Psi-Net "Spotter" (optional MOS): "Spotters" are Psi-Sensitives, Dominators and Mind Melters whose powers enable them to sense the presence of the supernatural, magic, evil, and/or see aura, read minds, sense emotions, glimpse the future and sense danger — all powers that enable them to identify or "spot" psychics, practitioners of magic, supernatural beings and non-humans, even when disguised as humans. Dog Boys and Psi-Stalkers are frequently used in this capacity.

Most also have the following skills and bonuses in addition to their standard training (use instead of MOS skills):

Camouflage (+10%)

Detect Ambush (+15%)

Detect Concealment (+10%)

Find Contraband, Weapons & Cybernetics (+14%)

Recognize Weapon Quality (+10%)

Lore: One of choice

+1 on initiative

O.C.C. Skills:

Mathematics: Basic (+20%)

Radio: Basic (+15%)

Streetwise (+10%)

Interrogation Techniques (+20%)

Intelligence (+10%)

Surveillance Systems (+10%)

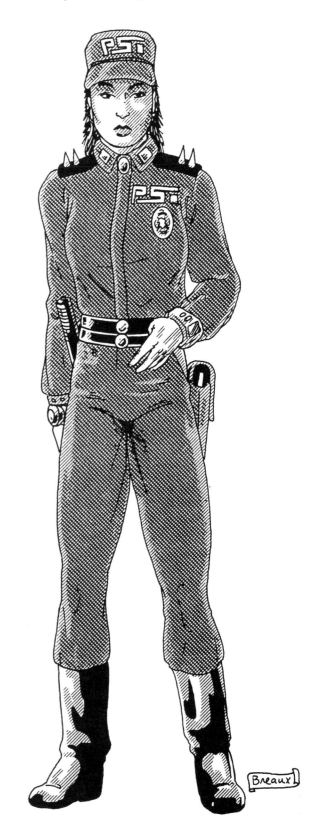

Land Navigation (+15%)
Lore: Psychic (+20%)
Pilot Hovercraft (+10%)
Physical skill of choice.
W.P. Blunt
W.P. Energy Pistol
W.P. of Choice
Hand to Hand: Expert

Hand to hand expert can be changed to martial arts (or assassin if evil) for the cost of two O.C.C. Related Skill selections.

O.C.C. Related Skills: Select four MOS skills from one of the following areas of special training: Communications, Electronics, Espionage, Mechanical, Medical (typically crime sciences), Piloting, Science or Technical — all of these special MOS-type skills are areas of specialty and get a +15% skill bonus — or select the "Tracker" or "Spotter" MOS.

Five other skills can also be selected from any of the available categories at level one, and two additional skills at levels four, eight and twelve.

Communications: Any (+10%)
Domestic: Any
Electrical: None, unless selected as an MOS.
Espionage: None, unless selected as an MOS.
Mechanical: None, unless selected as an MOS.
Medical: Paramedic (+5%) only, unless selected as an MOS.
Military: None, other than O.C.C. skills.
Physical: Any
Pilot: Any (+5%)
Pilot Related: Any
Rogue: Any (+2%)
Science: Advanced Math only (+15%), unless selected as an MOS.
Technical: Any (+10%; only 25% of all PRP agents are literate)
W.P.: Any
Wilderness: None

Secondary Skills: The character gets four secondary skills at level one, and one additional at levels three, seven, and ten. These are additional areas of knowledge that do not get the advantage of the bonus listed in parentheses. All secondary skills start at the base skill level. Also, skills are limited (any, only, none) as previously indicated in the list.

Standard Equipment: New style Coalition "Dead Boy" body armor or street clothes, energy rifle and energy sidearm of choice, four extra E-clips for each, neuro-mace, vibro-knife or saber, silver plated survival knife, silver cross, four tear gas grenades, two flash grenades, two flares, robot medical kit, pocket laser distancer, portable language translator, two sets of handcuffs, utility belt, air filter & gas mask, uniform, and dress uniform.

Equipment Available Upon Assignment: Special body armor, including military issue (special request for extraordinary circumstances), access to explosive ordnance (rifle grenades, mini-missiles, hand grenades, etc.) if necessary for the mission, any types of weapon, extra ammunition, optical enhancements, sensory equipment, camera, recording and surveillance equipment, electro-adhesive pads, automatic lock pin release gun, and other items. Non-regulation (including military) weapons, armor, equipment and vehicles may also be issued depending on the situation. Plus the character

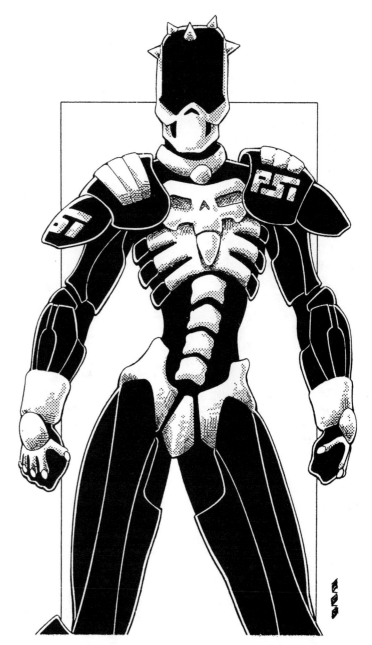

has access to PRP and ISS computers, data files, and department facilities.

Vehicles are usually limited to a simple motorcycle, hover cycle, or hover patrol car. Occasionally, power armor and robot vehicles.

Most human Psi-Net/PRP Inspectors have medium level security clearance while experienced and trusted veterans will have high clearance.

Money: Most psychics employed by Psi-Net or any of the ISS branches are *provided* with a nice, four room apartment (on levels 10-18 in the fortified super-cities; no charge), full medical benefits (including cybernetic prosthetics and bio-systems), as well as access to ISS, NTSET and PRP facilities. His monthly salary is 4000 credits. The character starts off with 2D6x1000 credits.

Cybernetics: Non-psionic Psi-Net agents typically have a clock calendar, gyro-compass and universal headjack with an ear implant and amplified hearing. Many later get augmented eyes. **Note:** Many city law enforcers will have the letters "PSI" emblazoned on their armor and uniforms (unless undercover).

The Burbs

"Burbs" is the slang term for the shanty towns that spring up around cities and strong holds within the Coalition States, particularly around the great, fortified super-cities. Like the *suburbs* of old, they are sprawling communities surrounding a large city. However, they are a far cry from the manicured residential communities that once surrounded the cities of pre-Rifts Earth. Most Burbs are slums composed of hovels inhabited by hoodlums, refugees, immigrants, "Rejects," and the dregs of society.

The Burbs were originally supposed to be a temporary holding zone for human refugees who wanted to apply for citizenship in the Coalition States, and/or petition for work or residence in one of the great walled cities. Peasants, farmers, wilderness folk, and refugees from other kingdoms throughout North America come in droves to the well defended, prosperous and peaceful Coalition cities. Unable and unwilling to accommodate everybody, the local CS officials are forced to push the multitudes away, beyond their city limits. Here, on the outskirts of salvation, many of those told to come back or *wait* several months or years before they are evaluated and accepted as a resident or citizen, pitch a tent or build a shack and *wait*. Many of the refugees and Rejects refused admission have no place better to go so they stay as well. Long ago, the CS government made the mistake of letting them stay, figuring sooner or later they would leave, but they didn't. In fact, most Burbs continue to grow, with new ones occasionally springing up and old ones expanding with urban sprawl. As time passed, such temporary communities became permanent or semi-permanent and have attracted hundred to hundreds of thousands of hopeful refugees, squatters and riffraff, as well as the criminal element and nonhumans.

In the early days, the Coalition Military would forcibly remove the squatters, sometimes escorting them hundreds of miles away, but many would return in a few weeks, joined by other hopeful newcomers, to rebuild. No matter how many times the people would be routed and the shanty towns leveled, they kept coming back. To complicate matters, at least a third really were eligible candidates for citizenship or work permits, placed on waiting lists and forced to languish with the less fortunate. Consequently, lethal force was not an option. The CS refused to kill their own kind — for while most of the Rejects were crude, uneducated, and unskilled, they were human. Even when extreme violence was used, the refugees kept coming. Finally, the CS government gave up and allowed the shanty towns to flourish, "like weeds outside the garden," as General Cabot once commented.

Zero Tolerance

Although the Coalition government has accepted the existence of the Burbs, they are not thrilled by their existence and have established some harsh policies concerning them. These policies are designed to keep the Burbs weak, submissive and non-threatening. They also give the CS the right to intercede, invade, and attack the Burbs to protect their own interests without formally declaring war or having good cause — the slightest suspicion can incite the Coalition to take extreme action and measures. The inhabitants of the Burbs must accept these conditions as realities or face the wrath of the Coalition Army.

1. The inhabitants of the Burbs are *not* citizens of the allied States. Their problems are not the concern of the Coalition States. Consequently, they enjoy none of the rights, privileges or protection of the CS. They are entirely on their own. Whatever hardships befall them is not the concern of the CS. This hard policy has allowed deplorable living conditions, poor sanitation, disease, malnutrition, crime and violence to claim the lives of thousands of people every year without the CS lifting a finger.

2. The Burbs are unauthorized and unrecognized communities who have invaded the Coalition States. Their people have no rights, no claim to land, and exist in a political no-man's zone. The inhabitants are undesirables, Rejects or squatters who are *non-entities* in the eyes of the Coalition. The CS does not acknowledge any government, ruling body, organization or leader that may rise from the Burbs. Any declaration of independence or sovereignty is an act of war!

3. Violence and insurrection against the Coalition States, its people, property and holdings will not be tolerated. The CS *will* respond accordingly.

4. The harboring of nonhumans, enemies of the allied States and/or wanted criminals is an act against the CS and will be considered an act of war. The CS *will* respond accordingly.

5. The establishment of a militia or military is not allowed (gangs and small groups of mercenaries or champions don't count). To do otherwise is an act against the CS and will be considered an act of war. The CS *will* respond accordingly.

6. The practice of magic is forbidden. The CS *will* respond accordingly.

7. The study, practice, teaching, and distribution of the forbidden knowledge of magic is illegal and will not be tolerated. The CS *will* respond accordingly.

8. Use of unauthorized and illegal technology, including bionic reconstruction, M.O.M. conversion (creating Crazies), Juicer augmentation, genetic alteration (mutation and superpowers), cyber-snatching and similar will not be tolerated. The CS *will* respond accordingly.

9. The worship of supernatural monsters, demons, intelligences and the inhuman in general, is illegal and will not be tolerated. The CS *will* respond accordingly.

10. The harboring of nonhumans, including D-bees used as cheap labor or slaves, is illegal and will not be tolerated. The CS *will* respond accordingly. All D-bees should be reported to the CS for capture and extermination.

11. Affiliation with or support of Coalition Enemies, including Tolkeen, Free Quebec, Naruni Enterprises, the Pecos Empire and others is considered an act against the allied States and cause for war. The CS *will* respond accordingly.

12. Rights and the authority of the Coalition States supersedes all others!

13. The CS authorities, in its sole discretion, shall use the military, ISS and any other force or measures to protect its people, property and holdings, keep the peace, and enforce some measure of law and order upon the Burb communities as it sees fit. The CS has the right of search and seizure, and complete jurisdiction over the Burbs regarding matters of investigation, crime, defense and national security. The CS *will* respond accordingly.

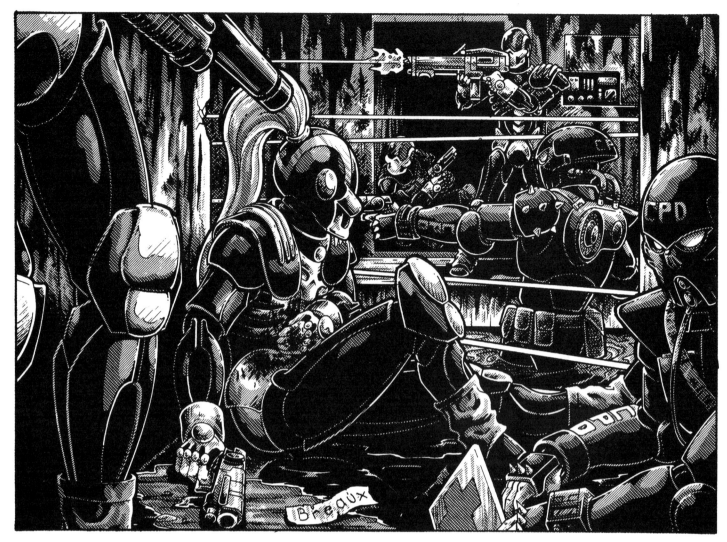

Many Burbs are lawless and morally debased communities. The majority are ruled by gangs, criminal organizations or powerful individuals (Juicers, 'Borgs, psychics, wizards, merchants, etc.; good and evil). Some are even controlled by monsters lurking in the shadows where they pull the strings of their human puppets. Since there are no formal laws or official ruling body, anarchy prevails and the level of violence, crime, corruption and mayhem can change dramatically from one Burb to the next — sometimes from one neighborhood to another in the very same Burb! Most Burbs are considered sprawling, lawless dens of iniquity where visitors can purchase all kinds of contraband and lose themselves in the masses. This is not entirely true.

First, some Burbs are surprisingly pleasant, orderly places to live. These are usually communities where one or more strong leaders and enforcers/protectors/champions maintain some modicum of order, justice and civility.

Second, the CS government *demands* that the Burbs maintain some measure of self-enforced laws to keep order. When they do not, and the lawlessness and/or violence becomes too great to ignore, these communities are placed under *martial law* and shaken down or purged. In some cases, they are evacuated and bulldozed! Martial law or destruction of a Burb can also occur when subversive rogues, spies, terrorists, practitioners of magic, or supernatural forces are suspected of controlling it or is being supported by the inhabitants. Again, this only becomes a concern to the CS authorities when it threatens the safety of the city and CS citizens, or becomes too blatant to be ignored.

Consequently, the unspoken law of the Burbs is, be subtle, careful, don't cause the human city any reason to worry, don't make too much noise, don't threaten CS authority, and don't make a fuss, because where the CS is concerned, what they don't see doesn't bother them. Many gangs and organizations consider their minions to be out of line if they do something that brings the CS on their heads. In many instances, those responsible for causing a CS investigation, martial law, or worse, a purge or retaliatory strike, are treated like pariah and often driven from the community (word of their folly travels like wildfire through the other Burbs so they may not be welcome anywhere in the immediate area). If the retribution of the CS is too terrible and costs hundreds of lives or the loss of businesses and important revenues, those held responsible often pay for their carelessness with their lives.

The Coalition Military or government can tear a Burb down and/or harass its inhabitants whenever they want to. Remember, the inhabitants of the Burbs are not CS citizens and their communities are not recognized as any sort of political entity, so they have absolutely no rights! Thus, the CS Army can enter a Burb, burst into a home or business, trash the place, threaten any of its people, beat, rape and even kill inhabitants with impunity. Any resistance on the part of the "Rejects" or attacks leveled against the CS authorities can only instigate serious trouble. Riots, destruction of a neighborhood or wholesale slaughter are the least of the probable aftermaths of a confrontation with the CS Military or ISS. The worst is *martial law*. Both the Coalition

Military and the ISS can impose and enforce its own rule and domination over a Burb that is considered to be openly hostile or harboring dangerous refugees, supernatural monsters or practitioners of magic. Martial law brings a strong police presence and strict, often brutally enforced laws, restrictions, curfews and regulations. The people living in a Burb under martial law are subjected to constant harassment, search and seizure, and interrogation. The CS authorities have absolute freedom to conduct themselves any way they see fit, and can use any degree of violence to keep the peace and/or eradicate the trouble. A Coalition grunt can beat or kill a man, woman or child with little fear of reprimand from his superior, unless the incident was extremely unwarranted and causes a commotion. As usual with all things regarding the Burbs, the quieter incidents are kept, the less likely there is going to be any involvement by CS superiors. High visibility and outrageous atrocities cannot be ignored and the soldier may find himself court martialed or have an accident while on duty in the Burbs.

Even when the Burbs are *not* under martial law, both the Coalition Military and ISS maintain a presence via frequent patrols, investigations and shakedowns. **Shakedowns** are surprise raids to "flush some of the rats into the open and see what we get." Such raids are typically directed at rogue scholars and scientists, practitioners of magic, nonhumans and organized crime, particularly brazen Black Market operations. **Purges** are full military invasions that can devastate entire neighbors, see the slaughter of dozens, the imprisonment and/or routing of hundreds and, occasionally, the obliteration of some or all of that Burb.

For the most part, the military and ISS don't really care if the inhabitants of the Burbs kill each other, die from disease, enslave and mistreat D-bees, struggle against supernatural predators or destroy themselves in any way, provided their internal conflicts and troubles do not directly affect, frighten or threaten the human citizens of the nearby city(s) or the security of the Coalition States. A Coalition Grunt will step over the dead body of a D-bee without so much as a, "what happened here?" The body of a monster or demon *may* elicit an investigation to make sure there aren't more lurking around or building an army of worshipers or minions that might threaten the citizens of the neighboring CS communities. The body of a human is more likely to raise an eyebrow, provided the deceased is not a vagabond, gang member or known criminal. The murder of a respected citizen from the city who foolishly visited a Burb, even if he was a scoundrel involved in criminal or morally reprehensible activities, will always warrant a thorough investigation and may be reason for a shakedown or a purge.

The flagrant and constant brutality, cruelty and injustice at the hands of Coalition officers is a direct result of the zero tolerance policies. However, the majority of CS troops and law enforcers do conduct themselves with some degree of morality and compassion. They don't, as a rule, go around pushing, beating, harassing, raping and killing just any Reject who gets in their way. In fact, many would-be citizens cooperate with CS authorities and try to turn to them when they have serious problems. Some soldiers and ISS operatives who are regularly assigned to a particular Burb are considered friends and protectors. The Coalition troops are most savage and relentless when hunting down wanted criminals, murderers, nonhumans and enemies of the CS.

The Six Big Problems with the Burbs

Note: The Military and ISS both have jurisdiction in the Burbs and share the responsibility of maintaining some measure of order. This include SAMAS and Sky Cycle fly-bys, regular street patrols and shakedowns. The primary focus of the ISS and the CS Military presence in the Burbs is the protection of CS citizens from the denizens of these foul refuges of the desperate and unwanted.

1. Bureaucratic Red Tape. The CS government has difficulty screening and processing acceptable applicants into the great cities. There is currently a *three year* waiting period even for desirable applicants. Only the most desirable and those with connections or vast wealth to properly grease the wheels of bureaucracy can acquire citizenship and residence in *less than a year.*

2. Refugees & Rejects. There are thousands of human refugees who have been *rejected* as "undesirable," but they refuse to leave!

Undesirables, commonly known as "Rejects," include people who have a criminal record, are known to associate with D-bees or practitioners of magic (or have in the past), are too old, sickly, lack social skills and/or have no work skills suitable for life in the high-tech cities. The latter two categories are typically peasant farmers, unskilled laborers and vagabonds from across the wilderness with the dream of a better life in the fabled wall-cities.

Many of those rejected for citizenship have no place else to go, and/or see life, even in the Burbs, as better and safer than other alternatives left to them (and gives one a good idea of just how terrible and frightening life can be outside the Coalition States). Consequently, they stay and struggle to eke out an existence in the Burbs. Many live straight and narrow lives with the hope of being reconsidered for citizenship, even though this secondary list currently has a waiting period of 11 years! Others join the CS military to prove their loyalty and to get on the *short Reconsideration List* (only a six year waiting period). Sadly, while they try to prove their worth in the Army, their families are left to make a life in the squalid and dangerous Burbs, where any accusations of wrong-doing can lead to a longer waiting period and even exclusion of that family member from reconsideration. This leads to the other big problem with the burbs, crime.

3. Crime. Human applicants forced to wait years for their chance to be considered for CS citizenship and/or city residency often find themselves stuck in the Burbs with little resources at their disposal and surrounded by rough and roguish people (human and inhuman). The unskilled, penniless, and often socially retarded "Rejects" are in an even more desperate state. For both of these groups, turning to *crime* is one way to make ends meet — for some it is the only way. Consequently, crime runs rampant in the Burbs, particularly robbery, mugging, smuggling, drug dealing, the sale of contraband, prostitution, gambling, blood sports, carjackings, vandalism, assault and battery, cybersnatching, rape and murder.

Street gangs also represent a serious danger. Gangs are active in establishing and protecting their "turf" as well as engaging in criminal activity. Some gangs rule half of the Burb. Visiting mercenaries, Juicers, Crazies, Headhunters, D-bee gangs, bandits, practitioners of magic, young toughs, hoodlums and supernatural predators also offer their share of trouble.

4. The Black Market is run by an efficient cartel of organized crime bosses and their gangs. It represents the biggest and most powerful criminal organization operating on the continent. It has a strong presence in many sections of the Burbs and typically has its hand in 40-60% of all illegal activities in the community, particularly the operation of body-chop-shops, prostitution rings, gambling, blood sports arenas, smuggling, and the sale of weapons, drugs and other illegal contraband.

5. The decimation of dangerous ideas. The unorganized mass of refugees and hopefuls living in the Burbs attracts all kinds of opportunists and parasites. In addition to con men and crooks, it also attracts *rogue scholars, rogue scientists, practitioners of magic, D-bees* and people of all kinds with dangerous ideas and views of life. Although not criminals in the usual sense of the word, the education of the masses is forbidden by the CS, so the scholars and teachers who dare to defy such edicts are branded as criminals, brutalized by the police and often executed on the spot! *Erin Tarn* is effectively the patron saint and hero of most scholars and free thinkers. She has also earned the position of Enemy Number One on the Coalition's most wanted list!

6. D-bees and Demons. The anarchy, lawlessness and opportunities of the Burbs also attracts the inhuman. D-bees desperate for work and better lives for their families have become the illegal, second-class citizens in a shadowy underground. Many will work for a third of what humans will work for, and will take the most degrading and dangerous jobs. Others are involved in crime or prey upon the humans who persecute and take advantage of them. Still others are vagabonds, drifters, drunks and bums.

Then there are the supernatural predators. The Burbs are wonderful hunting grounds. Without a formal army or police presence to combat them, hunting is easy and prey plentiful. Like the other denizens of the Burbs, these fiends have learned that keeping a low profile means they are less likely to be hunted. Preying on D-bees for example, rarely warrants investigation. Literally hundreds of D-bees could be disappearing from the streets and back alley of the Burbs and the CS authorities could care less. However, extend the hunting grounds beyond the Burbs, into the city or surrounding CS territories, and attack a CS citizen, and the authorities will come down upon the villain(s) like the wrath of god. Preying upon innocent humans, particularly women and children, or notable members of the Burbs will also get the Coalition Military or ISS involved in tracking down and eliminating the threat. Likewise, a perceived "infestation" of demons and supernatural beings will bring the CS authorities to investigate and exterminate the demonic vermin. From time to time, the Coalition Military and/or ISS will engage in purges to flush out and exterminate D-bees and monsters. Humans believed to willingly worship, serve, or protect supernatural or alien beings are typically slaughtered right along with their inhuman masters as traitors to humankind.

Burbs: Big & Small

Population Breakdown of the Average Burb:

2-5% Supernatural beings and/or creatures of magic.
15-20% D-bees
10-15% Psi-Stalkers, mutants and human psychics.
15-20% Human warriors, mercenaries, and professional criminals.
40-58% Ordinary humans; mainly the uneducated and unskilled.

Chi-Town is the largest of the five fortress cities in the area; the others only go to level 22 and hold only a half million people comfortably. Several other cities without the fortified walls of the super-cities rarely exceed a population of 200,000. The renovated coastal city of Waukegan will be the largest of the fortress super-cities, with 40 levels and able to accommodate 2.5 million inhabitants (its current population is approximately 700,000 — Chi-Town's is 1.3 million and will remain the seat of CS power). Around all these cities are the Burbs. Some cities like Waukegan and Chi-Town have a Burb population as large as the their civilian population. Others have comparatively tiny Burbs with a total population of only a few thousand refugees and Rejects.

The smallest Burbs are little more than a gathering of strangers and nomads. Most of these are small villages composed of tents and ramshackle buildings made from scraps and the gutted husks of vehicles. These can have as few as 20-100 people and are the most likely to be temporary dwelling places that fall victim to roaming gangs, thugs, bandits, monsters, disease, or the Coalition Military. These places never have large, permanent structures nor attract merchants, although a smuggler, travelling show, cyber-doc or con man may temporarily set up shop.

The larger, more established Burbs resemble and function as towns or small cities in and of themselves. At most, the atmosphere is similar to the boom towns of the pre-Rifts American wild west, where there are shootouts in the streets, the community never seems to sleep, and there's always something going on (whether you want it to or not). These are the communities where organized crime and the Black Market abound, and where one can find just about whatever illegal substance, pleasure or information he may be looking for. Of course, the Coalition Military patrols these places regularly and frequently sets up "sting" operations to capture criminals and spies. Bounty hunters, mercenaries, slavers, scholars, mutants, psychics, practitioners of magic, Juicers, Crazies, 'Borgs, City Rats, adventurers, D-bees and demons also call the Burbs home, or use them as a fuel depot to rest, resupply or get lost in a sea of faces, human and inhuman.

The Burbs are generally thought of as slums and shanty towns, but that is not always the case. Some are very old and established communities that have existed for 50-80 years. Some have paved streets and buildings that stand 10 and 12 stories tall and a range of neighborhoods from shanty towns and slums to nice residential sections and a modern downtown area. While some Burbs are always dilapidated garbage heaps, others are so nicely kept and friendly that visitors might mistake them for part of the city or a CS town. Chi-Town has some of the oldest and largest Burbs of all the allied states — Free Quebec and Iron

Heart are next in line. This is because most refugees are attracted to the largest, most prosperous and famous communities.

The ruins of **Old Chicago** is not officially a Burb and the Coalition Army is constantly running off squatters. Despite their efforts, it is constantly inhabited by small bands of adventurers, practitioners of magic, entities and creatures of magic. It is said only those looking for ancient secrets, in search of magic and the foolish, stay in Old Chicago for any length of time. Nobody has ever tried to rebuild the haunted ruins because ley line activity is strong and the place is constantly invaded by strange beasts and affected by dimensional anomalies. However, these very things attract the supernatural and practitioners of magic. A small RCSG outpost has been recently established in the ruins to conduct studies on Rifts and to help keep the place free of intruders.

Note: Travelling shows, Freak Shows and Carnivals all frequent the Burbs and outlying towns on both sides of the CS border. See **Rifts® World Book One: Vampire Kingdoms** for information on how to create and use traveling shows, as well as data on some different D-bees, aliens, creatures of magic and, of course, vampires.

The Denizen of the Chi-Town Burbs

The following are just some of the more notable D-bees known to inhabit many of the Burbs around the fortress city of Chi-Town and other nearby cities. The descriptions do not include psychics (see **Rifts® RPG** and **Rifts® Psyscape**), Psi-Stalkers, Simvan Monster Riders, and other races/R.C.C.s described in the **Rifts® Role-Playing Game**, the sourcebooks or optional characters from **Rifts® Conversion Book, Vampire Kingdoms, Atlantis,** and others. These characters can be used as NPC villains or as optional racial character classes.

Note: Nobody knows exactly how many D-bees of a particular species or race exist in North America or the Burbs. Among the most numerous and notable D-bee races, there are typically less than a half million found throughout the continent; the smallest may number no more than a few dozen. In many cases, a particular D-bee race may be common only to one small geographic region. D-bees often band together in small tribes and communities. Vast armies and gatherings of D-bees, aliens and monsters, like the Xiticix, are rare in North America, but places like Atlantis, Africa, Europe, China and Japan are examples where large communities of nonhumans and so-called demons have built expansive empires and number into the millions.

N'mbyr Gorilla Man R.C.C.

The N'mbyr (pronounced Nim beer) are nicknamed "Gorilla Man" because they resemble Earth Gorilla's or apes. Their facial features are simian, and their arms are long and powerful, their legs comparatively short which contributes to the illusion of being related to Earth apes. They are an aggressive and strong people, given to intense emotions and destructive fits of anger. Their powerful bodies and upper body strength make them excellent for construction work, lifting, carrying and general labor. They also make excellent climbers and warriors. They enjoy hard labor, sports (particularly wrestling and football), and physical challenges. Most are tough, but good natured. However, even the nicest Gorilla Man can fly into a rage and fight or maul a comrade when provoked. The violent outbursts by the N'mbyr is just part of their nature and may be linked to their psionic abilities and/or some survival mode suitable for their indigenous environment.

The N'mbyr arrived to Rifts Earth through a dimensional anomaly at the Old Chicago ruins, so they are most common to the Midwest, particularly Illinois, Arkansas, Missouri, and the Magic Zone.

Alignments: Any.

Attributes: I.Q. 2D6+4, M.E. 2D6+2, M.A. 2D6, P.S. 4D6+10, P.P. 3D6, P.E. 3D6+6, P.B. 2D6, Spd: 2D6.

Average Size: 6 to 7 feet tall (1.8 to 2.1 m)

Weight: 160 to 250 pounds (72 to 112.5 kg)

Hit Points: P.E. attribute number plus 1D6 per level of experience. **S.D.C.:** 3D4x10

M.D.C.: By body armor or magic.

Horror Factor: 10

P.P.E.: 6D6.

Natural Abilities: Keen vision, nightvision 120 feet (36.5 m), and psionic powers.

Violent outburst (Special): Although not quite a beserker rage, the N'mbyr lose control when they lose their temper. They lose their temper when angry, embarrassed, frightened or frustrated. When this happens, the N'mbyr will attack the person(s) responsible for his feelings and beat him/them into submission.

Loss of control provides the following considerations, bonuses and penalties: Bonuses during violent outbursts: +10 to P.S. (equal to a supernatural P.S. of 19; 1D6 M.D. from a punch or kick, 2D6 M.D. with power punch and one M.D. point from bite), +6 to save vs horror factor, +2 to save vs mind control, possession or psionic attack, +1 attack per melee round!

Penalties during violent outbursts: -2 to dodge, -30% to perform skills, incapable of pulling his punches (may accidentally kill somebody), and is not afraid of anything (i.e. too consumed with hostility to recognize that he's outnumbered, overpowered, can't win, etc.). Furthermore, when the character loses control, he becomes so single minded that he forgets about his assignment/mission/goal as well as friends or personal well being. All he can think about is lashing out to smash his enemy(s)! This also means the character forgets about his phenomenal physical strength which increases when angry or upset.

Psionics: All N'mbyr possess 1D4+2 *physical* psionic powers, while 20% are major or master psychics that fall into the Eruptor classification.

Eruptors possess 1D4+1 physical powers plus one of the following super-psionic abilities: Electrokinesis, hydrokinesis, pyrokinesis, telekinesis or telekinetic force field.

Eruptor bonuses: Double the normal range and duration and increase damage by 1D6 points.

I.S.P.: M.E. attribute number x3, plus 10 I.S.P. per level of experience.

Magic: None. Most N'mbyr aren't particularly interested in the pursuits of magic, preferring to rely on their natural physical and psionic powers.

Combat: Via hand to hand training; typically expert, martial artist, or assassin hand to hand.

Available O.C.C.s: Any Men of Arms or vagabond or wilderness scout, but in each case, reduce the selection of O.C.C. Related Skills and Secondary Skills by half. Tends to be physical; few are literate. Juicer and Crazy conversions which don't work on the D-bee's alien physiology.

Weapons & Equipment: The clothes on their back, a knife or mace, an energy weapon of choice, and some personal items. Favorite weapons include the nuero-mace, vibro-blades, and heavy weapons. Any type of armor can be worn.

Bionics & Cybernetics: Tend to avoid them, but will consider a more powerful prosthetic limb if the natural one is lost. Most also avoid M.O.M. implants, but some have elected to get Juicer augmentation.

Money: As one of the downtrodden, second-class nonhumns of the Burbs the D-bee typically gets slave wages. Player characters start with 2D6x10 credits and some very basic supplies.

Note: Most speak their native N'mbyr language, American (+20%) and one of choice (+15%), in addition to O.C.C. skills. Many are attracted to drugs and alcohol which only causes greater mood swings and potential violence.

Tirrvol
Sword Fist R.C.C.

The Tirrvol (pronounced "tear vol") are huge, barrel-chested aliens who cannot be missed in a crowd. Their upper torso is incredibly developed and strong. The neck is almost serpentine in its length and flexibility, ending in a short, round head with small round eyes, tiny pointed ears, slits for a nose and a large muzzle for a mouth. Their skin is a light grey color and thin and wrinkly like the hide of an elephant or rhino. The Sword Fist get their name from their most unique and obvious feature, their long, ivory colored, sword-like appendages. A sharp, mega-damage bone or horn extends into a bony blade where the fingers should be, and a bony hook protrudes from where the thumb would be on humans. The Sword Fist is amazingly adept at using their sword hands for things other than combat and can actually operate a computer and some simple machines. However, use of the sword hands is comparatively limited. Consequently, evolution has been good to the giant humanoid, giving him prehensile toes and double-jointed legs. Thus, the Sword Fist can operate a machine and even drive a vehicle using his feet!

The Tirrvol is a light mega-damage being, but warriors frequently undergo bionic augmentation to get *cyber-armor* similar to the Cyber-Knight. This armor typically protects the chest, shoulders and the Tirrvolian's long neck. They are fierce in battle and masterful swordsmen. Most are honorable, compassionate warriors of a good alignment who stand up against tyranny

and the forces of evil. Many have become champions of light and more than a few are rumored to have joined the Cyber-Knights.

The Sword Fist is highly intelligent, but they tend to speak in short, simple sentences. Some scholars have speculated that human languages are difficult for the creature; its natural language is a series of whistles, clicks and grunts reminiscent of Earth dolphins and whales.

Nobody knows where the Tirrvol originate or where they come from. Although a few hundred live in the Burbs in the State of Chi-Town, they are comparatively few, with perhaps fewer than one thousand throughout the Americas.

Alignments: Any, but most (60%) are good. Of the evil alignments, aberrant is the most common.

Attributes: I.Q. 3D6+1, M.E. 3D6+1, M.A. 3D6+1, P.S. 5D6+6, P.P. 3D6+6, P.E. 3D6+6, P.B. 1D6, Spd: 3D6. Strength is considered to be supernatural and does mega-damage.

Average Size: 8 to 12 feet tall (2.4 to 3.6 m)

Weight: 250 to 500 pounds

Hit Points & S.D.C.: A mega-damage creature.

M.D.C.: P.E. attribute number ×3, plus 2D6 M.D.C. per level of experience. In addition, most get cyber-armor and some also use magic.

Horror Factor: 12

P.P.E.: 4D6 points

Natural Abilities: Natural mega-damage creatures, keen vision, good hearing, heals twice as fast as normal humans plus sword hands and other limbs regenerate within 3D4 weeks if broken or severed. The leg joints (including ankles, knees and hips) are double-jointed and the feet and toes are prehensile, enabling the D-bee to use them like hands. However, the feet are not quite as agile and articulated as human hands, so they don't offer the same precision or proficiency — all skills requiring manual dexterity or precision suffer a skill penalty of -10%, including piloting, mechanics, medical, demolitions and so on.

Magic: None. Most Sword Fist aren't particularly interested in the pursuits of magic, preferring to rely on the their natural physical powers. This might again reflect the humanoid's difficulty in speaking human languages, making spell casting difficult.

Psionics: All Sword Fist have the psionic powers to see the invisible, sense evil, sixth sense, plus one psionic sensitive power of choice. I.S.P.: M.E. ×2 plus 1D6 per level of experience.

Combat: Via hand to hand training; typically expert, martial artist, or assassin hand to hand.

R.C.C. Combat Bonuses: These are in addition to hand to hand and attribute bonuses: +2 on initiative, +1 to parry, +1 to roll with impact, +1 attack per melee round, and paired weapons. The Sword fist is also +1 to save vs horror factor at levels 1, 2, 4, 6, 8, 10, 12, and 15, plus gets the following special (natural) W.P. sword ability: +1 to strike, parry and *disarm* with sword fists at levels 1, 3, 4, 6, 8, 10, 12, and 14. +1 to pull punch at levels 1, 2, 3, 5, 7, 9, 12 and 15. Critical strike (double damage) with the roll of a natural 17-20! Critical strike from behind. Normal cutting and stabbing damage is equal to the character's supernatural P.S.; power punch does double damage. The Sword Fist is so skilled that a successful pulled punch/strike can inflict whatever amount of damage the creature may desire to inflict, including S.D.C. damage as low as 2D6 points.

Available O.C.C.s: Any Men of Arms, scholar or adventurer O.C.C.s, except Juicer and Crazy conversions which don't work on the D-bee's alien physiology.

Weapons & Equipment: The clothes on their back, light to heavy body armor, utility belt, backpack or satchel, flashlight, portable language translator, knife, an energy weapon of choice (typically a pistol), and some personal items. Favorite weapons are its sword arms and items that can be used with the feet. Any type of armor can be worn.

Bionics & Cybernetics: Tend to avoid them, except for cyber-armor.

Money: Sword Fist easily find work as enforcers, hit men, mercenaries, soldiers, bodyguards, detectives and heroes. Consequently, they tend to be among the more affluent nonhumans. Player characters start with 3D4x1000 credits and some basic equipment.

Note: Most speak their native dolphin-like language, American (+20%) and one of choice (+20%). 01-70% can also read American or a written language of choice. All language skills are in addition to O.C.C. skills.

Quick-Flex Alien

The Quick-Flex Alien is the classic D-bee, because at a quick glance, he or she doesn't look different than a human. A long look or closer inspection will show the character's large eyes, long face and pinholes for a nose. Otherwise, the D-bee is your basic bipedal humanoid and can pass for human if clad in armor or when facial features are obscured. However, this race has a much higher metabolism than humans which means they a bit smaller (rarely exceed five foot, six inches/1.65 m), are alert, agile and incredibly fast. Their reflexes and speed are roughly equal to a Juicer or Crazy, plus they are ambidextrous. This makes the Quick-Flex Aliens superb gunmen, snipers, assassins, thieves, pilots and acrobats. They love adventure and fast moving vehicles. They also like adorning themselves with tattoos on their arms and chest.

The Quick Flex Alien are common to North America, particularly the mid-west, with an estimated one million scattered across the country.

Alignments: Any

Attributes: I.Q. 3D6, M.A. 3D6, M.E. 3D6, P.S. 3D6, P.P. 3D6+6, P.E. 3D6, P.B. 2D6, Spd 6D6+25

Average Size: 5 to 5 feet, 6 inches tall (1.5 to 1.65 m)

Weight: 100 to 150 pounds (45 to 67.5 kg)

Hit Points: P.E. plus 1D6 per level of experience.

S.D.C.: 3D6 plus those gained through physical skills and O.C.C. **M.D.C.:** From body armor or magic only.

Horror Factor: Not applicable.

P.P.E.: 2D6 points

Natural Abilities: Basically the same as a human except for hyper-activity, enhanced reflexes, great running speed and can leap eight feet (2.4 m) high or lengthwise from a standing still position! Add four feet (1.2 m) from a running start.

Magic: None. Most Quick Flex aren't particularly interested in the pursuits of magic, preferring to rely on the their natural physical powers.

Psionics: None

Combat: Via hand to hand training; typically basic or expert.

R.C.C. Bonuses (in addition to skill and attribute bonuses): +2 on initiative, +1 attack per melee round, +1 to strike using modern weapons/guns or bow and arrow, +2 to roll with impact, +2 to pull punch, paired weapons, automatic dodge (same as the Commando hand to hand ability).

R.C.C. Penalties: Tends to be jumpy and hyper — can't sit still, easily bored. Worse, the Quick-Flex Alien has a short attention span, which means complex skills and studies are difficult to master. Except for skills gained from the Rogue R.C.C., the character is -10% on all skills (regardless of O.C.C. bonuses) except physical and rogue skills whenever a human O.C.C. is selected. This attentions deficit also makes the study of magic unlikely.

Quick-Flex Rogue R.C.C: This character class is a cross between thief and city rat:

R.C.C. Skills: None of the R.C.C. skills and Related skills of the R.C.C. suffer from the learning penalty.

Speaks American and one language of choice (+20%)

Escape Artist (+20%)

Land Navigation (+10%)

Find Contraband (+10%)

Prowl (+10%)

Physical skill of choice

Streetwise (+14%)

Pick Locks (+20%)

Pick Pockets (+15%)

W.P. Energy Pistol

W.P. Automatic Pistol or Sub-machinegun

Hand to Hand: Basic

Hand to hand basic can be changed to expert for the cost of one R.C.C. Related Skill or to martial arts (or assassin if evil) for the cost of two skills.

R.C.C. Related Skills: Select six other skills from any of the available categories. Plus one additional at levels 3, 6, 10 and 14.

Communications: Any

Domestic: Any (+5%)

Electrical: Basic only (+5%)

Espionage: Sniper and Wilderness Survival only.

Mechanical: Basic only (+5%)

Medical: First Aid only.

Military: Etiquette and Recognize Weapon Quality only (+10%)

Physical: Any

Pilot: Any

Pilot Related: None

Rogue: Any (+6%)

Science: Math only.

Technical: Any (+5%)

W.P.: Any

Wilderness: Any

Secondary Skills: The character gets six secondary skills at level one, and one additional at levels three, seven, and ten. These are additional areas of knowledge that do not get the advantage of the bonus listed in parentheses. All secondary skills start at the base skill level. Also, skills are limited (any, only, none) as previously indicated in the list.

Available O.C.C.s (optional): Instead of selecting the Quick Flex Rogue R.C.C. the character can select any Men of Arms, scholar or adventurer O.C.C.s, but tends to avoid extreme types of augmentation, such as Juicer or Crazy conversions and full bionic reconstruction as well as proffessions that require a lot of studying; this D-bee prefers to work with his hands (they make great pilots and Operators/mechanics). Juicer and Crazy conversions will work on the Quick Flex Alien, but life expectancy after the augmentation is 25% less than usual because of the alien physiology.

Weapons & Equipment: The clothes on their back, light body armor, utility belt, backpack or satchel, flashlight, portable language translator, knife, a pair of energy pistols of choice, and some personal items. Favorite weapons are pistols of all kind and vibro-knives. Any type of armor can be worn but the character prefers light body armor or a Naruni force field.

Bionics & Cybernetics: Tends to avoid them, because they usually slow the D-bee down!

Money: As one of the downtrodden, second-class nonhumans of the Burbs, the D-bee typically gets slave wages. Player characters start with 1D6x100 credits or stolen valuables and some very basic supplies.

Note: Most have forgotten their native language and speak American (+20%) and one of choice (+10%), in addition to O.C.C./R.C.C. skills. Most (90%) are illiterate scavengers, vagabonds, thieves/rogues, mercenaries or adventurers.

Vanguard Brawler

The Vanguard Brawlers are notorious as leaders of street gangs and finding work as bounty hunters, slavers, hit men, enforcers, bouncers, bodyguards and mercenaries. While they will work for most any race, they tend to congregate among their own kind, typically gathering in family clans and gangs. Brawlers are tough, streetwise thugs who use their fists, violence and intimidation to get what they want. Despite their strong arm tactics, they are cunning, resourceful, excellent strategists and good leaders (in a mafia kingpin sort of way).

The D-bee has a tough, scaly, mega-damage skin, but it is only sufficient to withstand a few energy blasts, but then, most Vanguard Brawlers only need a few seconds to vanquish their opponents. Light to heavy body armor is often worn as well, particularly to protect the head, arms and legs. Two rows of sharp, hook-like spines protrude from the back and must have once served as a natural defense — any creature leaping onto the Brawler's back impales or gouges itself on one or more spines (typically 3-6 spines per row). The exact shape, size, and number of spines are different on every brawler and can be used as a means of identifying individuals, who all tend to look very similar. The color of the skin is a pale blue-green with larger scales and nodules that are a lighter yellow or powder green. The nose is small and located directly between the snake-like eyes.

There are believed to be less than a half million Vanguard Brawlers throughout the continent; most are in the Midwest.

Alignments: Any, but 33% are anarchist and 66% evil.

Attributes: I.Q.: 3D6+2, M.A. 2D6, M.E. 3D6, P.S. 4D6+4, P.P. 3D6+4, P.E. 4D6+4, P.B. 2D6, Spd 3D6

Average Size: 6 to 7 feet tall (1.8 to 2.1 m)

Weight: 220 to 320 pounds (99 to 144 kg)

Hit Points & S.D.C.: A mega-damage creature.

M.D.C.: P.E. x2 plus 1D6 M.D.C. per level of experience, and/or from body armor or magic.

Horror Factor: 11

P.P.E.: 1D6 points

Natural Abilities: Keen hearing and sense of smell (can track by scent at 30% +2% per level of experience, +10% to follow a blood scent), can see the infrared spectrum of light, and is a natural climber (base climb skill is 68/56% +2% per level of experience) as well as being a physically powerful mega-damage creature.

Magic: By O.C.C. only, but most Brawlers don't pursue magic. Note that the D-bee's high P.E. makes most Vanguard Brawlers resistant to magic, disease and poison.

Psionics: None

Combat: Via hand to hand training; typically expert, martial artist, or assassin.

R.C.C. Bonuses (in addition to skill and attribute bonuses): +2 on initiative, +1 attack per melee round, +2 to roll with impact, +2 to pull punch, +1 to save vs disease and poison, and +1 to save vs possession. +1 to save vs horror factor at levels 1, 2, 3, 4, 5, 6, 8, 10, 12, and 14.

R.C.C. Penalties: Clearly inhuman in appearance, making disguise impossible. The spine on the back makes it difficult to wear human body armor or clothing — requires customization.

Vanguard Brawler Thug R.C.C: This character class is a street warrior.

R.C.C. Skills:
    Speaks American and one language of choice (+20%)
    Basic Math (+20%)
    Land Navigation (+15%)
    Find Contraband (+15%)
    Intelligence (+16%)
    Streetwise (+16%)
    Track (humanoids; +10%)
    Pilot Hover Vehicle (+10%)
    W.P. Energy Rifle
    W.P. of choice
    Prowl (+10%)
    Body Building
    Boxing or Wrestling (pick one)
    Gymnastics or Acrobatics (pick one)
    Hand to Hand: Expert
    Hand to hand: expert can be changed to martial arts (or assassin if evil) for the cost of one R.C.C. Related skill.

R.C.C. Related Skills: Select five other skills from any of the available categories. Plus two additional skills at levels 2, 5, 8, and 12.
    Communications: Any (+5%)
    Domestic: Any
    Electrical: Any
    Espionage: Any
    Mechanical: Basic only (+5%)
    Medical: First Aid only.
    Military: Any (+10%)
    Physical: Any
    Pilot: Any
    Pilot Related: None
    Rogue: Any (+6%)
    Science: Math only.
    Technical: Any (+10%)
    W.P.: Any
    Wilderness: Any

Secondary Skills: The character gets five secondary skills at level one, and one additional at levels three, six, nine and twelve. These are additional areas of knowledge that do not get the advantage of the bonus listed in parentheses. All secondary skills start at the base skill level. Also, skills are limited (any, only, none) as previously indicated in the list.

Available O.C.C.s (optional): Instead of selecting the Vanguard Brawler Thug R.C.C., the player can elect to make his character most any Men of Arms, scholar or adventurer O.C.C.s. Note that Juicer and Crazy augmentation does not work on the alien physiology. Partial bionic reconstruction is fairly common, but most Brawlers who have undergone full conversion become bitter and meaner than usual.

Weapons & Equipment: The clothes on their back, light body armor, utility belt, backpack or satchel, flashlight, portable language translator, knife, a pair of energy pistols of choice, and some personal items. Favorite weapons are rail guns, plasma guns, and other heavy weapons. They also like vibro-blades and magic weapons. Any type of armor can be worn but the character will need to modify it to accommodate the spikes in its back.

Bionics & Cybernetics: Tends to avoid them, but may get as much bionic augmentation as desired.

Money: As one of the downtrodden, second-class nonhumans of the Burbs, the D-bee gets paid poor wages for manual labor, but can earn good to excellent money as a mercenary or thug. Player characters start with 1D4×1000 credits or equivalent in stolen valuables, as well as some basic supplies.

Note: Most speak their native language, American (+20%) and one of choice (+10%), in addition to O.C.C./R.C.C. skills. Most (70%) are illiterate thieves/thugs, mercenaries or adventurers.

Trimadore

The Trimadore is a strange looking D-bee humanoid with a long, thick neck, comparatively small head, long thin appendages, hands with two fingers and a thumb, and wide feet. The Trimadore are generally quiet, peaceful people with a knack for electronics, mechanics and building. They are constantly taking equipment apart, studying it and putting it back together. They are also excellent at jury-rigging different systems and cobbling things together. Trimadore usually make their own body armor from scrap parts and are always puttering around with something. Their mechanical aptitudes make them ideal for becoming Operators or Techno-Wizards.

Overall, the Trimadore people are gentle giants who like to build, so, while there are some adventurers and warriors, most avoid combat. There are believed to be less than a quarter of a million Trimadore in the world.

Alignments: Any, but most are anarchist and unprincipled.

Attributes: I.Q: 3D6, M.A. 3D6, M.E. 3D6, P.S. 3D6, P.P. 3D6, P.E. 3D6, P.B. 2D4, Spd 3D6.

Average Size: 7 to 8 feet tall (2.1 to 2.4 m)

Weight: 180 to 220 pounds (81 to 99 kg); tall, thin and lanky.

Hit Points: P.E. plus 1D6 points per level of experience.

S.D.C.: 2D6 plus any acquired from physical skills.

M.D.C.: By armor only.

Horror Factor: 9

P.P.E.: 1D6 points

Natural Abilities: Perfect 20/20 vision, good hearing, a keen sense of touch and an innate mechanical aptitude (almost on a savant, genius level). The long arms offer an extended reach.

Magic: Techno-wizardry fascinates the Trimadore who find this new alien technology to be wonderful. Other areas of magic are not pursued.

Psionics: Limited. All Trimadore possess the powers of mind block, object read, speed reading and telemechanics. I.S.P. 2D4×10 plus M.E. attribute number and 2D4 I.S.P per level of experience.

Combat: Via hand to hand training; typically basic or expert.

R.C.C. Bonuses (in addition to skill and attribute bonuses): +2 on initiative, +1 attack per melee round, +2 to roll with impact, +2 to pull punch, +1 to save vs disease and poison, and +1 to save vs possession. +1 to save vs horror factor at levels 1, 2, 3, 4, 5, 6, 8, 10, 12, and 14.

R.C.C. Penalties: Clearly inhuman in appearance, making disguise impossible.

Trimadore Mechanic R.C.C: This character class is a natural Operator/Mechanic.

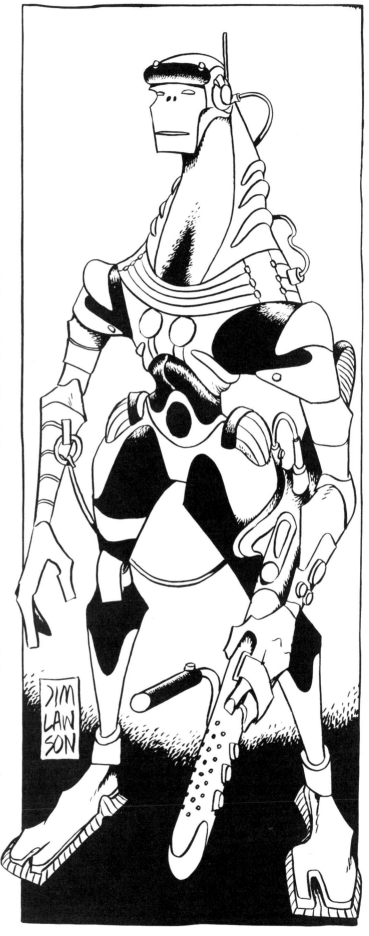

R.C.C. Skills:

    Speaks American and one language of choice (+20%)

    Literate in Earth language of choice (+15%)

    Basic and Advanced Math (+30%)

    Pilot Hover Vehicle (+10%)

    Pilot of choice (+10%)

    Military Fortifications (+10%)

    Computer Operation (+20%)

    Computer Programming (+10%)

    Electrical Engineer (+10%)

    Mechanical Engineer (+15%)

    Armorer (+20%)

    Recognize Weapon Quality (+20%)

    W.P. of choice

    Hand to Hand: Basic

    Hand to hand: basic can be changed to expert for the cost of one R.C.C. Related Skill or to martial arts (or assassin if evil) for the cost of two skills.

R.C.C. Related Skills: Select six other skills from any of the available categories. Plus two additional skills at levels 3, 6, 9, and 12.

    Communications: Any (+10%)

    Domestic: Any

    Electrical: Any (+10%)

    Espionage: None

    Mechanical: Any (+10%)

    Medical: First Aid only.

    Military: Any (+10%)

    Physical: Any

    Pilot: Any (+10%)

    Pilot Related: Any (+10%)

    Rogue: Computer Hacking only (+6%)

    Science: Any

    Technical: Any (+10%)

    W.P.: Any

    Wilderness: None

Secondary Skills: The character gets five secondary skills at level one, and one additional at levels four, eight and twelve. These are additional areas of knowledge that do not get the advantage of the bonus listed in parentheses. All secondary skills start at the base skill level. Also, skills are limited (any, only, none) as previously indicated in the list.

Available O.C.C.s (optional): Instead of selecting the Trimadore Mechanic, the player can elect to make his character a Scholar, Cyber-Doc, Operator or Techno-Wizard.

Weapons & Equipment: The clothes on their back, body armor of their own construction (50-100 M.D.C.), utility belt, backpack or satchel, tool kit, flashlight, multi-optic band, visor, portable language translator, pocket computer, knife, an energy weapon of choice, and some personal items. Favorite weapons are lasers and multi-weapon systems.

Bionics & Cybernetics: Tend to avoid major bionic reconstruction, but may get numerous implants and augmentation.

Money: Their incredible skill puts these odd looking D-bees in high demand and nets them good money as an Operator/mechanical engineer. The player character starts with 2D4×1000 credits or equivalent in stolen valuables as well as some basic supplies.

Note: The Trimadore, also known as Fixers, are one of the rarer D-bees of North America, with less than 100,000 believed to be on Earth. All are literate in at least one language (plus their native tongue).

Kremin Cyborg

The Kremin are alien cyborgs who came through a Rift to explore the planet. They are fascinated by magic and the multitude of alien life forms. They have only just begun to explore other worlds through their own fledgling experiments in spanning space and time through dimensional travel. Rifts Earth being something of a dimensional vortex, drew the explorers to it. However, their last communique with their homeworld, minutes after their arrival on Earth, indicated that their dimensional portal was tearing itself apart and that it would be a while before repairs could be made to get it back on line. The cyborg explorers were on their own. The Kremin 'Borgs are confident that their comrades will some day reopen the dimensional door and rescue them. Till then, be it months, years, or decades, they continue their mission to explore strange new worlds and civilizations, to boldly go where no Kremin has gone before!

The exact goals of the Kremin are unknown. They claim to be ambassadors from a peaceful world with the purpose of making contact with other civilizations to exchange ideas, art, technology and resources. Although they claim to be peace loving, they don't seem to be taken aback by the violence and turmoil of Rifts Earths. However, most Kremin fight only in self-defence and seem to try to avoid direct contact or alliances with any of the planet's inhabitants, human or D-bee — they simply observe. While this may support their claims of being peace loving, nobody really knows anything about them. All that is truly known is that they are bionically augmented beings similar to humans, the tech level of their bionic systems are slightly more advanced than Triax, and they are presumably from another dimension. The Coalition States have declared them to be dangerous alien invaders and has issued a standing order to destroy all Kremin on sight. As a result, the alien 'Borgs have fled the CS territories and can be found scattered throughout the rest of the continent, particularly in the western wilderness, Texas, Minnesota, Free Quebec and Michigan. Whether they are friend or foe is yet to be determined. **Note:** Only three dozen Kremin Cyborgs are believed to have come to Rifts Earth. The CS has already destroyed nine, dissecting and studying several — that's how they know the approximate tech-level of the bionic systems.

Alignments: Unknown; most appear to be anarchist and unprincipled but psionic blockers built into the cyborgs' brains prevents reading their thoughts.

Attributes: I.Q. 3D6, M.A. 3D6, M.E. 3D6+4; all physical attributes are bionic: P.S. 22+1D6, P.P. 22+1D4, P.E. not applicable, P.B. 6+1D6, Spd 132 (90 mph/148 km).

Average Size: 8 feet tall (2.4 m)

Weight: 600 pounds (270 kg).

Hit Points: Not applicable; full conversion borg (alien).

S.D.C.: A mega-damage cyborg.

M.D.C. by Location (alien alloys):

    Head — 110

    Hands (2) — 30 each

Arms (2) — 95 each
Feet (2) — 50 each
Multi-Weapon Blade & Sheath (1) — 60 each
Legs (2) — 130 each
Main Body — 280

Horror Factor: 9

P.P.E.: 1D4 points

Natural Abilities: Not applicable; see bionics.

Magic: None

Psionics: None

Combat: Hand to hand: expert.

R.C.C. Skills: +1 to save vs horror factor at levels 2, 4, 6, 8, 10, 12, and 14. Also see bionic systems.

R.C.C. Penalties: Clearly a cyborg of some kind, making disguise impossible.

Kremin Cyborg R.C.C: Skills are fundamentally the same as the CS Technical Officer, see **Rifts® RPG**. Use the 'Borg experience table. The language translator allows the Kremin to speak all Earth languages at 96% efficiency.

Weapons & Equipment: Starts with a Multi-Weapon Blade, its standard bionic systems and a utility belt, backpack, satchel, tool kit, flashlight, an Earth energy weapon of choice, and some personal items. Favors heavy weapons, variable lasers and vibro-blades.

Bionics Systems of Note: Finger and headjack, amplified hearing, built-in language translator, full optics, molecular analyzer, voice amplification, built-in radio receiver and transmitter, laser finger (tool), climb cord, and various secret compartments.

Bionic Alien Systems Include: 1. Psionic dampers and blockers implanted in the living brain of the Borg. These implants prevent psychics from reading surface thoughts, emotions, seeing aura, sensing good or evil, or conducting full telepathic probes; effectively a permanent *mind block*. They also make the Kremin 'Borgs +2 to save vs psionic attacks, +3 to save vs illusions and hypnosis, and +6 to save vs possession.

2. Retro-Mechanic Nano Restorers: These are internal housings that contain rechargeable nano-machines that can repair internal and external damage to the cyborg, a sort of mechanical regeneration process. Severe damage is likely to require raw materials from Earth equivalents such as mega-damage plating, circuitry, and, if a bionic limb has been destroyed, entire bionic limbs and components. The magic of the nano-systems is that they take these less advanced Earth equivalents and integrate them into the more advanced Kremin Borg. When the conversion and modification process is complete, the Borg will be fully restored and look as good as new!

3. Energy Fist: Each hand has four buttons or short rods protruding from the hand, just behind the knuckles. These can generate an energy field that enables the 'Borg to punch, doing 4D6 M.D. or to fire a short blast that also does 4D6 damage; 500 foot range (152 m), but limited to four punches or two blasts per melee round (needs time to generate spent energy).

4. Multi-Weapon Blade: The chief weapon of the Kremin 'Borg is a blade that vaguely resembles a Japanese short sword. The weapon can cut like a vibro-blade (does 2D6 M.D.), stun by touch (a jolt that knocks its victim off his feet, causing him to lose two melee attacks and initiative; does

5D6 S.D.C. damage), or fire an energy blast that does 6D6 M.D. damage; range 1200 feet (366 m); payload: 12 blasts before needing to recharge in its special sheath.

Money: Whatever they accumulate here and there. The player character starts with 1D4×1000 credits as well as some basic supplies.

Note: The Kremin are rare with fewer than 30 believed to be wandering the Americas (possibly as many as 100, not more).

Monsters Common to the Burbs

Devil Sloth

The Devil Sloth is a monstrous mound of muscle, spines and claws. It gets its name from the pair of horns on the top of its head, demonic appearance and sloth-like claws. However, the mega-damage creature is not a supernatural demon, but a scavenger that rummages through the garbage and waste of the burbs and feeds on it. They are touchy creatures who don't like to be disturbed and startle easily. When startled, cornered, hurt, defending a mate or young, or when it feels threatened, the monster stands on its hind legs and bellows a horrible shriek. This tactic is used to warn interlopers to leave or die. A moment later, the monster strikes at its antagonist with slashing claws and biting mouth. If it kills its attacker or person who startled it, the monster will eat him, otherwise it fights only to escape or frighten away the thing that is threatening it. The only other time a Devil Sloth will attack a humanoid is when it is starving or the person is weak and dying. Aggressive and defensive, Devil Sloths have been known to challenge troops in power armor and attack robot vehicles.

Devil Sloths' have a high animal intelligence and can be trained like a dog. However, even trained animals are still jumpy and lash out when startled or feel threatened. Simvan monster riders love 'em. They are also used in gladiatorial arenas for blood sport spectacles. The creature is about as common as bears once were in North America. They seem to roam the woodlands of Michigan, Illinois, Arkansas, the Magic Zone, Ohio Valley and forests of the south and east. Most Devil Sloths' hunt, scavenge and travel alone, in mated pairs or in small groups of 3-5 members. According to rumors, the Devil Sloth came from the St. Louis Rift before the CS began their efforts to contain the portal.

Alignments: Considered anarchist or evil; animal predator.
Attributes: I.Q: equal to an I.Q. of 1D4+2 (high animal I.Q.), M.A. 1D6, M.E. 1D6, P.S. 6D6+6, P.P. 3D6, P.E. 4D6+6, P.B. 1D6, Spd 4D6; P.S. is considered to be supernatural.
Average Size: 10 to 16 feet tall (3 to 4.87 m)
Weight: One to two tons!
Hit Points & S.D.C.: A mega-damage creature.
M.D.C.: 2D4×100
Horror Factor: 15

P.P.E.: 6D6+10 points

Natural Abilities: The lumps or nodules on the head are a combination eyes and sensory clusters that enables the creature to see the invisible, see all spectrums of light, and sense the supernatural identical to Dog Boys. It's interesting to note that the Devil Sloth hates supernatural beings and will either flee or attack and fight to the death. Keen hearing and sense of smell enable it to track decaying food or by blood scent at 80%. It is also a good digger, swimmer 70%, and climber 60%. The beast heals twice as fast as most animals.

Magic: None

Psionics: None

Combat: Five attacks per melee round. Claws inflict mega-damage equal to its supernatural P.S.; bite does 1D6 M.D., body block 1D4 M.D.

R.C.C. Bonuses (in addition to skill and attribute bonuses): +5 to save vs most diseases, poisons and toxins, +6 to save vs horror factor.

Vampire Flat Worm

The Vampire Flat Worm is a parasite and predator that frequently infests and plagues the inhabitants of the most squalid and overcrowded parts of the Burbs. Once infected, they are difficult to exterminate.

The hideous thing is some sort of alien creature that hides under garbage dumps, in sewers, under debris and in dark, dank places during the day. A night predator, the creature crawls out of hiding on its hundred tiny legs in search of prey, weaving silently through the darkness. Being so flat and able squeeze through small openings, the hideous thing can sneak just about anywhere. Its prey is typically a person who is sitting still, slumbering or drunken. The Vampire Flat Worm crawls up to its victim, raises its body like a snake ready to strike and lunges forward, impaling its victim with two pair of blood sucking fangs. Once attached, the thing may try to entangle its prey like a python to keep it from escaping or fighting back. However, unlike a python, it cannot constrict or strangle, only hold onto and pin or restrict the movement of its victim. Once attached, it will drain its prey of 1D4 pints of blood. The horrible creature will return to easy prey every night until the person is killed. The Vampire Flat Worm's favorite prey are helpless, homeless people living in the streets. It may also feed on the recently deceased and animals as well.

The Vampire Flat Worm is neither a worm or a supernatural creature, but an S.D.C. creature that can only attack other S.D.C. creatures.

Alignments: Considered anarchist or evil; animal predator.

Attributes: Most are not applicable; I.Q.: equal to an I.Q. of one (low animal I.Q.), M.A. N/A, M.E. N/A, P.S. 1D6+4, P.P. 1D6+6, P.E. 3D6+6, P.B. N/A, Spd 1D6+6

Average Size: 4 to 10 feet long (1.2 to 3 m)

Weight: 10-30 pounds (4.5 to 13.5 kg)

Hit Points: 4D6

S.D.C.: 6D6

M.D.C.: Not applicable.

Horror Factor: 14

P.P.E.: 2D6 points

Natural Abilities: Prowl 76%, climb (like an insect) 88%, swim 50%, thermo-sensors and infrared vision.

Magic: None

Psionics: None

Combat: Two attacks per melee round. Bite 1D6 or tail slap 1D4. Once the worm attaches itself it, pulling it off will do 3D6 damage and the thing can drain a pint of blood in five minutes.

Bonuses: +1 on initiative, +2 to strike, +3 to dodge, +5 to save vs diseases, poisons and toxins; effectively impervious to horror factor.

Spiny Ravager

This monster makes the Fury Beetle look small and calm by comparison. The Spiny Ravager is an extremely aggressive predator that is not afraid of humans or most other life forms. In fact, humans and humanoids have seemed to become its favorite prey. The largest and most aggressive will actually raid the smaller, outer Burbs by quietly prowling up to them, then loping into the streets or a busy area, pouncing on terrified people and gobbling them down. A Spiny Ravager can bite a human in half with one bite and the largest can swallow them whole! When the monster has had its fill and all easy prey are gone and/or defenders attack to drive it away, the hideous beast runs away. The problem is, like a maneating lion, once the Spiny Ravager has tasted human (and D-bee) flesh, and knows where to find such delectable, easy prey, it will return time and again.

This walking nightmare is as big as a CS tank, standing 15-25 feet (4.6 to 7.6 m) tall and measuring 25 to 60 feet (7.6 to 18.3 m) long! It has a high animal I.Q. and is a cunning, vicious, and often relentless predator. Like a playful cat, the monster will frequently toy with its prey, using hit and run tactics as well as hiding, playing dead and lurking from behind concealment or underwater, and so on. Spiny Ravagers have been known to follow and pick-off members of a traveling caravan or tribe, one by one, until all are devoured. Being a mega-damage creature itself, even a mega-damage vehicle is no guarantee of protection. The monster is notorious for capturing vehicles, especially small trucks, cars and land rovers, by pinning the vehicle with the weight of its body and tearing open doors or clawing through the roof to get at the passengers inside. They also enjoy chasing hovercycles, motorcycles and low flying prey and try to catch them in their teeth. However, once enraged, the Spiny Ravager may become reckless and fight foolishly and until its death. Such a fighting frenzy occurs when the beast is provoked, angered, trapped, injured or just pissed off!

The eyes are the speckled mass on the side of its head, but the large mounds on the head are sensory pods that enable the creature to smell and hear. Thus, another hunting ploy is to lay quietly underwater with only the sensor pods and part of its back above the water's surface, then leap out when it hears or smells prey nearby, and attack. The heavy plating and spines on its back offers it armored protection equal to any robot in the Coalition Army. With the monster's eyes on the sides of its head and sensory cluster on top, it can bite, head butt, lunge and claw at opponents of any size with little fear of blinding itself or damaging sensory organs. The tail provides balance and serves as a rudder when in water. Its large, spindly legs are powerful and capable of frightening speed and leaps.

Perhaps the strangest feature of this creature is the body sack dangling from the neck, behind the chin. This is a second stomach, but what makes it so strange is that four small, working arms and claws are attached to it. The arms are used primarily as precision cutting and tearing tools to dismember and collect the body parts of its prey. They are especially useful when the Spiny Ravager leaps on top of large prey, pins the prey with the weight of its body and large limbs, and lets the small ones rip it apart. During combat, the small, clawed arms can slash and rip at an opponent at the same time the Spiny Ravager is snapping with its mouth or raking with its large front claws, as well as parry. The small arms and hands are also used to feel around in the dark and to groom itself.

The recent appearance of the Spiny Ravager just in the last two years, suggests it is another monster from a random Rift. They are found primarily in the Midwest which further suggests that they probably came out of one of the Rifts in the Magic Zone or Michigan. Although the beast may look insect-like with a chitinous exoskeleton of plating and spines, it is actually a huge, warm-blooded predator.

Simvan Monster Riders absolutely love 'em as mounts, pets and watchdogs. Spiny Ravagers are found throughout the plains and light forests of North American (US & Canada), Mexico, and Midwest — they don't seem to care for dense forests or jungles. The CS has recently begun a campaign of extermination because the monster's population has exploded 200% in the last year; thousands (perhaps as many as 15 or 20 thousand) are believed to exist. Without a natural predator to hunt the giant beast, their numbers have increased at an alarming rate. The only good thing about them is that they seem to find Xiticix as tasty and easy prey as humans. Spiny Ravagers usually hunt as lone individuals, pairs or small groups of 3-5.

Alignments: Considered an evil animal predator. Many wilderness folk consider them demons.

Attributes: Most are not applicable; I.Q.: equal to an I.Q. of 1D6+2 (high animal I.Q.), M.A. N/A, M.E. 3D6, P.S. 1D4×10+15, P.P. 2D6+10, P.E. 5D6, P.B. 1D4, Spd 58 (40 mph/64 km)

Average Size: 15-25 feet (4.6 to 7.6 m) tall and measuring 25 to 60 feet (7.6 to 18.3 m) long.

Weight: 12-30 tons

Hit Points & S.D.C.: See M.D.C.

M.D.C. by Location:
  * Tongue (1) — 50
  * Eyes (2) — 30 each
  * Sensory Clusters (4) — 90 each
  * Small Front Arms (4; lower) — 40 each
  Large Front Legs (2) — 155 each
  Large Back Legs (2) — 200 each
  Tail (1) — 200
  Spiny Lower Body — 1D4×100
  ** Main Body — 2D4×100

  * A single asterisk indicates targets that are small and/or difficult to hit. The attacker must announce a "called shot," take his time to aim and strikes at -4 to hit.

  Shooting out the eyes does blind the monstrosity, but its other senses are so acute that all combat bonuses are only reduced by half! Destroying the eyes and the four sensory organs on the top of its head will completely blind it.

  ** Destroying the main body kills the creature.

Horror Factor: 18

P.P.E.: 1D6×10 points

Natural Abilities: Hold its breath for 3D4 minutes, prowl 46%, climb (like an insect) 68%, swim 90%, thermo-sensors, can see the invisible and all spectrums of light, recognize scent 75%, track by scent 65%, track by blood scent 90% — it can recognize and follow the scent of blood up to a mile (1.6 km) away. Keen hearing enables the creature to target and attack prey out of its line of vision and makes sneaking up on it virtually impossible. The Spiny Ravager can leap 20 feet (6 m) high and 60 feet (18.3 m) long. Furthermore, it seems impervious to poisons, toxins, and diseases, and is resistant to heat and cold; it can withstand extreme temperatures (normal S.D.C. fire does no damage).

Magic: None

Psionics: None

Combat: Four attacks per melee round. Bite does 1D4×10 damage, claw attack with giant arms/legs 6D6 M.D., head butt 3D6 M.D., tail slap 2D6 M.D., a pouncing leap does 6D6 M.D. and has a 01-80% chance of pinning/immobilizing vehicles half its size!

Bonuses: +3 on initiative, +3 to strike, +2 to parry, +3 to dodge, +3 to save vs mind control and illusion; effectively impervious to horror factor!

The Prosek Regime

Note: Reprinted in part from **Rifts® Sourcebook One**.

Emperor Karl Prosek

Circa 105 PA

Emperor Karl Prosek and his son, Joseph II, have been waiting for the day to launch their new campaign for military conquest and expansion for over five years. They have been patient, slowly building their secret army, making strategic alliances, and getting everything into position. They are like a pair of master chess players about to engage in their ultimate challenge, and they are ready.

Karl Prosek is an evil megalomaniac whose every action is motivated by his lust for power, fame, and glory. He has manipulated the humans of the Coalition States for years and has laid the frame work for *his* empire with care and precision. It is built on a firm foundation that should last for generations.

Emperor Prosek is a masterful strategist, administrator, and manipulator, yet his son, *Joseph Prosek the Second*, is a manipulator without peer and, if one can imagine it, even more ambitious than his father. His son's skillful efforts as head of propaganda have been instrumental in securing the people of Chi-Town's unanimous and undying support as well as establishing the right "atmosphere" within the government itself. The propaganda machine and the many loyal spies that it employs will continue to be an important aspect of the Coalition's continued success.

Karl Prosek and his son's aggressiveness and ingenuity have persevered and won the day, time and time again. This has encouraged like-minded opportunists to join them in their quest for power and immortality.

Karl Prosek is a powerful and capable leader with a head for strategy and tactics, both in the military and political arenas. He is a quick thinker, resourceful, and cunning. His keen mind and unrelenting nature makes him a formidable foe and strong, willful leader. He has meticulously and intelligently arranged the power structure of the government and the social, economic structure of Chi-Town, and to a lesser degree, the other Coalition States, to support his position of power, as well as having won the hearts and minds of the people 100 percent.

The Emperor is a slim, healthy man in his late 50's. His dark hair is full but greying at the temples, which seems to add to his striking appearance. His wife and youngest son were killed years ago during a terrorist attack by the Federation of Magic. His sole surviving heir is his eldest son, Joseph Prosek II, named after his famous grandfather (Karl's father, General Joseph Prosek the First).

Emperor Prosek

Alignment: Diabolic Evil

Hit Points: 58; **S.D.C.:** 20

Weight: 165 lbs (74 kg); **Height:** 6 feet (1.8 m); **Age:** 61

P.P.E.: 11

Horror/Awe Factor: 14

Attributes: I.Q. 19, M.E. 21, M.A. 24, P.S. 13, P.P. 10, P.E. 9, P.B. 11, Spd. 9

Disposition: Stern, demanding, merciless, calculating, manipulative, yet charismatic; seen as a strong leader/father figure. Tends toward megalomania and obsessed with control and a lust for power. His dreams of power and glory are the motivating forces behind his most every action. He loves and trusts his son implicitly.

Experience Level: 11th level scholar/diplomat/leader; increased a notch since the stats presented in the Sourcebook.

Magic Knowledge: None, other than in a historical or scholarly sense. He uses his practical knowledge about the history of magic and sorcerers to inflame the people to support his crusades.

Psionic Powers: None

Combat Skills: Hand to hand basic.

Attacks per Melee: Four

Bonuses: +1 on initiative, +1 to strike, +2 to parry and dodge, +2 to damage, +4 to roll with impact, +4 to pull punch, +5 to save vs horror factor, judo body flip, and critical strike on a roll of natural 19 or 20.

    Other bonuses: I.Q. +5% skill bonus (included in skills listed), M.E. +3 to save vs psionic attack, M.A. 80% likelihood to evoke feelings of trust or intimidate.

Weapon Proficiencies: W.P. Knife (includes vibro-blades) and W.P. Automatic Pistol, both at 11th level proficiency; W.P. sword, W.P. Energy Pistol and Energy Rifle are all at 6th level proficiency.

Weapons: Usually carries a .45 automatic pistol (4D6 S.D.C. weapon), S.D.C. dagger (1D6 S.D.C.) and vibro-knife (1D6 M.D.) on his person at all times. When in the field he adds a CP-30 laser pistol and a C-12 heavy laser rifle (his rifle of

choice) to his armaments, but can use any of the CS assault rifles, pistols, and weaponry. He owns an extensive collection of Pre-Rifts S.D.C. weapons that include knives, swords, revolvers, pistols, and rifles. All are in perfect working condition, complete with ammunition.

Emperor's Body Armor: The emperor's dress body armor is specially reinforced and composed of a new, lightweight, molecular bonded armor that affords him greater protection; 120 M.D.C., weighs 15 lbs (6.8 kg), and has all the usual "Dead Boy" armor features. The armor is always worn when beyond the protective walls of the city and even during public addresses.

Skills of Note: Literacy 98%, languages include English, Techno-can, Spanish, and Dragonese, all at 98%, basic and advanced math 98%, lore: demons & monsters 98%, anthropology 98%, biology 90%, computer operation 98%, radio: basic 98%, writing 90%, pilot automobile 98%, pilot hover craft 98%, pilot jet pack 84%, swim 98%, intelligence 78%, wilderness survival 90%, land navigation 82%, concealment 65%, streetwise 64%, and hunting.

Note: Also see the original write-up in **Rifts® Sourcebook One** for some additional history and insight about Karl Prosek and the Coalition States.

Joseph Prosek II
Head of Propaganda

Colonel Joseph Prosek II is the heir apparent to the throne. There is no doubt in anyone's mind that he will be the next great Emperor, and will be as capable as his father, perhaps more so. Although it will be a decade or two before his father will step down, Joseph is already setting his goals and making plans. He is completely loyal to his father as the two genuinely share the same vision of the future for their Empire. Joseph is patient and too clever to pressure his father into retirement, besides, he wields nearly as much power as his father and recognizes the Emperor as a valuable resource. Thus, Joseph the Second, cheerfully serves at his father's right hand. He is a capable administrator, good tactician, excellent strategist, and thinks quick on his feet. With more experience he will exceed his father as the manipulator supreme and has already been instrumental in winning the hearts and minds of the people. Having won them, they are now his to control for the next generation or two.

Like his father, young Prosek lusts for power and control. However, unlike his father, Joseph views it all as a colossal game, and he is the master of that game. He loves challenges and thrives on competition and crisis (it tests his abilities). Joseph hates defeat and embarrassment, and while it may make him angry, he never loses sight of his objective or allows himself to be driven to make a foolish move.

Joseph is often seen in the company of his father or one of their trusted generals. Neither Prosek is seen in public without an entourage of guards and assistants.

Alignment: Aberrant Evil

Hit Points: 52; **S.D.C.:** 30

Weight: 182 (81.5 kg); **Height:** 6 ft, 3 inches (1.9 m)

Age: 29

P.P.E.: 9

Attributes: I.Q. 17, M.E. 23, M.A. 19, P.S. 18, P.P. 18, P.E. 20, P.B. 15, Spd. 15

Disposition: Quiet and calm, yet confident and decisive; exudes strength and leadership. He is also calculating, deceptive, cunning, and merciless. His strategies are elaborate and based on the long term — like a calculated chess move that sacrifices the pawn or the knight to put oneself in better position for a decisive kill. He loves his father dearly and would never do anything to hurt or belittle him. The two work in total union in the fulfillment of the same dream.

Experience Level: 8th level Military Specialist; he has grown in experience over the last five years and is more confident and capable than ever before.

Magic Knowledge: Only lore and historical data.

Psionic Powers: None

Combat Skills: Hand to hand assassin

Attacks per Melee: Four

Bonuses: +1 on initiative, +4 to strike, +5 to parry and dodge, +3 to roll with impact or pull punch, and +7 to damage (S.D.C.).

Other bonuses: I.Q. +3% skill bonus (included in all skills listed), M.E. +4 to save vs psionic attack, M.A. 55% likelihood to evoke trust or intimidation, P.E. +3 to save vs magic and poison.

Weapon Proficiencies: W.P. knife, W.P. sword, W.P. energy pistol, W.P. energy rifle.

Weapons: Any he desires.

Skills of Note: Includes all applicable skill bonuses. Literacy 98% (special education), demon and monster lore 95% (special education), languages include English, Techno-can, and Dragonese, all at 98% (special education), basic math 98% (special education), computer operation 83%, computer programming 68%, computer hacking 53%, cryptography 78%, radio: basic 93%, radio: scrambler 83%, surveillance systems 83%, T.V./video 73%, forgery 68%, pick locks 78%, intelligence 76%, read sensory equipment 83%, weapon systems 88%, pilot hover craft 98%, robot combat: elite (SAMAS and UAR-1 Enforcer), and body building.

The Prosek Family

Emperor Prosek has no other direct heirs. His wife, younger son, brothers and father have all perished at the hands of the enemies of humankind. The Emperor has no interests in remarrying and delights in the accomplishments of his son Joseph. However, there are other family members in the Prosek line.

His late brother, Kenneth Prosek, married a gentle woman named Camellia, and sired two sons, Edmond and Ryan Prosek, and two daughters, Lisa and Meggan. **Edmond Prosek** is currently a Brigadier General and involved in the campaign against Quebec. **Ryan Prosek** served in the military for only six years (retired a lieutenant, the rank he began with) and is the *black sheep* of the family. Ryan is a playboy and a drunk who has no aspirations for power or glory, although he very much enjoys the wealth and prestige that his family name bestows upon him. **Lisa Prosek** has kept her family name even though she has recently married a research military scientist in the RCSG division — Captain Matthew Campbell. Meggan is the youngest, 21, and is currently going to college on the upper levels of Chi-Town.

Quentin Turnbull (51) is a second cousin and old childhood rival. The two men dislike each other intensely and haven't spoken in 20 years. Quentin, his wife Joyce, their son, Martin, and daughters, Victoria and Katherine, all feel cast away and ostracized by their famous relatives. This has made them all very bitter, particularly Martin who covets the power and position of his cousin, Joseph II. The Turnbull family are middle-class and live on level 21 of the great city of Chi-Town. Both Quentin and Martin are cybernetic specialists, but as of late, Martin has considered starting a life of adventuring (he's 27) and exploring the world.

Rumors have persisted for years that Joseph I took a beautiful female prisoner as his mistress during his Bloody Campaign against the Federation of Magic in 12 P.A. As the story goes, the woman, a young sorcerer, fell in love with him and gave birth to a baby boy. Some versions of the story paint Joseph I as a hard man who took what he wanted and tossed her aside after she became pregnant. Others suggest that he loved her as much as she did him, but that he could not bring back a mistress who was also a practitioner of magic. Thus, he set her free when he returned home, unaware that she was with child. If this is true, then Karl Prosek could have a half brother someplace in the Magic Zone — possibly even a sorcerer and a member of the Federation of Magic. Karl has never given these "wild tales" any credence, and ignores them as the fantasies of his enemies. Joseph II has done some cursory investigations but can find no evidence to substantiate the claims.

General Cabot

Military Counsel to the Emperor

General Marshall Cabot is an old friend of the family who knew the late Joseph Prosek the First, and was like an uncle to Karl and a great uncle to Joseph the Second. He loves both father and son, and sincerely believes they are the great saviors of mankind. Furthermore, he is impressed by the Empire they have built and believes they have earned everything they have made for themselves, regardless of their methods. Calculated ruthlessness is a virtue in the General's eyes.

General Cabot is a great military hero and military leader with few peers, particularly when it comes to battle tactics, strategy and organization. Even being in his twilight years, the general is still a resourceful, brave and bold soldier who is inventive and never afraid to take a reasonable chance. Without a doubt, Cabot is one of the great military minds of all time (he finds it amusing that his pawn, the bombastic *General Underhill*, should hold that official distinction). General Cabot was instrumental in creating and organizing the Chi-Town military nearly from its inception, and has shaped it into what it is today. He knows every aspect of its structure, disciplines, resources, capabilities, officers, and troops.

Cabot is one of the few people who the two Proseks confide in completely. He has been as instrumental in creating Chi-Town as a power base for the Coalition States and as a tool for the two Proseks themselves. He enjoys their trust, affection, power and wealth.

Alignment: Aberrant Evil
Hit Points: 56; **S.D.C.:** 24

Weight: 200 lbs (90 kg); **Height:** 5 ft, 10 inches (1.75 m)
Age: 83 (considering retiring, although he's in amazingly good health)
P.P.E.: 8
Attributes: I.Q. 19, M.A. 17, M.E. 16, P.S. 12, P.P. 11, P.E. 13, P.B. 8, Spd. 6
Disposition: Quiet in public, but outspoken when dealing with Emperor Prosek and Joseph Prosek. Clever, experienced, confident, resourceful, imaginative, a true master of military strategy and tactics; a general's general.
Experience Level: Fifteenth (15) Technical Officer (tech & science)
Magic Knowledge: None other than tactical knowledge and lore.
Psionic Powers: None
Combat Skills: Hand to Hand Expert
Attacks per Melee: Five (5)
Bonuses: +2 to strike, +5 to parry and dodge, +2 to roll with impact or pull punch, and +3 to damage (S.D.C.).

I.Q. +5% skill bonus (included in all skills listed), M.E. +1 to save vs psionic attack, M.A. 45% chance to evoke trust or intimidation.
Weapon Proficiencies: All energy W.P.s, W.P. heavy, W.P. automatic rifles, and W.P. blunt
Weapons: Favorite weapons include the neuro-mace, C-14 Fire Breather, and NG-57 Ion Blaster (pistol).
Body Armor: The new "Dead Boy" armor.
Cybernetics: Headjack, clock calendar, gyro-compass, bio-system polarized eyes to simulate perfect vision, artificial kidney and heart.
Skills of Note: Literacy 98%, basic math 98%, advanced math 98%, computer operation 98%, computer programming 98%,

computer hacking 90% (special), chemistry 98%, chemistry analytical 98%, anthropology 98%, languages include American, Spanish, Techno-can, Euro, and Dragonese all at 98%, demon and monster lore 98%, faerie lore 98%, writing 75%, general athletics, running, swimming 98%.

General Ross Underhill

Commander of the 4th CS
Mechanized Infantry Division

General Underhill is a decorated hero of nearly one hundred (94) military campaigns waged against inhuman enemies, including the famous *Legion of Dragons* and *Federation of Magic*. He is respected by the people and, thanks to a masterful propaganda campaign by the young Prosek, heralded as the greatest military leader since Joseph Prosek the First (some say the greatest of all time).

Indeed, General Underhill is a superior strategist and a fabulous leader. He is always with his men in the thick of battle and is famous for never demanding of his men anything he would not do himself. He has even been known to defy Emperor Prosek if it meant preventing the futile slaughter of his troops or a tragic tactical error. The Emperor, in turn, has officially acknowledged General Underhill as the greatest and noblest military mind in Coalition history!

Despite the General's loyalty to his troops and his skill as an undefeated defender of Chi-Town and the Coalition States, he is a glory-hound, a fascist, and a fanatical human supremacist; therefore, he is more than a bit of a fool, often controlled by ego

and emotion. Most everything about the General is extreme, from his personality to the risks he takes on the field of combat. The calculating Emperor and his trusted advisor, General Cabot, recognize General Underhill's extreme personality, have fed his egotistical delusions and nurtured his fanatical views to capture the General's complete loyalty and confidence. Emperor Prosek knows the strength and fervor of fanaticism and uses it like a deadly weapon. General Underhill is one such personal weapon used like a scalpel to surgically remove obstacles to his vision of a better world, his world.

General Underhill has been active in organizing the troops for the Tolkeen Campaign and securing the perimeter of the State of Chi-Town as they prepare for war. However, he will *not* be included in the siege on Tolkeen. Instead, General Underhill is likely to be placed in charge of defending Chi-Town. To keep the general from getting bored and discontented, he has also been given authority to organize reconnaissance, seek and destroy squads and Special Forces teams to explore territories and communities rumored to harbor monsters. This includes Kingsdale, the Magic Zone, and New Lazlo (Ann Arbor Michigan), and what was once the states of Nebraska, Kansas, Oklahoma and Texas/the State of Lone Star.

Alignment: Anarchist

Hit Points: 69; **S.D.C.:** 40

Weight: 140 lbs; **Height:** 5 feet, 8 inches (1.65 m)

Age: 44

P.P.E.: 6

Attributes: I.Q. 14, M.E. 15, M.A. 20, P.S. 22, P.P. 18, P.E. 21, P.B. 10, Spd.12

Disposition: Loud, gruff, outspoken, honest, fanatically loyal to his soldiers and to humans. Totally merciless and cruel in combat against all non-human adversaries and humans who support non-humans. He is known for his holier-than-thou and flamboyant attitude, making him both a larger than life champion of humankind and an irascible rogue. His men love him and will follow him into hell if he led the way.

Experience Level: 10th level Military RPA Elite Soldier (SAMAS)

Magic Knowledge: None

Psionic Powers: None

Combat Skills: Martial Arts

Attacks per Melee: Five (5)

Bonuses: Combat: +4 to strike, +7 to parry and dodge, +7 to damage (S.D.C. damage; P.S. bonus), +4 to roll with impact/punch, +3 to pull punch, critical strike on a roll of natural 18-20, judo body throw, all kick attacks, and paired weapons.

Other bonuses: +3 to save vs poison and magic (P.E.), 60% likelihood of evoking trust or intimidation.

Weapon Proficiencies: All energy weapon W.P.s, W.P. Automatic Pistol, W.P. Automatic rifles, W.P. Heavy, W.P. Knife, W.P. Chain, W.P. Blunt.

Weapons: Favorite weapons include neural mace, vibro-knife, C-14 "Fire Breather," C-50 "Dragonfire," the CV-212 variable light frequency laser rifle, and rail guns. He now always enters combat in a Super SAMAS (in his opinion, power armor is the single greatest piece of infantry equipment ever invented)!

Bionics: Left arm is bionic. P.S. 20, P.P. 18, energy-clip port in arm, laser finger blaster (1D4 M.D.), explosive finger joints

(3 on little finger), forearm blaster: particle beam (6D6+6 M.D., 1000 ft range). Also a bionic lung.

Cybernetics: Gyro-compass, clock calendar, universal headjack, amplified hearing, and sound filtration system.

Skills of Note: Boxing, body building, gymnastics, general athletics, climbing 85%/75%, swimming 95%, demolition and demolitions: disposal 82% each, robot combat: elite, pilot tanks and APCs 84%, pilot hovercraft 98%, radio: basic 98%, radio: scramblers 85%, first aid 98%, streetwise 52%, wilderness survival 70%, land navigation 68%. The General is illiterate.

Adventures & Settings Regarding the Coalition

Players and Game Masters should regard the **Coalition War Campaign** as a catalyst for epic adventure. Everything just got all shook up and nobody knows where the pieces will fall. Everything and everybody is in motion. The events that will unfold will see the birth of heroes and nations and the fall of others.

The Coalition States are a marvel of technology and force of will. From an outsider's point of view, they may appear to be an unstoppable juggernaut destined to conquer the continent. From a player's point of view, one might wonder how a lowly player character stands a chance against them.

First, don't be like Emperor Prosek and his High Command and *overestimate* the strength and power of the Coalition States. While they are a major force in North America, they are not the only power. There are other forces in place even as the Emperor rolls out his "New Army." Ask yourself these questions and think about the many, *possible* ramifications.

Just how powerful is Tolkeen? What has Emperor Prosek set into motion by attacking them (and others)? For the first time ever, the Cyber-Knights, as a group, have taken a side in a conflict, and against the Coalition.

Other independent nations, kingdoms and dictatorships see the handwriting on the wall, and don't like what it says. Will they also join Tolkeen against the Coalition? Some may, others will establish their own "coalition" of united kingdoms. And some may turn to darker forces to protect themselves.

There are many sleeping giants in North America, known and *unknown*, that the Coalition's Campaign of Unity may awaken. The Coalition Army and most people see the **Xiticix** as low intelligence "bugs" to be exterminated, but will the Coalition act in haste and foolishly stir up a hornets' nest before they are prepared for the consequences? **Archie-3**, the robot intelligence and would-be god, has quietly observed the CS and humankind for decades, but this new offensive might entice him to take a more direct hand in matters. Exactly what he might do is impossible to guess. Archie is a strange and unpredictable being. What about **Lazlo**? Nobody thinks of it in terms of military power, because it

is a peaceful kingdom, how will it use the people and power at its disposal? How dangerous is the **Federation of Magic** and how will they respond?

What madness and dark force that exists at the very heart of the Coalition States themselves? Not everybody is content playing second fiddle to the Great Prosek family.

Furthermore, in a world that is linked to countless other planets, civilizations and dimensions, times are ever changing. Who knows what might emerge from the Rifts tomorrow and suddenly change the balance of power?

Perhaps the most frightening question of all is, what will happen if the Coalition States, for all their good and evil, should fall? Will the Emperor's predictions of anarchy, human slavery, human genocide and wanton destruction at the hands of inhuman and supernatural invaders come true? Will North America become a place like *Wormwood*? Or will more peaceful and enlightened communities like Lazlo rise up and bring to life a new era — a Golden Age — for all people?

Of course, Emperor Prosek and his High Command may bring a new age of power for the States, successfully conquering kingdom after kingdom and crushing all who stand in their way. Tolkeen may be obliterated, Lazlo a shattered relic of what could have been (perhaps *should* have been) and Free Quebec the enslaved sixth member of the allied States (Arkansas being the fifth).

What villains and profiteers will emerge to add to the woes of a people in conflict?

Any way you look at it, the Coalition's War Campaign spells action packed adventure full of suspense, tension, intrigue, treachery and surprises.

Adventures can be epic events that will turn the tide of history or small adventures about the individual people, places and events that fall through the cracks and have little impact on the overall scheme of things. Both can be incredibly fun and dramatic. Remember that the environment of nations at war will always create situations (albeit they may be temporary) that could

Hook, Line and Sinker™

Quick, down and dirty adventure ideas

HLS created by Jolly Blackburn
Rifts® Adventures written by Kevin Siembieda

What is a Hook, Line & Sinker?

Hook, Line & Sinkers™ is the popular Game Master's tool created by Jolly Blackburn. The idea behind it is simple — give the Game Master just enough information to spark his own creative energies and then step out of the way. They come in handy when the G.M. has nothing else prepared, or finds the party has outpaced him and the prepared adventure suddenly ends.

The Explanation:

Hook: The current situation or location of the adventuring party.

Line: An opportunity for adventure that presents itself to the party. A line is normally presented as a short paragraph. Think of the line as the "bait" to lure the party into an adventure.

Sinker: The clincher to the line. The sinker presents the G.M. with a dilemma that makes the situation a true adventure.

The Adventures: The following are just a *handful* of possible adventures fueled by the Coalition's War Campaign. See the **Rifts® Index: Volume One** and **Rifts® Game Shield & Adventures** for more HLS and fully plotted adventures. **Rifts Mercenaries and Juicer Uprising** may also provide ideas, characters and equipment for adventures.

The Big One

Hook: With the Coalition so involved in the war effort against Tolkeen, they have "reemphasized" their resources and manpower. This has left a tiny, little known, secondary military outpost on the southern border of the Coalition State of Missouri at a quarter of its normal strength (at least temporarily). The outpost does not represent any particular strategic value, which is exactly what makes it vulnerable.

Line: A gang of rogues plans on hitting the base and stealing tons of CS weapons, ammunition and power armor! The gang can be angry Juicers frustrated and fuming over the failure of the Juicer Uprising, a bunch of Crazies, D-bee freedom fighters, Tolkeen loyalists, mercenaries, bandits, etc. **Note:** It is ideal if the player characters were party to the actual raid. This is appropriate (not to mention a fun adventure in itself) if the leader of the gang had, or claimed, good intentions (or seemed to offer easy pickings if the group is composed of selfish characters).

The base falls with relative ease. Sure enough, the base has just received a shipment of the latest, most advanced CS weapons and equipment. Indeed, this is the motherload, the jackpot, "The Big One!" Enough stuff to equip a small army!! Items include cases of CP-40 and C-50 rifles (at least 720 of each, but no extra E-clips), 144 suits of the new C-4 "Dead Boy" armor, two

never exist under any other circumstances. People, organizations, unlikely heroes, unexpected alliances, unimagined villains and predatory monsters (both human and inhuman) will seem to crawl out of the woodwork. Carpetbaggers, bandits, dictators, madmen, prophets and self-proclaimed saviors may all rise to join the fray.

Where your characters fit into all this is of your choosing. Cut that imagination loose, pick a side, and rock and roll!

Scarab Command Cars, 12 suits of Mauler power armor, 12 Hellfire Scouts, and six Hellraisers (the rogues get at least four of these). Plus, the base's standard complement of "old style" C-12 rifles, C-18 pistols, body armor and basic equipment for its skeleton crew of 48 soldiers, including six Command Cars and a facility for recharging E-clips.

Sinker: This one is a triple-zinger.

1. The NPC rogues go wild with delight and start smashing open crates and grabbing what they will. Within a few moments, they turn into a freewheeling, booze swilling mob, shooting up the place with their new "toys" — they ignore any attempts our heroes might make to control the situation. A fight will break out if the player characters try to use force. This will become a free-for-all.

2. Drunk with power, the rogues, never as well intentioned as they seemed, run into the night, armed to the nth degree. Within 24 hours they have launched their own campaign of terror, robbing places, shooting up towns, and doing whatever they please. Best of all (to their way of thinking), the Coalition gets the blame for their villainy!

The player characters who helped them get this stuff may (should, if a good alignment) feel responsible for bringing these maniacs to justice and protecting the communities at large from their acts of banditry and cruelty. Even if they weren't involved in the heist, they will hear about the goings-on and are likely to be attacked (robbery attempt) by one of the factions. The original band that robbed the outpost has splintered into 1D4+2 different groups. To make matters worse, some have joined up with their "buddies" and have shared their loot, so one or two of the forces our heroes may be up against could number into the dozens.

3. The CS Army isn't happy. The "loot" was a shipment on its way to an outpost in Lone Star. It was reported missing three hours after its delivery time was missed. The CS has dispatched six special strike teams (each a squad composed of different CS forces) to seek out and destroy the perpetrators, and to recover what they can. Unless the player characters present during the robbery *personally* deactivated the outpost's security system (the rogues fail to deactivate the entire system), our heroes and their misbegotten allies were all taped on micro-security cameras. Thus, their appearance, at least as they look in their armor and adventuring gear (if they never took it off), if not their faces, is known to the CS. They are regarded as dangerous criminals and *enemies of the Coalition States* — penalty for their crimes: execution! Any character in the possession of CS equipment will be suspected of complicity and attacked. Furthermore, characters trying to stop the mayhem may be suspected of being part of it and regarded as part of the rogue band. Life as a fugitive can be hell.

Stalag of Doom

Hook: An evil CS commander and a partial company of soldiers (94) beyond the borders of CS Territory have systematically collected 1D4x1000 D-bees and placed them in a "work camp." At this work camp, the prisoners are subjected to brutality, torture and experimentation.

Line: The player characters learn of this hell-hole and resolve to rescue the thousands of innocents trapped there. Their CS opponents are all armed with "old style" weapons, armor and equipment, although among their resources are two Abolishers and a SAMAS squad (10).

Sinker: Among the prisoners are CS soldiers who defied the Commander's orders to build the camp and subject the D-bees to torture. Of the forty-six who defied him, only 16 are still alive.

The work camp is unauthorized by the High Command, who will find its very existence to be abhorrent and "inhumane." An example of something horrible that slipped through the cracks.

If the CS authorities learn about the stalag, they will shut it down and mercifully execute the poor tortured D-bees. If they learn about it after it has been shut down, the High Command will methodically hunt down, capture and court-martial the Commander and all troops who followed him. After a military trial, the Commander (if he escaped the player characters) and his officers will be executed. Other CS troops who participated in this horrific affair will have their citizenship revoked and either be imprisoned for life or banished forever from the Coalition States and its territories. The soldiers who defied their insane Commander and endured months (perhaps years) of torture will receive commendations and the coveted *Imperial Medal of Honor*.

Player characters, including mages, humans and nonhumans, involved in destroying the camp and/or bringing the insane Commander and his rogue soldiers to justice, will not be charged or in any way persecuted. They won't be heralded as heroes either, nor get public credit for their role in the matter. The entire incident will be swept under the carpet and kept as quiet as possible.

Resistance

Hook: A reputable mercenary leader is gathering mercenaries to join his troops in the defense of Tolkeen. Word through the grape-vine will provide the location of his current recruiting station — he's constantly moving to avoid Coalition assassins.

Line: Fight for freedom, stop imperial aggression, save Tolkeen, kick some Coalition ass, and the usual war time hype.

Sinker: The mercenary leader is on the Coalition's payroll. His recruiting is all a trick to lure dissidents and anti-Coalition supporters (especially potential combat personnel) into the open. Recruits who sign up are sent to a predetermined location where they are apprehended (typically when their guard is down) by CS power armor troops and Commandos. Humans are interrogated and imprisoned, practitioners of magic and nonhumans are taken away and quietly executed.

Those who meet, inquire and leave without signing on, are hunted down by CS wilderness scouts (with two Juicers) or Special Forces disguised as adventurers or mercenaries. Nonhumans are assassinated. An *attempt* is made to capture humans for interrogation, possible CS recruitment or imprisonment. Those who exhibit great resistance or represent too great a threat are killed on the spot.

The Price of Freedom

Hook: The player characters either join forces with or become loosely affiliated with a group of gung-ho freedom fighters or bandits or mercs turned freedom fighters. Their common bond is a mutual hatred of the Coalition States and/or a desire to save Tolkeen, Free Quebec or some other CS target.

Line: The players gladly join such a worthy cause and dream of heroics and fame.

Sinker: It becomes apparent (quickly or slowly) that their comrades in arms are just as bad, or worse than the Coalition (extremists or evil)! The problem is likely to be two-fold; one, our heroes may be privy to information that would compel them to oppose their fellow freedom fighters. The player group can first try to reason with their associates, but are likely to have no success and find themselves physically standing against them or let a tragedy unfold.

Second, their comrades are likely to take the attitude of, "either you're with us or against us." Again leading to violence and is likely to label them as enemies for life.

The moral: Evil and fanaticism comes in all shapes and sizes, often waving the banner of a good cause.

In the Front Door

Hook: The Coalition Military has begun to engage in the Emperor's *Campaign of Unity* and are looking for Service Specialists to assist them in their efforts. Human mercenaries and laborers are most wanted. Service Specialists are needed for the Tolkeen and Quebec Campaigns as well as positions along CS borders.

Line: This could be a chance for the player characters to infiltrate and spy on (in a peripheral way) the Coalition Army!

Hook: What do they do? Spy, steal, sabotage — all are tough to do in a way that seriously hurts the CS. Are they discovered to be D-bee sympathizers? Do they escape? Are they forgotten or wanted men?

The Prophet

Hook: D-bee communities within 300 miles (482 km) are terr of what will happen to them. With the Coalition's *Cam of Unity* in full swing, a number of towns and villages ready fallen and thousands have been slaughtered.

Line: A human prophet, Cornelius Kayden, has appeared at a handful of villages near the CS border. He promises salvation and the protection of a great and powerful god; a promise made by scores of men and women just like him, except that Cornelius has already saved one defenseless village from Coalition invasion on three different occasions! As word spreads about this mighty prophet and his benevolent god, hundreds of D-Bees flock to him.

Sinker: Cornelius is a witch who has made a pact of union with some terrible alien intelligence from another dimension. The prophet and his god are using the war to gather a following of dedicated worshippers. Once enough *minions* and *pawns* have been gathered (tens of thousand are needed), the foul creature can enter Rifts Earth to build a proper empire. The desperate D-bees are unwittingly trading one evil for a greater one. Ironically, their behavior supports the Coalition's paranoia about enslaving supernatural monsters.

Cornelius is assisted and protected by three powerful, magic wielding demonic creatures (use demons from *Rifts® Conversion Book One* or create something new).

Dark Tunnels

Hook: A skirmish with the Coalition Army (could be anywhere) opens a hole in the earth (probably small) that leads to an underground complex (large or small).

Line: Going down to investigate, the place seems to be abandoned. It can be a pre-Rifts bunker that is empty or with some basic 21st Century weapons and supplies; ancient books, data disks and other *relics* can fetch a good price on the Black Market and from collectors in free states like Lazlo. If an old military bunker of the USA, there might even be a pair of Glitter Boys or a mega-damage tank or APC. Of course, the power supplies for them would be drained and getting them or any large equipment out through the small opening will require some excavation, which will attract attention.

The underground complex might be an undiscovered UTI/Vallax alien hideout not discovered during the Juicer Uprising, or some other alien or D-bee construct.

Sinker: The place isn't abandoned and the inhabitants aren't happy to see intruders! If a Vallax hideout, the enemy includes two Vallax and a half dozen Newcomer Androids and/or Juicer

Techno-Zombies (see **Rifts® World Book 10: Juicer Uprising**).

If a pre-Rifts bunker or other construct (subway tunnel, underground parking structure, basement, etc.), the ruins may have another entrance and could be inhabited by D-bee refugees, supernatural critters, or even be a CS trap.

Sleepers

Hook: A skirmish with the Coalition Army (could be anywhere) opens a hole in the earth (probably small) that leads to an underground complex (large or small).

Line: Going down to investigate, the place seems to be a pre-Rifts Military bunker of some sort, deep in the ground. Parts are collapsed, completely buried, but one section is intact. It's powered by an independent nuclear power plant. Inside are dozens (hundreds?) of frost covered capsules. Inside are humans from before the Great Cataclysm!

Sinker: Are they friends or foes? A potential new ally or a new menace? Why were they put into suspended animation? Were they just participants in an experiment that never got completed when the Rifts came and reshaped the Earth? Are they solders or super-soldiers? Superhuman Mutants? Criminals? Aliens? Are there more behind a secret wall (perhaps an entire army of thousands)? What secrets do they hold? If soldiers, do they have a secret cache of weapons and armor someplace (behind the next wall or miles away at some other secret place)?

Do you release them from their cryogenic slumber?

To the Rescue

This is a real simple, all-purpose, expand as you want, adventure plot that can be used over and over again.

Hook: A cry for help. The pleas can come from a lone child, woman, human, D-bee, etc., or from an entire community.

Line: Our heroes go to help.

Sinker: The character(s) or community calling for help really is a good guy or innocent, and really is in distress. The problem is the enemy threatening them is a CS squad or platoon! In the alternative, any old enemy of the player group, or hideous opponent the group was hoping to avoid or deal with later, will do.

Strange Bedfellows

Hook: Our heroes catch wind of a murderous plot by the Federation of Magic to attack the CS. They have boasted about the devastating blow this will have on the CS and how dozens will die and thousands will suffer!

Line: The target of the attack is a sprawling farm community. CS help may be miles away, and by the time the military arrives, the innocent farmers will be slaughtered and their crops destroyed. According to rumors, an evil Ley Line Walker has uncovered some ancient, terrible Spell of Legend that will create a blight that will destroy acres of crops. The word is that the magic could destroy three quarters of the Missouri and Iowa croplands, dealing the Coalition a terrible blow.

There are two problems with this scenario. One, hundreds of thousands of people will suffer, including thousands of D-bees and wilderness folk who also count on CS crops and food processing. Second, the sorcerer doesn't know exactly how the spell works or whether he can control the blight; the fear being that it might spread throughout Mid-America and may kill all vegetation. His own lieutenant has begged him not to unleash this magic. When he refused, his lieutenant tried to kill him, but failed (he was killed). Even if he can control the magic crop destroyer, he alone will hold its secrets, and he has already made it known that he will use "the power that brought the Coalition States to its knees," against others in order to build his own empire.

Sinker: Our heroes also know the location where the power-mad sorcerer will work his magic, which means *they* can stop him! Ironically, if they do try to stop the sorcerer, the player characters will find themselves fighting to protect the Coalition States!! The CS authorities won't respond in sufficient strength or numbers to the rumors of danger or go to the wrong location.

The sorcerer needs the energy of a ley line nexus close to the target area, tonight (or in few days if the group needs time to prepare or get to the location; something that could be an adventure in and of itself). The spell is actually a ritual that must be cast during a lunar eclipse (soon). The sorcerer will sacrifice a captive CS Psi-Stalker to initiate the ceremony (further evidence of his evil).

This will not be an easy battle. The mage is ready for trouble and is powerful (6-9th level). Suggested adversaries: He is escorted by 3D4 low level supporters (1-3rd level warriors and vagabonds), 1D4 low level sorcerers (2-3rd level), one powerful warrior (Juicer, Crazy, D-bee, cyborg, power armor, golem, etc.; 6-8th level) and one fellow practitioner of magic (4-6th level or equivalent demonic being).

D-Bee Vagabond
1 0,000-1,900
2 1,901-3,600
3 3,601-7,200
4 7,201-14,400
5 14,401-24,500
6 24,501-35,000
7 35,001-45,000
8 45,001-65,000
9 65,001-85,000
10 85,001-115,000
11 115,001-145,000
12 145,001-185,000
13 185,001-250,000
14 250,001-310,000
15 310,001-375,000

ISS Peacekeeper,
RPA Elite SAMAS Pilot
1 0,000-1,925
2 1,926-3,850
3 3,851-7,450
4 7,451-14,900
5 14,901-21,000
6 21,001-31,000
7 31,001-41,600
8 41,601-53,000
9 53,001-73,000
10 73,001-103,500
11 103,501-139,000
12 139,001-189,000
13 189,001-239,000
14 239,001-289,000
15 289,001-339,000

CS Dog Pack,
CS Grunt/Infantrymen
1 0,000-1,950
2 1,951-3,900
3 3,901-8,800
4 8,801-17,600
5 17,601-35,600
6 35,601-50,600
7 50,601-70,600
8 70,600-95,600
9 95,601-125,600
10 125,601-175,600
11 175,601-225,600
12 225,601-275,600
13 275,601-325,600
14 325,601-375,600
15 375,601-425,600

CS EOD Specialist,
CS Nautical Specialist
1 0,000-2000
2 2,001-4,000
3 4,001-8,200
4 8,201-16,400
5 16,401-24,500
6 24,501-34,600
7 34,601-49,700
8 49,701-69,800
9 69,801-94,900
10 94,901-129,000
11 129,001-179,100
12 179,101-229,200
13 229,201-279,300
14 279,301-329,400
15 329,401-389,500

NTSET Psi-Hound,
Vanguard Brawler Thug,
CS EOD Specialist,
CS Nautical Specialist
1 0,000-2050
2 2,051-4,100
3 4,101-8,400
4 8,401-16,800
5 16,801-25,560
6 24,561-35,800
7 35,801-50,400
8 50,401-70,800
9 70,801-95,400
10 95,401-130,800
11 130,801-180,400
12 180,401-230,800
13 230,801-280,400
14 280,401-331,800
15 331,401-392,800

Quick Flex Rogue R.C.C.
Trimadore Mechanic R.C.C.
1 0,000-2,300
2 2,301-4,600
3 4,601-9,200
4 9,201-18,400
5 18,401-26,500
6 26,501-36,600
7 36,601-51,700
8 51,701-74,800
9 74,801-100,900
10 100,901-140,000
11 140,001-193,100
12 193,101-235,200
13 235,201-290,400
14 290,401-350,600
15 350,601-425,800

ISS Specter,
CS Technical Officer,
CS Military Specialist
1 0,000-2,120
2 2,121-4,240
3 4,241-8,480
4 8,481-16,960
5 16,961-24,960
6 24,961-34,960
7 34,961-49,960
8 49,961-69,960
9 69,961-94,960
10 94,961-129,960
11 129,961-179,960
12 179,961-229,960
13 229,961-279,960
14 279,961-329,960
15 329,961-389,960

NTSET Protector/Hunter,
CS RCSG Scientist,
ISS Intel Specter
1 0,000-2,140
2 2,141-4,280
3 4,281-8,560
4 8,561-17,520
5 17,521-25,520
6 25,521-35,520
7 35,521-50,520
8 50,521-71,000
9 71,001-96,100
10 96,101-131,200
11 131,201-181,300
12 181,301-231,400
13 231,401-281,500
14 281,501-341,600
15 341,601-400,700

Psi-Net Agent,
Special Forces
1 0,000-2,200
2 2,201-4,400
3 4,401-8,800
4 8,801-17,600
5 17,601-27,800
6 27,801-37,900
7 37,901-55,100
8 55,101-75,200
9 75,201-100,300
10 100,301-145,500
11 145,501-190,600
12 190,601-245,700
13 245,701-295,800
14 295,801-345,900
15 345,901-415,100

CS Juicer,
CS Commando,
CS Strike Cyborg
1 0,000-2,150
2 2,151-4,300
3 4,301-8,600
4 8,601-17,200
5 17,201-25,500
6 25,501-36,000
7 36,001-52,000
8 52,001-73,000
9 73,001-98,000
10 98,001-134,000
11 134,001-184,000
12 184,001-240,000
13 240,001-295,000
14 295,001-385,000
15 385,001-450,000

CS "Fly Boy" RPA,
ISS Psi-Stalker,
CS Ranger/Scout
1 0,000-2,100
2 2,101-4,200
3 4,201-8,400
4 8,401-17,200
5 17,201-25,400
6 25,401-35,800
7 35,801-51,000
8 51,001-71,200
9 71,201-96,400
10 96,401-131,600
11 131,601-181,800
12 181,801-232,000
13 232,001-282,200
14 282,201-342,400
15 342,401-402,600

Experience
Point Tables